POWERS OF FATE

A Story of Love and Courage Born Amid the Ruins of War-Torn Italy

By

Mono V. D'Angelo

BEST REGARDS,

Mono D'Angelo

2002

ISBN: 1-4033-1257-5 (Ebook)
ISBN: 1-4033-1258-3 (Softcover)
ISBN: 1-4033-1259-1 (Hardcover)

Library of Congress Control Number: 2002103601

This book is printed on acid free paper.

Printed in the United States of America
Bloomington, IN

1stBooks - rev. 05/22/02

To Mom and Dad.

My greatest regret is that it took me over half a lifetime

to realize what courageous and fascinating people you were…

ACKNOWLEDGEMENTS...

Thank you,

To my wife, Ingrid, for believing in this novel and my desire to write it. To Margo LaGattuta, without who's superb editorial skills, this work would have never flourished. To Cecilia Schneider, my online critique partner, for her vision and enthusiasm. To Mr. Norman P. Klein, for granting me permission to reprint his haunting photograph of Fort Dix, New Jersey on the front cover. To Mr. David H. Lippman, noted World War II historian, for generously sharing his extensive knowledge of this period in American history. And to Angela DiGiulio, for documenting her poignant memories of a war bride leaving Naples.

INTRODUCTION

By May of 1945, while American and British forces were overrunning the Nazi homeland, the ranks of the U.S. Army had swelled to over eight million men worldwide.

In 1942, an American soldier stationed in England married a young British girl. He became the first G.I. to take a war bride. Over the next ten years, an estimated 300,000 men in the U.S. ... do the same. ...., ... p.........., in Europe, American soldiers fell in love with, and married, the foreign women they met. When the war's end brought these young women to America, many were pregnant, carrying young children, or both. Like their soldier husbands, they too were only in their late teens or early twenties. At an age when life can be very uncertain, they made irreversible and often terrifying decisions to leave their families and homeland for the rest of their lives.

The war made falling in love easy for these young men and women. In a caldron of emotions ranging from the fear of death to the childlike giddiness of a new flirtation, there was little time for these women to know the persons inside the soldiers they married. Often, the reality of arriving in the United States and seeing their husbands in civilian clothes for the first time made many of these women feel as if they'd married strangers. In some cases, the lives they left behind were so significantly different from the lives of the men they married, it became impossible for them to completely embrace their new world. The promise of a better life in America was soon diluted by the shock of being immersed in a strange new culture, one in which many could not even speak the language. For some, their new lives were lonely and disappointing. Others, however, were delivered from abject poverty and into a wonderful life drenched in the American dream.

Powers of Fate is an intimate look into the lives of one soldier and the beautiful Italian girl he falls in love with and marries. Mario Carlucci is an Italian-American street hustler who is raised by his gambler father in a rough part of Detroit's Italian district. Antonella Cappodanno is the daughter of a successful businessman in Naples, Italy. Talented and beautiful, she becomes a highly sought-after fashion designer in pre-war Naples. Their lives could not have been any more different. Living half a world apart and having nothing in common except their Italian language, only the extraordinary events of World War II make it possible for them to find each other and create a life together. This is their remarkable story.

CHAPTER 1

Early 1930's, Detroit, Michigan

It is nearly 2:00 AM and Mario, accompanied by his older brother John, are heading for the Brass Rail, a dingy, after-hours nightclub. It is located in a rough part of Detroit better known for its cheap whores and tough street thugs. Mario stares into the black void beyond the reach of the car's headlights. He simmers in a silent rage, still fuming over having his new car stolen from the front of his father's home. He wants to "pay back" those who are responsible. Mario and John cruise the street around the seedy little club, searching for a parking space, while Mario's temper continues to mount.

Roberto Lucci, the "ringleader" of the gang of punks that has heisted the new Ford, will pay for his little "joy ride." John backs the black sedan into a parking place near the club and turns off the engine. Sitting in the darkened car, Mario's voice cracks with nervous energy as he considers what to do once inside the club. John listens in silence as Mario's fury begins to pour forth.

"I dunno how many guys this Lucci prick has with em, so let's just go in and look around for a few minutes. I don't know nothing about this dump…we gotta be smart."

"Are ya sure ya wanna go through with this tonight?" John asks with a slight hesitation.

"Look John, I'm gonna kick the shit outta this asshole tonight with or without ya, so if ya don't wanna go in, you can wait here," Mario screams.

John looks straight into Mario's eyes and says, "Let's go; you ain't goin' in there without me." John has always watched over his wild, younger brother. They share a bond of devotion that allows very little to come between them, and tonight is proving to be no different.

Entering the club, they approach the crowded bar and order two Crown and waters. Nursing their drinks slowly, Mario carefully looks the place over, mentally noting the location of the men's room, the bouncers, and in particular, Roberto Lucci's table. He watches Lucci sitting with a small group of gruff-looking hoodlums, casually drinking and getting friendly with several "working" girls. Mario determines that the bouncers are stationed far enough from the men's room to make it difficult to hear anything coming from inside. He says to John, "When Lucci gets up ta take a leak, I'll follow him inta the shitter and talk some fuckin' sense into him." John agrees to remain outside the men's room door and discourage any unwanted attention. Then they wait, like two young lions stalking their prey.

Mario is the middle son of Giuseppi Carlucci, an Italian immigrant from Sicily, who settled in the Detroit area shortly after arriving in the United States. His family consists of Giano (John), the eldest of his three sons, Mario, and Giuseppi (Joe) the youngest. Shortly after arriving in this country, Giuseppi lost his young wife to tuberculosis, forcing him to raise the three boys alone. Rumor has it that he has links to the Detroit Mafia, but no one has ever proven a connection. He is a notorious gambler and, although he runs a legitimate business selling fresh seafood, the back room of his storefront is where he really makes his money. There are regularly scheduled card games, mostly canasta, but some poker, both played for very high stakes.

The "old man," as the boys respectfully call him, has a reputation for running honest games, and this reputation attracts some of the most well-known but fearsome "Mafioso" found in Detroit during the early 1930's. Giuseppi treats all of his friends with great respect, and he is well liked by all who know him. Even the police are willing to ignore his little side business, as they prefer to enjoy the fresh fish from his store, frequently at no cost.

The three boys have grown up in this twilight world of the honest businessman and prolific gambler, greatly influenced by the exciting life their father appears to lead. They work the storefront during the day and serve drinks and food in the back room in the evening, learning the ways of professional card players.

At fourteen, Mario drops out of school to spend all of his time working the store and watches the card games with a growing fascination. Giuseppi's skill at the card table is more than pure luck. His friendly, easy manner conceals an ability to remember most cards played in a single hand. The ability to calculate the odds of pulling the needed cards gives him an incredible advantage over his hapless opponents, and he wins in modest amounts, careful not to kill his own game with greed. He never reveals this talent to anyone, including his sons, until many years later. Without a mother's influence, the three boys migrate into the world their father has created around them.

Now in their late teens, the boys are well aware of Giuseppi's reputation and influence. They begin to take advantage of that reputation by offering certain cops the best portions of the daily seafood shipments to forget a traffic ticket or look the other way if a small problem occurs. They regularly abuse Giuseppi's relationship with the local police without his knowledge. They acquire a taste of their father's lifestyle and begin to enjoy it, but the old man remains unwilling to open the door to his world for them completely.

Giuseppi will not allow his sons to participate in his card games, still considering them too green to play well, and they tire of being just waiters in their father's world. Mario and John grow too ambitious to continue to work in the store, and they decide to find jobs in one of the many auto factories in town. But neither of them is prepared to give up gambling, the "habit" they have inherited from their father. Mario, in particular, enjoys the excitement of matching his gambling skills against strangers. He becomes extremely fond of shooting dice. Knowing he can play the game practically anywhere appeals to his sense of excitement like nothing else ever has. There are frequent crap games in the factory during shift breaks and lunchtime, and he plays every chance he can.

On a steamy, Friday afternoon, one such crap game takes place in a dimly lit, little workshop located deep in the bowels of the hulking old plant. It is payday and the game is big, with players shouting out their bets and wagering huge amounts of money. Mario loves the furious action of these heavy games. He plays with a grit not many are willing to challenge. His fierce, growling style tends to back off all but the most aggressive competitors, and he wears his growing reputation like a badge of courage, daring anyone to tear it from his chest. But Mario also knows that, if he goes broke, the old man will usually bankroll him for awhile until his luck changes. Often his father's safety net clouds his judgment, and he bets with reckless abandon, usually with disastrous results, but tonight he cannot lose. Money is wagered in all corners of the small, smoke-filled workshop, as one man after another takes his turn rolling the small ivory cubes.

Groups of players typically cluster together, usually along ethnic or racial lines. The Italians, the Irish, and the Blacks bet against each other repeatedly, and the racial tension adds to the already intense atmosphere of the game. But for Mario, tonight is becoming much more than just another night of craps. He rarely rolls the dice, preferring instead to place his side bets with the other groups, and successfully covers most of the bets in front of him. The evening continues to produce one good run after another, with piles of cash filling his hands and pockets. He has a knack for reading the other players, and he can feel when their luck is about to change. He makes the good bets, beating the shooter repeatedly, and before long, John begins following his lead. They ride Mario's winning streak as far as they dare and, after a few hours, decide to leave with their growing pile of cash before trouble breaks out.

After leaving the plant, Mario and John climb into the "old man's" car and begin to count up their winnings. They are shocked to discover how much they have actually won.

"Eight-hundred and fifty bucks, do ya fuckin' believe it?" squeals Mario. "I got a great idea. Let's go get our own car. Ya know we need our own car. Jus' think of the women we can find."

"I don't know Mario, maybe we oughtta wait and think about it for a while," his brother replies.

"Aw, fuck that John. We ain't never gonna get another chance like this again. If we leave right now, we can be drivin' home inna brand new Ford tonight," Mario barks back.

John's temper begins to reach its breaking point at Mario's attempt to have his way with the money they have just won. He snaps back at his brother,

"Goddamn it, Mario, maybe I don't wanna spend my money onna fuckin'car. Didja ever think a that?"

"Oh bullshit, John. Whodda hell don't wanna new fuckin' Ford for Christ's sake?" growls Mario with a mystified look on his face.

John realizes that this argument might go on indefinitely, and he finally tires of arguing with his brother,

"OK, Mario, you win. But ya better get two sets of keys."

Mario laughs out loud, like a kid at Christmas. He slaps John on the back and says,

"You ain't gonna regret this. Trust me." John shoots a wide grin at his brother and says, "Why don't I believe you?"

They drive off to find a dealer, pool their money and pay cash for a brand new Ford sedan. Because Mario has contributed most of the money for the purchase, he drives it away from the dealer and heads home, while John follows in their father's car.

The smell of the leather seats, the clean, sparkling paint job, and the roar of the powerful V-8 engine has Mario feeling smug and cocky. He never imagined that owning a brand new car could feel so good. After a short ride through the neighborhood to show off, Mario finally drives home to show the old man the car before he and John go out for the evening. Pulling up in front of the large, two-story house, they honk the horn wildly until Giuseppi appears on the porch. He stands there and glares at the brand new Ford, but the boys notice he does not appear very pleased. Standing in front of the car, John looks at Mario and says,

"I don't get it. He looks pissed off. Why da fuck would he be pissed off?"

Mario doesn't understand it either and says,

"We just need ta explain it to him, that's all."

In spite of his brash talk, Mario's stomach is twitching like a dying fish out of water. Giuseppi has always cast a long shadow over his three sons, and this moment feels no different. Mario draws a deep breath, walks up to the porch, and asks,

"Well Pa, what do you think?" The old man asks,

"Where inna the hell do you git theesa car, Mario?" Mario swallows hard and responds,

"Well, uh, you see, me and John, we won a lotta money shootin' craps at the plant, so...so we decided ta buy a new car and not have ta borrow yours so much. Ain't it a beaut'?"

Giuseppi clenches his fists and his face reflects a crimson-colored anger, which is about to explode. He screams,

"What kinda fuckina dumbasses are you two for spending so mucha money like a that?" Giuseppi has always been very careful not to make his gambling success too obvious; becoming deeply upset that his sons did not understand the need to do the same.

"Ifa you spend a lotta money when alla the neighbors know you no hava any, they gonna starta to aska questions. I'ma no need any goddamn questions," he rages on. Mario and John are surprised as well as disappointed in the old man's reaction. They believe they have done something he should be excited about, but instead he is chewing them out. Mario rarely challenges his father, but this time he cannot remain quiet. He says,

"Pa, you're wrong. No one would screw around with us for buyin' a new car. Why the hell would they care?"

Giuseppi shakes his head in disgust and walks into the house, frustrated that his two sons do not understand what he's trying to tell them. The boys are unsure how to appease their father, so they climb back into the car and drive into town to go nightclubbing. They visit a number of their regular hangouts and show off the car to their lady friends, making dates and planning to have some good times over the next few months. They are both aware of what a new car will mean to their relationships with the numerous women they know, and it is already starting to pay off. After a long night of club-hopping and women-chasing, they return home early in the morning, park the car in front of the house, and go in for the night.

On Saturday mornings, Mario usually enjoys sleeping in after being out late. Early this morning, however, he is awakened by John and Joe yelling and cussing in an angry mood about something downstairs. He gets up to see what's going on. Still half asleep, he inches his way slowly down the flight of stairs when John comes running up to him.

"Some motherfuckers' stole our car! They took our brand new car!"

This reality stuns Mario from his morning drowsiness, and he bolts out the front door, only to see the empty parking space where he parked the new Ford last night. His face begins to redden and he charges around the tiny front lawn like a caged bear. Pacing furiously, with one hand on his hip and the other clenched into a fist, he bellows,

"Goddamn it…GODDAMN, wait'll I find out who did this. Those bastards are gonna pay for this and pay hard."

By now, Giuseppi has also been awakened by all the commotion, and when he steps out onto the porch, Mario and John immediately begin pleading with him to do something.

"Pa, you can help us find our car, right?" quizzes John.

Giuseppi is uncertain whether or not he can help his sons recover their stolen car, but he decides not to do anything too hastily. He sees the theft as a valuable lesson to his sons. His circle of friends is impressive. Many who enjoy his card games are upper level Capos with various mob connections in the city. Following the car theft, he enters the house and calls his good friend, Antonio Bomarito.

Antonio is one of his oldest gambling associates and, between the two of them, they exchange thousands of dollars in gambling debts every year. They are proud and honorable men, true to the Sicilian traditions they have grown up with, and know each other to be totally trustworthy. But there the similarities abruptly end. Unlike Giuseppi, Antonio is known for being cold and ruthless, his brutal reputation founded on rumors of baseball bat attacks and senseless shootings. He never allows anyone to stand in his way when there is something he wants. Giuseppi knows, if anyone can find his son's car, it is Antonio. After Antonio answers the phone, Giuseppi greets him in their Italian tongue,

"Antonio, come sta?"

"Giuseppi, boun giorno, Io fa bene, grazi tante," Antonio replies.

They always greet one another in Italian, out of respect for their Sicilian homeland, but quickly resume speaking English.

"Howsa your family? Are those three boys of yours makina you crazy yet?" Antonio chuckles. He has no children of his own and admires Giuseppi's family. He frequently speaks with great envy of Giuseppi's good fortune in having three sons to carry on his family name. Giuseppi begins laughing at Antonio's question and responds,

"They are maka me olda before my time, I'ma telling you. I'ma gonna trow them alla outta my house before I die from a goddamn a heart attack."

Antonio laughs even louder; then Giuseppi changes the subject and asks,

"Howsa your business theesa days?

"Its good, you know. I make a lot of money from booze and runnin' a coupla gambling joints," Antonio replies.

"Are you gonna play cards inna my place again?" Giuseppi asks.

"Of coursa, you know I will. I always like a to take a your money," Antonio jokingly answers.

Their conversation rambles on, covering many different subjects for the next few minutes. Old friends, news from Sicily, and an endless list of matters pertaining to their businesses are the standard topics of discussion between these two familiar yet different men. Near the end of their conversation, Giuseppi asks,

"*Amico mio*, John and Mario justa bought a new car anna this morning we find ita is stolen. Canna you helpa me get it back?"

"Where dida your sons getta new car?" Antonio asks with curious interest.

After Giuseppi explains how John and Mario had come to own a car, Antonio says,

"Whena was it stolen?"

"Lasta night…from inna front of my house."

Antonio assures him he will look into the matter, and Giuseppi knows enough not to say any more about it. He thanks his friend for whatever he can do, saying he is looking forward to taking more of his money. They both laugh and say good-bye.

Mario and John continue pacing around the house, cursing and threatening to "kill the son of a bitch" who has stolen their car. Joe, often the victim of John and Mario's teasing, views the theft of the car as an opportunity to even the score with his older brothers for a change. He is more mild-mannered than they are and finds their angry frustration amusing. In a slow, monotone voice, he adds,

"Your car's probably somewhere in Tennessee by now. You ain't never gonna see the damn thing again." This only serves to inflame Mario and John even more, so they chase him from the house, threatening to kick his ass if he didn't shut up. Joe runs from the house laughing like a screeching hyena and heads off to the fish market for his usual busy Saturday. The morning drags by slowly. Mario grows angrier and more frustrated. He finally decides to approach his father and find out if he will do something.

"Pa, can't somma your friends find out what happened to our car?" he whines.

Giuseppi nonchalantly listens as Mario all but begs for his help but says nothing of his earlier phone conversation with Antonio Bomarito. He lookes at Mario and calmly replies,

"I willa try do something, but I'm a no sure I canna help."

Mario stomps away in an even angrier mood and storms out of the house to cool off. Giuseppi watches his earlier prediction coming back to haunt his sons and hopes they will learn a valuable lesson in how to win smart.

Later that day, Antonio Bomarito calls Giuseppi and, once again, the conversation begins in Italian. After the traditional exchange of greetings Antonio says,

"Giuseppi, someone willa call you very soon and tella you where you canna finda the car."

"Thanka you, Antonio. I ama very grateful for your help. Isa there anything I canna do for you inna return?" Giuseppi asks.

Antonio replies with a chuckle, "No, I'ma happy to helpa out an old friend. But, the nexta time we play canasta, a few good cards once is a while would be nice."

They both laugh at Antonio's little joke, but Giuseppi knows his debt will not be forgotten.

A short time later, the Detroit police call and inform the family that they have found the Ford sedan abandoned in an alley not far from the fish market. Mario and John rush to where the car is and find it unharmed and intact. They are ecstatic about having their new car returned and, when they drive it home, they find Giuseppi standing on the porch with his hands on his hips, saying nothing. He returns to the kitchen to prepare his lunch, leaving his sons to wonder if he's had anything to do with the car's return.

John and Mario are pleased to have their car back, but they are not about to let the situation end there. The police say a gang of local hoodlums have been busy stealing cars around the area and they are likely responsible for the theft. The police are unsure why it was left where it was, and unharmed no less, but think Mario and John are lucky to get it back in one piece. After such a joy ride, most stolen cars are found severely damaged or not at all. Mario and John know nothing of their father's request for help from Antonio Bomarito, but since the old man is quite well known to the police already, they say nothing more than 'thank you,' wanting to avoid any further questions. Mario has had earlier run-ins with the punks who stole the car and knows where they often hang out. He decides to make sure they will not bother his family again.

About twenty minutes after Mario and John enter the Brass Rail, Roberto Lucci gets up and heads for the toilet. Mario's heart begins to race while watching Lucci move away from his table. He gulps down his drink as he prepares to follow him. After Lucci enters the men's room, Mario and John stand in front of the door and go over the plan one more time. They are breathing very heavily from the surge of adrenaline pulsing through their blood. John says,

"OK, go get this over with. I'll make sure no one bothers you."

He paces nervously in small circles outside the heavy, mahogany door as Mario cautiously enters the granite-walled room. There he finds Lucci, standing in front of a urinal, relieving himself. As Lucci turns and zips up his pants, he looks up and sees Mario glaring at him.

"What the fuck do you want?" Lucci growls.

Without saying a word, Mario pulls a blackjack from his coat pocket. The leathery, rough texture of the lead-filled bludgeon only serves to heighten Mario's vicious mood. He suddenly swings it in a wild but powerful stroke, striking Lucci on the wrist.

Lucci recoils in pain and screams,

"Are you fuckin' crazy? What's this all about?"

Still silent, Mario swings the blackjack again, this time hitting Lucci on the side of his head, just above the ear. Blood explodes from the large wound, spraying a light, pink-colored mist all around. A heavy flow begins gushing down the side of his face and, after Lucci grabs his head, Mario kicks him in the groin, dropping him to the floor. With Roberto Lucci lying on the floor in a pool of his own blood, Mario stands over him and bellows out a stern warning,

"You're a real stupid motherfucker for takin' a car that don't belong to you, Lucci, especially mine. You didn't think you was gonna get away with it, did ya?"

Small, pearl-like puddles of saliva are visible in the corners of Mario's mouth. They disintegrate into a translucent, wet cloud that drifts down onto the fallen Lucci as Mario screams out his final threat,

"If ya fuck around with anyone else in the Carlucci family, you're gonna have me to deal with again."

Mario then kicks the moaning Lucci in the stomach, walks out of the men's room, telling his brother it is time to leave. They hurriedly find their way out of the club, while Lucci's friends begin to look for him. After John and Mario climb into the car, Mario begins yelling,

"I sure showed that son of a bitch who he's fuckin' with."

John keeps asking what he has done to Lucci, so Mario pulls out the blackjack and waves it in front of him, screaming,

"This is what I did to the stupid son of a bitch. I taught em' a fuckin' lesson he won't forget." John gets a little nervous and asks,

"How bad ya hurt him?" Mario says,

"He ain't dead, but he won't make that mistake again." They drive home in an eerie silence, saying nothing more about the bar fight.

John parks the car in the same place it was stolen from, and they go into the house. He steps into his room and closes the door behind him, saying nothing more to his brother. Mario climbs the stairs and flicks on the single overhead light bulb in the tiny bathroom located next to his room. After relieving himself, he stands in front of the small medicine cabinet mirror and stares into his reflection for a moment. There he sees tiny droplets of Roberto Lucci's blood on his cheeks and forehead. A feeling of anxiety and panic sweep over him, and he grabs a small towel, soaks it in cold water, and scrubs his face with harsh, violent strokes. He hangs his head and stares at the pink tint on the towel, suddenly feeling a little frightened. His thoughts are all over the place right now, and he is not sure how he should be feeling after what he has just done to Roberto Lucci. He returns to his bedroom, slumps onto the old, tattered chair in the corner, and lights a cigarette. Sitting alone in the dimly lit little room, he wonders how badly Roberto Lucci has been hurt.

Mario had had numerous fights in the neighborhood as a young boy, but this one is far more serious than any he has been in before. Of Giuseppi's three sons, he clearly has the most violent temper. Following the death of his mother, Mario became an angry child. At the time of her death, he was the most vulnerable of Giuseppi's three sons and suffered the loss more profoundly than his brothers did. John, being five years older, relied on his maturity to cope with their mother's passing. Joe was very young and never really knew their mother, his youth insulating him from the pain of her passing. Mario, however, was nine years old, and her death affected him much more severely. He longed for a mother's comfort and care, as well as her love. He later became angry over losing that part of his childhood and this anger frequently spilled over into his day-to-day behavior. Following her death, Mario could no longer cope with school and struggled to get along. His bitterness diminished when he reached his teen years, but his angry temper would remain with him for a very long time.

Sitting in the stillness of his darkened room, Mario can feel a sense of guilt begin to settle over him. He sees the white underbelly of his conscience suddenly exposed, and he has never accepted that frailty as part of his being. He feels no pride in what he has done this evening, but he will never admit to such feelings. To do so, he believes, would be viewed as weakness, and he does not want anyone to think he is not as strong as he portrays himself to be.

Giuseppi has never been the kind of father who shares open affection for his sons, and now that they have grown into young men, he seems even more distant to Mario. Combined with his mother's death, his father's coldness has formed an impenetrable barrier around Mario's emotions, and he expects his life will always be entangled in confrontations such as the one this evening. He knows no other way to live and has never considered his future or set any goals. He lives his life one day at a time, waiting for the next crap game or willing woman to come along. He can never imagine himself having a wife or family someday or even living away from his father.

After finishing his cigarette, Mario kicks off his shoes, removes his trousers and lies down on his bed. He feels both mentally and physically exhausted and looks forward to the darkness to help blot out the image of a battered Lucci lying in his own blood. But as tired as he is, he will not sleep well tonight. In his own mind, he does not see himself as much different from the hoodlum he has just beaten up.

CHAPTER 2

Napoli, Italia, early 1930's

Antonella runs further and further ahead of her father, while he shouts,

"Antonella, la vigilanza era voi sta entrando e non funziona in chiunque," reminding her to be careful not to fall. He smiles, even as his youngest daughter pays him little attention. She has a wildness in her that both pleases and concerns him. Strolling along the Via Pozzuoli while holding the hand of Lucia, Antonella's older sister, Pirrone enjoys these casual Sunday outings with his two daughters, but he wonders why Antonella behaves so differently from other little girls in Napoli.

Pirrone Cappodanno spends many leisurely Sundays strolling along the shores of the Mediterranean with his family. He treats these outings as special occasions, making sure family members wear their finest clothes. Dressed in a long, black coat and a colorful tie and donning his fine hat and walking stick, he appears elegant and charismatic. A handsome and successful businessman in Napoli, he is very proud of his two beautiful daughters and only son. More recently, however, Giancarlo, the oldest of his three children, has found these outings to be too time-consuming, frequently choosing to remain at home and complete his schoolwork. He is more serious than his two sisters, already planning to join his father's business one day. Pirrone's wife, Assunta, delights in her husband's pleasure in these family outings and looks forward to enjoying lunch in one of the many outdoor restaurants found along the oceanfront.

Assunta Cappodanno shares a good life with Pirrone, raising their family and keeping their home in order. She willingly accepts her traditional role as a subservient wife and mother. Her family traditions dictate that women marry and raise their husband's children; she knows no other way to live. Life in Napoli has been this way for many generations, and she fully expects her daughters will follow the tradition. She, too, has seen the difference in Antonella's behavior and harbors a mother's natural concern for her daughter's well being. Neither Assunta nor Pirrone have seen Antonella's aggressive ways as a harbinger of her artistic talents.

Antonella continues to race ahead of her family, periodically turning and shouting,

"Papa, can we stop here and eat our lunch? Please, Papa?" pointing to one of the many trattorias along the oceanfront. Pirrone

finds her desire to stop at almost every trattoria she passes highly amusing. He often laughs out loud at the numerous times she changes her mind.

"Yes, Antonella, we can stop here. This trattoria is very nice," he responds with a broad smile on his face. They gather beneath a red and green umbrella, feasting upon caprese, a plate of fresh tomatoes and provolone cheese and Pirrone's favorite mid-day meal. Antonella and Lucia order bruschetta and begin to negotiate with their father in a game they all love. Lucia asks,

"Papa, we will share a piece of our bruschetta with you if we can have some of your caprese."

Lucia and Antonella smile and giggle with one another, as Pirrone appears to study the question with a mocked expression of concern on his face. He leans over, carefully examines the bruscetta on the plate before them and says,

"Well, this bruschetta looks very delicious. Perhaps I should taste some of it."

Pirrone is no longer able to maintain a business-like scowl, and they all explode in laughter as Lucia and Antonella help themselves to their father's lunch. Assunta looks on at the often repeated game between Pirrone and his daughters and teases him, saying,

"Pirrone, you will never refuse them anything, will you?" He offers his wife no answer, but the adoring look on his face needs no explanation.

Facing the clear, blue waters of the Mediterranean, they dine while watching an endless parade of ships come and go. Lucia and Antonella find those ships a constant source of fascination, asking Pirrone an endless string of questions.

"Papa, where do the many ships come from?" Antonella inquires.

"They sail here from far away lands with unusual names, such as Istanbul, Beirut, and Singapore," he replies.

"Why do they all come to Napoli?" asks Lucia.

"They come to trade many things - coffee, tea, and sugar for olive oil and wine," he answers as simply as possible.

His business thrives upon the ships in the harbor, but he does not try to explain the complicated world of importing and exporting to his youngest children. Of course, the questions never stop, but Pirrone devotes these Sundays with his family to answering curious questions from his beautiful daughters, and he never tires of it.

Antonella is nine years old and Lucia is eleven. Both girls attend school in Bagnoli, one of the many small cities surrounding Napoli. The school has begun planning its annual Festival dei Fiori, which always includes a musical presentation by a select group of students. Antonella is aware of the festival, particularly the musical show. She enjoys singing and has a strong, powerful voice, but

Assunta and Pirrone pay little serious attention to that talent. Her interest in the festival increases daily, and she asks her mother,

"Mama, I want to sing in the music show at our school. But how can I become part of such a show?"

"Antonella, I believe you must ask the festival organizers in your school if you can sing in the musical, and they will have to decide," answers Assunta.

The next day, Antonella bursts into their home and begins skipping through each room, clapping her hands with joy and screaming,

"Mama, Mama, dove tu?"

She cannot wait to share the wonderful news she has received at school that day. Antonella's explosive excitement makes it nearly impossible for Assunta to understand what she is trying to tell her. After watching Antonella dash about for several minutes in joyful exuberance, Assunta calms her down, and asks,

"Antonella, please stop jumping and screaming for a moment and tell me what has happened to make you so excited."

"Mama, I have been permitted to sing in the music program at the school festival. Isn't that wonderful?"

"Oh yes, my darling, that is very exciting news. Just wait until your father hears of the show. He will be so surprised to know you will be singing in the festival," Assunta replies.

After kissing Antonella on the cheek, she inquires,

"Tell me how the festival organizers decided you can sing in the show."

"It was very easy Mama. I asked my teacher who decides which students will sing in the festival. She said several of the teachers choose the students, and then she asked me if I could sing. I told her of course I could and, after class, I sang for three teachers, and they decided right away I could be in the show," Antonella explains. A prideful Assunta tells her daughter,

"I am sure you will be the best singer in the entire festival." Mother and daughter hug each other amid their smiles and laughter.

Antonella then tells her mother,

"I must make a costume for the show. Will you help me sew one together, Mama?"

"Of course I will help you, my dear. We can shop for material tomorrow," Assunta replies.

The following day, Assunta, Antonella and Lucia walk the few blocks to the central market district and search for just the right material to be used in the costume. After hours of scouring the many shops there, Lucia finally locates a fabric with a color and pattern they all agree upon. They immediately return home to begin sewing the costume together. Lucia and Antonella discuss what the costume should look like, but disagree about the design. Lucia grabs the material, drapes it over her shoulder and says,

"Antonella, this is what such a costume should look like. It must be a long, royal gown, not a simple peasant dress."

"Oh, Lucia, how do you know such things? You have never been in a music show. I want the costume to be pretty, not royal," she argues.

They bicker back and forth over the design, neither one willing to relent and concede to the other's opinions. Lucia grows weary of arguing with her younger sister and storms from the house shouting,

"That's enough. You make the costume any way you like. I will not help you if all you are going to do is complain about my ideas."

During the next few days, Assunta patiently teaches Antonella how to cut out a pattern and use the sewing machine, but she has little time to assist her daughter with the design of the costume. Too impatient to wait for her mother's help, Antonella begins to design, cut, and sew it together herself, completing the ornate garment in less than a week. Just before dinner one evening, she models the newly finished costume in front of her family. The dress fits Antonella's tiny body perfectly. The sleeves are large and puffy, with tight bands at the elbows. The waistband holds the long flowery skirt at a perfect length to the floor, from front to back. The detailed quality of the stitching shows remarkable talent for such a young girl. The costume is not only perfect for the festival, but it is also designed and sewn together as if created by a professional seamstress. Looking on in wonder, Pirrone jokingly accuses Assunta,

"My dear wife, did you help Antonella finish this beautiful costume?" But Antonella proudly argues,

"Oh no Papa, she was too busy to help me. I made it all by myself." Pirrone glances at his wife, looking for validation of what Antonlla has just said. Assunta smiles and winks at him, subtly informing him that Antonella did sew the costume without any help. Pirrone proclaims,

"Antonella, you are a gifted and talented seamstress to be able to sew such a beautiful costume. Come here and let me have a closer look at you." She adores her father and always loves to please him. She promises,

"I will be the best singer in the festival for you, Papa. You will see." Pirrone's face brightens with pride, and he says,

"You will also be the prettiest singer in the festival,"

On the day of the festival, Antonella's heart pounds and her mouth feels as dry as beach sand. Spellbound by the excitement, her nerves are beginning to show. She has never performed in public before and is finding the experience both exhilarating and frightening. Assunta tries to calm her daughter's anxiety by telling her how very pretty she looks in her beautiful dress and that she will get over her nerves once the show begins.

Antonella steps onto the stage with four other young girls to a polite applause from the audience. Verdi's *LaTraviata* has been chosen as the music for the program. The five young girls have practiced the music many times and are prepared, but still nervous.

Following the opening song performed in chorale, each young girl sings a brief solo. The audience applauds after each girl finishes. Awaiting Antonella's turn to sing, her father and mother expect her recital to be similar to the shy and timid performances of the other girls in the program. Instead, Antonella's voice explodes in the crisp, clear tone of a young soprano, with professional-like vibrato and strong lungs. Pirrone is plainly visible to her, adding to the nervousness of the moment, but she completes her solo with confidence. Her talent is clearly superior to that of the other young girls, and at the end of her song, the audience bursts into a loud cheer, led of course by Pirrone.

Antonella springs from the stage with a broad smile on her face, and her surprised but proud parents greet her with proud hugs.

"How did you learn to sing so well, Antonella?" a stunned Pirrone asks.

"Papa, I sing all the time. You just work too much to hear me," she replies.

Pirrone's import/export business demands much of his time, keeping him away from home twelve to fourteen hours each day. Discovering such talent in his daughter thrills and pleases him, but he also feels a twinge of guilt for not knowing about Antonella's talents sooner. He silently wonders if there are other important moments in his family's life he's missed.

Antonella and her family stand in front of the stage with other families whose daughters are part of the pageant, all enjoying the excitement of the group's performance. Many admire Antonella's costume and begin to ask who made it. When she tells them it is her own design and work, several of her classmates immediately begin seeking her help to create costumes for other upcoming stage events. Pirrone's family does not recognize that this day marks the beginning of a life-long career for Antonella as a talented seamstress and fashion designer.

During the months following the Festival de Fiori, Antonella designs many other costumes for fellow students. Her talents become known, not only at her own school, but at other schools around Napoli. Her reputation as a talented seamstress becomes more well known and, even at her young age, she begins to receive payment for her work. Her school and church repeatedly ask her to sing on every occasion that she can. Antonella loves to perform on stage as much as she loves designing costumes. Admired by many of her young friends, she enjoys all the newfound attention.

Assunta encourages her daughter to practice her God-given operatic talent, saying,

"Antonella, you have a beautiful opera voice, you should practice singing different operas to improve it."

"But Mama, I enjoy singing the songs I hear from the street musicians along the oceanfront. My friends like that music, too, and they like it when I sing it for them," she snaps back.

Antonella's fiery personality and strong will prove to be more than Assunta wishes to contest. Her wild and vivacious young daughter will follow her own path and Assunta decides not to interfere.

For Pirrone and his family, life is a wonderful fantasy. His business is flourishing, his family prospers, and he enjoys many friends and acquaintances. His hard work and loving care provide the skills that reward him so generously. But the world he has carefully crafted will not last forever.

Returning home from school one afternoon, Lucia and Antonella notice a large crowd gathered in front of their apartment building. Giancarlo is running toward them with a terror in his eyes they have never before witnessed. His face is red and swollen and tears are streaming down his cheeks. When he grabs them, they can feel him trembling throughout his body. A flood of panic sweeps over the two sisters, and Lucia asks, *"Giancarlo, what is wrong?"*

"Its Papa...he...he...oh my God," he replies in a profound, sobbing voice.

His speech is punctuated with deep, involuntary gasps while he struggles to regain some control of his emotions. He forces himself to take several, exaggerated breaths, wipes his eyes and says,

"It's Papa; he became sick and then he died today. Oh dear God, I can't believe it." Lucia and Antonella do not understand or even believe what their brother has just told them. With a terrible fear beginning to claw away inside of her, Antonella says,

"Giancarlo, what are you saying? This cannot be true. You must be wrong."

"The doctor said he suffered a heart attack, Antonella; it is true," he replies.

Dropping their school bags and coats, they run to the apartment building as fast as they can, hoping to find that Giancarlo is mistaken.

After fighting their way past the crowd and into the apartment, they see Assunta sitting in a kitchen chair. Her hands are clasped against her face, and she is weeping uncontrollably. Her eyes are glazed and lifeless, her skin pale. The old wooden chair, upon which she sits, emits a subtle creak while she weaves back and forth. When Lucia and Antonella enter the room, they stare at their mother and confront the awful reality of what Giancarlo has told them. Assunta reaches out for her young daughters, wanting to hold them in her arms. Now they are all crying on this darkest of days. Badly shaken and trembling, Lucia asks Assunta,

"Mama! Wha…what should we do?"

She doesn't answer. She does not know. What she does know is that the world they loved and shared has just died with Pirrone. And the worst still lies before them.

Pirrone's death brings many terrible consequences. Preparing for his funeral, the children struggle with the eternal question of why their father has died. Pirrone did not appear seriously ill at any time before his death. Antonella pounds her fists against the walls while screaming angrily at God for taking her beloved father. She was certainly Pirrone's favorite, and she is already beginning to feel lost without his presence. She cries bitterly while trying to accept the awful truth. Assunta's grief prevents her from explaining the complex reasons for his death, and Antonella has to cope with this nightmarish experience with only her sister and brother to comfort her.

On the day of the funeral, the traumatic feeling of loss becomes too overpowering for Assunta, and Giancarlo has to help his mother with every detail. His role as the family leader begins to emerge from this ordeal. Like his mother and sisters, he is very frightened by the death of his father. Being the oldest child and Pirrone's only son, he feels not only the pain of loss but also the responsibility for his family shifting squarely onto his shoulders.

Pirrone Cappodanno's import/export business required his constant vigil. Without him, the business cannot remain successful. Assunta knows little of her husband's business affairs and, following his death, she seeks out several of his friends to assist her in trying to save it. But the nature of the business demands Pirrone's expertise. In the weeks following the funeral, most of Pirrone's customer's are forced to replace his services. Giancarlo had hoped to take over the business one day, but he is still too young to run such a complicated enterprise without his father's guidance. Finally, the family loses the business and begins to look for other ways to support themselves. Assunta begins to assist as a midwife in many childbirths. Her earnings are meager, however, and she finds it necessary to also work for local businesses taking in laundry. Her life has changed dramatically following Pirrone's death, forcing her to support her family for the first time.

Giancarlo continues his studies while working on the harbor docks. He excels in school and instinctively makes the important family decisions. Upon successfully completing his schooling in Napoli, he wishes to go on to the university but cannot afford to do so. Desperately wanting to further his education, he makes a difficult decision. When the time comes to reveal his decision to his family, he sits privately with Assunta one evening and says,

"Mother, I want to go to the university to finish my education. The only choice I have is to join the military. I have decided to enlist in the Air Corps."

Assunta listens to her son tell of his plan to join the military, and she begins to cry. She fears losing his guidance in raising her two daughters. He tries his best to comfort her, saying,

"Mother, if I go to the university, I can be a much greater help to the family. I can run a business as Papa did. He would want me to do this."

Although Asssunta understands the importance of what he is saying, the thought of living without Giancarlo terrifies her.

Giancarlo's decision causes even greater fear for Lucia and Antonella. Antonella has been designing clothes for many of Napoli's wealthiest families, and her growing reputation has helped the family to survive. Giancarlo watches over her business to insure that she delivers her beautiful gowns on time and collects her fees. But she is afraid that, without his guidance, her business will fail. Lucia tries to convince her that her gift, as Pirrone referred to it, could continue to help the family, saying,

"Antonella, we can run your business until Giancarlo returns from his military training and studies. You will be famous by then, and he will be very proud."

Despite Lucia's flattering words, Antonella remains very concerned. No matter how hard she tries to accept Giancarlo's decision, losing his love and protection increases her sense of abandonment. With the clouds of war hovering just beneath the European horizon, his absence will cast Assunta and her daughters into the hell that is about to engulf all of Europe.

The family becomes much closer during Giancarlo's last weeks in Napoli as he completes all of his preparations to leave. On his final day at home, Assunta prepares a wonderful meal for him, serving all of his favorite dishes. The rich aromas of garlic, seafood, and homemade pasta simmering together atop the small cook stove fill the apartment. Antonella cheerfully asks,

"Giancarlo, come and help me set the table. The food is almost ready." He laughs at her instructions, saying,

"Even today, you will not let me rest?"

"You will have time to rest on the train, dear brother. If you wish to eat Mama's wonderful meal, you must still work for it," taunts Lucia. Assunta watches her children tease one another, savoring the short time they have left together. She reminds them,

34

"Our dinner is ready now. Be sure to put the salad and bread on the table with the pasta."

It is the simple, loving tasks they perform as a family that seem to draw them even closer on this difficult day. They sit around the small dining room table, sipping Chianti and delighting in the delicious meal Assunta has prepared. The girls remain overly attentive to Giancarlo, making sure his last dinner with them is joyous and pleasant. But beneath the forced laughter, smolders the deepening fear of bidding their brother farewell as he readies to leave Napoli. While finishing dinner, Giancarlo asks his sisters,

"I have not finished my packing yet. Can the two of you help me when we finish our dinner?"

"Yes, yes. I will fold your clothes and put them in your bag," responds Antonella.

"And I will prepare a nice lunch for you to take with you. The food on the train cannot be as good as ours," adds Lucia.

Eager to make his last day at home as comfortable as possible, they cater to his every need. Antonella sings several of his favorite songs, while Assunta and Lucia help him complete his final preparations. The hands on the tiny table clock race around like vanes on a windmill, and all too quickly it is time to leave for the train station. Giancarlo puts on his coat and kisses his sisters and mother one final time. He picks up his suitcase, and they all leave the apartment. With reluctant and tentative steps, they walk arm and arm along the narrow streets of Bagnoli, savoring their last few moments together.

When she arrives at the station, Assunta's emotions overcome her calm façade, and she reaches out to Giancarlo, throws her arms around his shoulders and begins to cry in deep, heart wrenching gasps. He holds her tightly and tenderly kisses her forehead, saying,

"Please don't worry mother. I will be home soon, and everything will be better."

"Giancarlo, promise me you will take care of yourself. I love you very much," Assunta says.

"I love all of you too; you know that. My training will be over quickly; you will see," he replies.

His attempt to assure her of his safe return does little to ease Assunta's sadness over his departure. Her eyes and cheeks glisten from the flood of tears she has shed. Antonella and Lucia also find it impossible to remain strong and supportive, as they too begin to cry. Giancarlo places his arms around his sisters and embraces them in one last brotherly gesture. He promises,

"When I return from my training, we will never have to say goodbye like this again."

Unpredictable world events will prevent Giancarlo from keeping that promise. Stepping aboard the train will entangle him in the madness soon to sweep over the entire continent of Europe, and it will be over four brutal years before he can return to his family. He takes a window seat; one facing the platform, and the train slowly pulls from the station. He watches his mother and sisters wave goodbye with silky, white scarves, until they appear as mere specks in the dimming light of the late afternoon. When they are no longer visible, he slumps back into the seat. There he cups his face in his hands and begins quietly weeping from the mounting guilt he feels while the train speeds him away to an unimaginable future.

CHAPTER 3

Mario continues to wander aimlessly in the years following the car theft incident. Now in his early 20's, he has no steady girlfriend, still lives at home, and has not managed to become as successful a gambler as Giuseppi. His life drifts somewhere between the gangland underworld run by his father's gambling associates and a simpler, more conventional blue-collar existence found throughout this city of factories.

His working skills provide stability. He learns a trade as a machinist, joins the union and accepts this existence as his life for the foreseeable future. The lure of the dice, however, proves too tempting to ignore, and he habitually looks for opportunities to polish his skills and try his luck. The big games in the plant are played with regularity, but when his luck goes cold, he loses much more than he wins. On the days he does win, he usually calls one of his lady friends and spends the night buying dinner, nightclubbing, and sleeping with her until the money is gone.

John and Joe also begin to cultivate some basic job skills. They are not interested in following Giuseppi's unpredictable lifestyle. John becomes involved in the growing union activities beginning to impact the factories in Detroit and decides to accept the frequently violent role of union steward. In what will become a lifelong career for him, John's no bullshit personality and tough but effective negotiating skills become his trademark. The rank and file, as well as the plant management, recognize his reputation for fairness and common sense. Joe continues to run the seafood business, and Giuseppi rarely interferes. He is his own boss and finds it an appealing way to live. His hard work has turned the little fish market into a profitable business. Giuseppi's interests revolve around his card games, and he permits Joe to keep most of the money earned from the sale of the seafood. Joe's life is much less complicated than that of his brothers, and the tiny business suits him perfectly. It is an idyllic situation for him, but that will soon change.

John and Mario are working the afternoon shift when the foreman comes rushing up to Mario and says,

"Hey Carlucci, ya better go find your brother and get a holda your old man. He called an' said somethin' bout an emergency, an' the both of ya's need to get home right away."

The old man has never tried to contact them at the plant before. Mario and John figure there is something wrong and rush home to find a distraught Giuseppi, pacing around the house. Deep furrows are visible on his brow, and his thin gray hair has a tussled look, as if he's been running his hands through it. John asks,

"Pa, what's a matter? Why did ya need us ta come home so fast?" The old man takes a couple of deep breaths and says,

"Joe, he hada to be rush to da hospital today. I think he's a very sick."

"Where is he, Pa? What happened?" asks Mario with great concern. Giuseppi replies,

"He's inna St. Mary's Hospital, near downtown. We gotta go there right away. They tella me to come backa after they run a test or somathing."

They immediately climb into Giuseppi's car and drive to the hospital. After they arrive, the receptionist gives them directions to Joe's room. Entering the four-bed ward, they find Joe awake but clearly upset. His face appears white and chalky and his eyes red and glazed. He stares straight up at the ceiling for several minutes before speaking to his family, but then says,

"The doc says I got a heart problem, but he won't tell me what's wrong."

John asks, "What happened?"

"I dunno. I just felt some pain in my chest and got real dizzy, like I was gonna faint or something," Joe answers. Mario's short temper flares up and he begins to grumble,

"That's bullshit. Give me a coupla minutes and I'll get some goddamn answers."

John grabs Mario by the arm and says,

"Shut up, will ya. All you're gonna do is piss these people off, and we won't get anywhere."

Giuseppi stands next to Joe's bed, as if frozen in place. He finds it easier to let his sons deal with this crisis than try to take charge himself. He is very concerned over Joe's heart problem, but he will not openly express it. This emergency doesn't fit into any part of his life that he can relate to, so he remains quiet and stoic.

John's political savvy from negotiating for the unions begins to pay off. He calmly leaves the room, finds a nurse's station and asks,

"Can someone tell me something about the condition of Joe Carlucci?" The nurse on duty asks, "Are you a relative?"

"Yeah, I'm his brother. Can you find a doctor I can talk to?" The nurse says she will try to locate the doctor as soon as possible and ask him to see them. John returns to Joe's room, and they wait for several minutes until someone arrives. Moments later, a doctor enters the ward and asks,

"Hello, are you Joe's brother?" extending his hand to John.

"Yes, I'm John and this is our father, Giuseppi, and that's Mario, Joe's other brother," John responds.

"I'm Dr. Little and I'm sorry for keeping you all waiting, but I'm still running blood tests on Joe to try and determine what the

41

problem is." He begins to explain what he thinks the nature of Joe's illness might be.

"Joe was apparently born with a damaged heart valve, and only now has it begun to show up," the doctor explains. "This is not a life threatening illness, but it is very serious. Joe will never fully recover from this type of heart ailment."

The doctor's words are chilling. Joe's life is about to significantly change, but no one can determine exactly how. Joe lies in his bed listening to the doctor's report. He wonders if he'll still be able to work anymore or even recover. He has visions of living in a wheel chair or hospital for the rest of his life, and the thoughts terrify him. Worried and desperate for some encouraging news, he looks the doctor straight in the face and asks,

"What the hell does that mean? Am I gonna be sick for the rest of my life?"

"Not if you follow my advice and take care of yourself," the doctor replies.

Joe slams his head back on his pillow. He claws at the blankets with each hand, balling up a fistful of the old, worn fabric tightly between his bone-white fingers. His breathing is short and intense from the fear and anxiety of his newly diagnosed heart condition. He feels on the verge of panic. He nervously quizzes the doctor,

"Wha…What do I gotta do to get better?"

"It's not complicated. Watch your weight, cut out the smokes, and don't over exert yourself," he answers. With that simple advice, he returns to his other patients. Joe remains very upset and he looks over at his father. Giuseppi looks down at him and says,

"Everything willa be ok, you gonna see." After saying so little to comfort his son, he abruptly leaves the room.

After he's gone, John and Mario stay and watch over their brother. Mario paces around the room in tight, little circles. In mounting frustration, he begins shouting at John,

"I can't believe he just stormed outta here like that. Why'd ya let em do that?"

John says,

"Keep quiet, will ya? Yer only gonna make Joe more upset." Mario's face winces and he bellows,

"I ain't gonna keep quiet, John. I'm goin' ta talk to em right now. This is a bunch of crap, him walkin out like that."

He flies out of the hospital room, past the nurses' station and up the long corridor looking for the old man. He finds him sitting alone in a waiting room, his head cradled in his hands, and staring at the floor as if he were in a trance. When Mario approaches him, he notices his eyes are wet and red. Mario stops, stands there a moment, and looks at Giuseppi with bewilderment. He has never been witness to any open displays of emotion from his father, but the tears reveal a side of Giuseppi that Mario is unprepared for. Mario's anger turns more to sympathy in the next few minutes.

"Pa, are you all right?" he asks.

Giuseppi neither looks up nor answers Mario. He simply nods his head up and down in a slow, measured response, indicating he has heard the question. He has never been very good at being a caring father and, after watching Joe's reaction to the doctor's comments, he doesn't quite know what to say or do. His awkward attempt to help Joe were the only words he could think to say. A strange feeling of helplessness smothers his feeble effort to comfort his son and the only thing he could think to do was leave the room. His disheveled look and sulking posture reveal a sense of guilt, which Mario has never before seen.

Giuseppi finally raises his head and looks at Mario, only to see his son struggling with his own emotions. He sees a confused and pained expression on Mario's face as his son cannot find anything to say to him. Mario leaves the waiting room in silence, abandoning his father as Giuseppi had abandoned Joe moments earlier. This emotional chasm can only be conquered by a world crisis that will soon force both men to open their minds and hearts to each other as never before.

After Mario returns to Joe's room, he asks him where he's been. Mario said,

"I had ta find a men's room and take a piss," choosing not to say anything of his disturbing experience with Giuseppi. John has been trying to cheer Joe up, but without much success. With John and Mario keeping him company, however, he begins to feel less anxious over his condition. As the time passes, his fears recede, and he begins to believe his life is not necessarily over. He talks of his illness in his familiar, sarcastic manner, saying,

"I guess it could be worse. At least the bastards don't wanna slice me open."

Spurred on by Joe's mild humor, John and Mario begin teasing him, saying,

"Looks like you ain't gettin' laid anymore. That's way too exciting for you now," John jokes.

"Hell, I ain't gettin' none anyway, so what's the big deal about that?" Joe quips.

"At least I don't got Mario's short temper. There'll never be a cure for that," Joe adds with a giggle.

They all laugh over Joe's little jab at Mario and take it as a good sign that he will recover.

Spending most of the evening in the hospital, Giuseppi, Mario, and John leave after Joe falls asleep. They drive home without speaking, the rumble of the car's engine producing the only sound they can hear. The old man parks the car in its usual space along the curb. Without muttering a word, he opens the door, climbs out of the car and trudges up the porch stairs leading to the foyer. Mario knows how much Joe's condition has upset his father, but he continues to keep the waiting room incident to himself. He and John remain in the car for a moment, each deep into their own thoughts on the events of the evening. Mario breaks the silence first, and says,

45

"I'm too nervous ta sleep, John. Let's go someplace and get a drink."

John groans his disapproval, saying,

"Aw Christ, Mario, ya know I gotta get inta the plant real early tomorrow. I ain't goin' nowhere tonight except ta sleep."

John follows Giuseppi into the house, leaving Mario standing alone at the curb. Wanting to get his mind off of the unsettling night, Mario decides to go out anyway. He jumps into the Ford sedan and speeds away into the night. It is late, and all of his regular hangouts are either closed or about to close, so Mario heads for an after-hours blind pig he knows of. He is hoping to find either a crap game or one of his women friends who usually hang out there. Parking the car a short distance away, he hikes back to the plain-looking house. The place has a tough reputation and, in case of trouble, getting out of there on foot is a choice he'd like to have. Sounds of people laughing stream through the drape-covered windows. After Mario knocks on the door, he sees a pair of large, bulging eyes peering at him through four small panes of leaded glass. A large, burly man slowly opens the door. His name is Pietro and, at six-foot six and two-hundred and seventy-five pounds, he makes sure no one causes any trouble in the place. Under the left breast of Pietro's suit coat, Mario sees the telltale stub of a Smith and Wesson revolver. He recognizes Mario and, in a thick Sicilian dialect, asks,

"*Mario, dove il hell siete stati ultimamente?*" puzzled by Mario's lengthy absence from the place. Mario replies with a laugh,

"You must be running outta money, eh Pietro? That's the only fuckin' reason you'd ever worry bout me." Pietro chuckles, and in his best English, shouts,

"Oh bullashit, Carlucci. You know your girlafriend Lena? She has a been askin' bout you all over the fuckin' place tonight."

Mario dates a number of different women, and Lena is one of his favorites. He has been going out with her for about a year. She loves playing craps in the blind pig and met Mario one night while gambling at the same table. She was having a bad run of luck at the time and screaming and cursing, as the dice claimed the last of her money. Mario found her behavior amusing and her wild and shameless manners intriguing. She is an attractive woman in her mid-twenties, with long, flaming red hair worn loosely over her bare shoulders. Her eyes are somewhere between green and turquoise, her body like that of a movie star. Although she looks more like a prostitute, she never sleeps with anyone for money. Instead, she carefully chooses her lovers from the endless parade of men who want to be with her. Hopelessly addicted to gambling, Lena noticed that Mario continued to win that night, and she began to place her bets with him. She started to win back some of her lost wagers while unashamedly flirting with him.

Mario slips Pietro a customary five-dollar tip and enters the blind pig. The joint is crowded. Small groups of players are gathered in the many, smoke-filled rooms of the tattered mansion. People in expensive suits and gowns mingle with those in old, weathered coats and crumpled hats, all expecting to find the beginning of their next winning streak in this unlikely place. Mario browses through the many rooms in an effort to find Lena or a good crap game. It doesn't take him long to locate both. The telltale yelling and shouting of a crowded dice table comes from one of the game rooms. He follows the sounds of the crap game into a large, corner room, and there is Lena. As Mario approaches the table, he sees that Lena is having a good night. There is a large stack of chips piled neatly in front of her. Spotting Mario across the table, she flashes him a bright smile and screams,

"Mario, there you are! Where have you been lately?"

Before he can answer, she jumps up, runs around all the other players at the table, and gives him a long, wet kiss. He wraps his arms around her slender waist and pulls her tightly against himself. After giving him another big kiss and a seductive smile, she says,

"I feel so sexy when I'm winning, Mario. Maybe you'll be lucky tonight, too."

"I hope so. I could use a little luck tonight," he replies.

He squeezes in next to her at the tightly-packed table and pulls a wad of bills from his coat pocket. After ordering a Crown Royal and water, he buys some chips and places a few bets. People are playing at a frantic pace, and the dice change hands with surprising frequency. Mario's normal game strategy isn't working tonight. He can't get a feel for the shooters or find a tempo to the table. After a steady spiral of bad bets, his losses mount rapidly. The dark night has slowly given way to the first light of a new morning, and Mario's luck still deserts him. He has lost a sizeable sum of money and, after a long, frustrating night, he gives up trying to beat the table. Lena does a little better, managing to keep some of the winnings she accumulated earlier in the evening. Mario begins drinking even more Crown Royal and gets predictably drunk. He collapses onto an old, shabby-looking love seat, nursing one last drink and swirling Lena's long red hair between his fingers.

"Let's get outta here, Lena. I'm pretty fucked up," he moans.

"Sure baby, I know where we can go," she giggles.

Lena grabs his arm and pulls him to his feet. She escorts him out of the blind pig and guides him into the passenger's seat of his car. She smiles mischievously, while stuffing her hand into his pant's pockets in search of his car keys. After giving him another sensual kiss, she climbs into the driver's side of the car, starts the engine, and drives off to her upper flat. Lena has never owned a car and rarely drives. The stick shift on Mario's sedan is nearly impossible for her to manage in the tight evening gown she wears. She resorts to hiking the gown up well above her knees, which makes her driving even more erratic. The herky-jerky ride continually tosses Mario from side to side, his head thumping against the window glass several times. He is sleepier than he is drunk. When he wakes after yet another collision with the door window, he asks,

"Where the hell are we goin, Lena?" She laughs out loud, pats his thigh, and says,

"Don't worry, lover. We're going to my place. I'm gonna take good care of you." Lena enjoys sleeping with Mario and never passes up an opportunity to make love to him, even if he is a little drunk at the time. She continues driving through the deserted, early morning streets, putting only a random milkman or paperboy at serious risk. The first shafts of sunlight flash through the shadows of the city's ragged skyline and race across Mario's half-opened eyes. Neither fully asleep nor awake, he tries to find a comfortable position, eventually leaning onto Lena's shoulder. While Mario drifts in and out of a shallow sleep, Lena runs her right hand along the full length of his thigh, brushing his groin and hoping to arouse him. Pulling up in front of her flat, she turns off the car's engine and lights. She leans over and kisses him, exploring his firm body with her hands. She then whispers into his ear,

"Wake up, baby. We're here."

They are invariably good together. Even though he has been drinking heavily for most of the evening, he knows exactly what she is up to. He reacts by caressing her breast, while their kisses get steamier. With a smirk on her face, she backs away from him and says,

"I am glad to see you are awake enough to know what's going on."

"Oh, I know Lena, I know," he replies with a slight smile on his face.

She encourages him to get out of the car and helps him up the dark stairway to her upper flat. After she opens the door, Mario steps in and Lena follows, locking the door behind her. Mario is familiar with her place, and he easily makes himself comfortable. He kicks off his shoes, unbuttons his shirt and lies down on the overstuffed couch. Lena goes to the kitchen, takes two beers from the tiny icebox, and returns to the living room. Sitting on the edge of the couch, she asks,

"I got us a couple of beers, would'ja like one?"

Well aware that this day is far from over, Mario gives her a seductive smile of his own and says,

"Sure, I'm not goin anyplace for a while."

He takes a few sips from the long-necked bottle and places it on the small table next to the couch, as they look at each other in anticipation of being together again.

The numbing affect of the whiskey has all but worn off, and Mario seems to catch a second wind. Lena sees he is wide-awake and runs her tongue around the tip of the long necked bottle in a slow, erotic motion while sipping her beer. She loves to tease him when they are about to make love, knowing how aggressive it makes him. She places her beer on the table next to his, leans down, and begins to kiss him, her tongue darting and flicking against his. Mario enjoys her playfulness and, as she rubs her body against his, he begins to sober up fast. Lena takes great pleasure in touching Mario and is not the least bit hesitant to explore his body. Their kisses become more explosive, and she slides her hands under his open shirt, delighting in the feel of his taut, muscular chest. Rubbing his smooth skin stimulates her passion to even greater heights, and she places her hand between his legs once again, finding Mario highly aroused by all of her attention. In spite of her wild nature, she sleeps with only a few men. Mario is clearly one of her favorites. With their sexual intensity reaching its boiling point, she rises from the couch, turns her back to him, and asks,

"Would you mind unzippin' me, darlin?"

Mario stands and unzips the gown for her. She slides the dress off her shoulders and allows it to drop to the floor. Lena has a stunningly beautiful body, with perfectly shaped breasts, appearing slightly larger than the bowl of a champagne glass. Her waist is trim and her legs long and slender. Her firm, athlete-like buttocks accentuate them. While she stands there in just her bra and panties, Mario finds her as alluring as ever. She holds her hand out to him and leads him down the long hallway to her bedroom.

Lena unbuttons Mario's shirt and removes it, lightly kissing first his muscular chest and then his rippled stomach. She unbuckles his belt and undoes his pants, letting them drop to the floor. After pulling him onto the bed, she removes all of his remaining clothing. Their craving for each other becomes instinctive and primal, their embrace bordering on the edge of violence. They roll from side to side atop the small brass bed. Mario removes her bra and takes her into his mouth, first one breast, then the other. He rips her panties down her long slender legs, and she kicks them onto the floor. The touching of flesh along the full length of their bodies drives Lena crazy. She rolls on top of him, pinning his wrists against the fresh, white sheet. Her turquoise eyes stare at him with an insatiable hunger, and her russet-colored hair flails wildly as she begins to make love to him. Their lovemaking is physical, wanton, and at times, violent. Their shared, all-consuming desire lasts well into the early afternoon. They then fall asleep from delicious exhaustion, remaining that way until late in the day.

When Mario wakes up, he realizes he is late for the afternoon shift at the plant again and becomes very angry with himself. Scrambling from Lena's bed, he practically ignores her as he worries about how to make things right at the plant. Lena props herself up on her elbows and watches Mario dressing himself.

"Do ya have ta leave right away, baby? I can make you something to eat if you want," she inquires.

"No, I gotta try and git to work. I'm gonna catch hell as it is," he answers.

Mario's feelings for Lena can change suddenly. After spending the night making love to her, he is capable of running out of her flat without even saying goodbye. He does not love her. They are drawn together by sex and gambling, and those are the only common interests they share. Mario treats all of the women in his life in the same way. He never feels the need to enter into a long-term relationship with any of them. He finishes dressing and dashes out of Lena's flat.

Mario has missed work before and knows he will have to endure the anger of the foreman, as well as that of his brother, John. In the past, John has kept the foreman from firing Mario by getting the union's help in certain situations. But Mario's repeated irresponsibility has made John's influence far less affective. Mario calls John at the plant and says,

"John, it's me, Mario."

"Goddamn it, Mario. Where the fuck are you?" screams John.

"Look, I'm…I'm sorry. Tell the foreman that I'll git there inna half hour, okay?" Mario begs. John is seething and continues to shout into the phone,

"I ain't gonna keep doin this, Mario. I can't fix this shit forever, ya know. Ya better get your ass into work if you wanna hang on ta your job."

Mario hangs up the phone and hurries into the plant. In spite of his behavior, he believes John will always be there to help him get out of a jam. That is about to change.

CHAPTER 4

At sixteen years old, Antonella has managed to nurture her meager business as a seamstress into that of a respected, young, fashion designer. Women from some of Napoli's finest families regularly ask her to create something special for them. Her success is a tremendous help to the family, and they are all very proud of her. They now live in a modest but comfortable apartment that allows Antonella ample space for her sewing machine and cutting table. Assunta no longer has to work as much as she once did, choosing instead to help Antonella sew many of the dresses she designs. Lucia continues to work in a local trattoria and, between the three of them, they have found a life of relative happiness that didn't seem possible only a few years earlier.

Giancarlo has completed his studies and elects to remain in the military as a career officer. He has excelled in his pursuit of aviation training and will soon become a pilot in the Italian Air Corps. His visits home become more infrequent, however, as his commitment to his new career begins to demand much more of his time. He writes to the family often, telling them of the many exciting places he has visited and of his increasing success in the military. In spite of his letters, Assunta, Lucia, and Antonella miss him dearly, but they have found ways to survive on their own. They feel very proud of what he has accomplished, for not many young men from their part of Napoli have become successful military pilots. And like the proud mother she is, Assunta tells her neighbors of Giancarlo's achievements anytime they will listen.

Antonella decides to leave school and devote all her time to running her prospering business and supporting the family. The ever wild and passionate moods that have characterized her personality from her youth remain, however. She is now an attractive, young woman, with long, dark auburn hair and a beautiful face. Her rich, brown eyes are framed by ebony lashes and high, classic cheekbones. Her body has also matured, with firm breasts, long shapely legs and a curvaceous shape. Physically, she looks more like a woman of twenty than the sixteen-year-old girl she actually is. She creates quite a commotion among the young men in Bagnoli as she joins Assunta and Lucia during their beloved Sunday strolls along the Mediterranean. The clothes she designs for herself make her look even more beautiful and provocative, and many men, both young and old, stare at her with lustful interest. Assunta also notices this unexpected attention and constantly reminds Antonella,

"You are a young girl without a father to look after you. You must not dress so much like a grown woman. People will think you are immoral."

Antonella laughs loudly and says,

"Mama, I love to wear my clothes. It is good for my business. You need not worry. I can take care of myself, you know."

Once again, Assunta cannot persuade her daughter to follow the old conservative traditions of her family and, soon, Antonella's youthful fearlessness will lead her into trouble.

Antonella loves to swim in the Mediterranean. She walks the short distance to the beach on days she is not working and spends hours in the ocean. She enjoys the sound of the crashing waves, the heat from the pristine golden sands of her favorite beach, and the smell of the sea air. Accompanied by Lucia, she tirelessly swims long distances into the harbor and back. The salty Mediterranean makes swimming very easy, and they sometimes venture out near the large ships that are anchored in the bay. Even from a distance, the foreign sailors call out to them in strange languages, frequently waving candy or cigarettes at them to entice them to come aboard. Lucia understands the dangers lurking aboard those ships and warns Antonella,

"It is best just to ignore them and swim away from the ships. Then they cannot bother us." Antonella usually follows her sister's advice, but not without first teasing some of the sailors.

"Che cosa li hanno per offrirli?" she shouts in feigned interest, knowing they cannot speak Italian and have nothing to really give them.

On a warm and sunny summer day, Antonella tires of sewing and decides to go to the beach to swim alone. She tells Assunta,

"Mama, I must go to Senora Minelli's home to measure her for a new gown. I will return in several hours." Assunta is busy doing some laundry and does not bother to come into the same room with Antonella. She shouts from another room of the apartment,

"Do not be too late, Antonella. I want you to be home before nightfall."

Antonella has begun lying to Assunta more often in order to explore Bagnoli on her own. Lucia spends more time working in the trattoria and cannot join her sister as she has in the past. Being a strong swimmer, Antonella gives little thought to the dangers of swimming by herself. The brilliant sun scorches the beach, lifting shimmering ribbons of heat skyward. It is a perfect day to enjoy the ocean. Antonella roams the Via Pozzuoli, in no particular hurry, and soon arrives at her favorite place to store her street clothes. She steps into one of the red and white striped modesty huts at the edge of the beach to change into her bathing suit. Immediately after she leaves the hut, one of several young boys who recognizes her runs up to her and asks with obvious affection,

"Antonella, I will watch your beach bag while you swim if you like. Can I do that for you?" With a seductive smile on her face, she replies,

"Thank you, Giovanni. How very kind of you to offer."

With that comment, she leans down slightly and gives him a light kiss on the cheek. The boy is speechless, as the kiss, the only payment he hoped to receive, causes him to flush with embarrassing delight. Antonella has begun to learn how to use her beauty. With a charming smile and subtle touch, she has the boy ready to guard her belongings from the many thieves found all over Napoli. Rushing down the beach toward the ocean, she can see there are many ships in the harbor. The sounds of clanging bells and bellowing horns fill the air over the Mare de Napoli. Antonella runs into the surf and dives into the ocean, swimming away from the beach in her usual explosive style. Her love for the ocean allows her to swim about effortlessly. She is well conditioned and very fit from years of swimming long distances along this beach. She knows if she tires it is possible to simply float and relax on the surface until feeling ready to continue. After a short distance, she decides to lie motionless on her back for a moment, basking in the warm sun and the refreshing, cool water. The serenity of the moment is suddenly interrupted by a voice that calls out to her in English.

"Hello, Senorita. What are you doing so far from shore?" the voice asks.

Startled by the strange greeting, Antonella looks around and sees a young man in a small rowboat, only a few yards away, watching her. Feeling threatened by the presence of someone else in this private world she enjoys, her first reaction is to swim away from the boat. The young man follows her, while shouting,

"Please wait. I only want to help you get to shore safely."

Unable to escape the intruder, Antonella soon becomes exhausted and has to stop to catch her breath. The mysterious stranger rows the small boat much closer to her this time and smiles while extending his hand to her. At this close distance, Antonella can see he is a handsome young sailor from one of the ships in the harbor. His dashing looks ease her anxiety slightly, but in her most demanding voice she asks in Italian,

"I speak no English. What do you want?"

Shaking his head from side to side, he touches his hand to his temple, saying,

"I'm sorry. I do not speak Italian."

They stare at each other in a clumsy silence for several minutes, neither sure of what the other has said. He continues to politely smile at her and offers to help her into the small boat once again. Antonella's anxiety slowly fades, giving way to her ever-present curiosity. Lucia warned her to beware of foreign sailors, but Lucia has never actually met one. To Antonella, this handsome young man could not be one of the evil men Lucia so often refers to. She swims alongside the boat and reaches up, hanging onto the old, battered rub rail. This man with a boyish appearance stands up and stretches his arm to her, offering to lift her into the boat. With her courage bolstered by his kind smile, Antonella finally grabs his hand and, in one swift motion, lets him pull her into the boat. She sits on the seat furthest from him, pulling her wet hair from her face while nervously watching his every move. After a few cautious minutes, she says,

"Thank you for your help. Where are you from?"

The sailor is from England, and he has been in Napoli for three days. He crews aboard a cargo ship named the Channel Star and expects to remain in Napoli for a week while waiting to unload cargo. Unsure of what she has just said, he replies,

"My name is Steven, and I'm British." Aware that Antonella cannot understand him, he points to his chest with his first two fingers and slowly repeats,

"I am Steven; do you understand?"

Antonella realizes he is giving her his name and, mimicking his gesture, she points to herself and replies,

"Ah yes, I think I understand. Your name is Steven. I am Antonella."

When the British seaman figures out she has just revealed her name, he extends his hand to shake hers and says,

"It's very nice to meet you, Antonella." Antonella smiles as they shake hands. Although she cannot understand him, she begins to feel more comfortable in the boat with him. But midday has given way to late afternoon, and she must return home. She points toward the beach and asks,

"Can you please take me to the beach? I must go home right away."

Steven also points in the same directions and quizzically asks,

"You want to go back to the beach?'

Antonella nods her head in agreement, and he begins rowing the dory back to the shore. She hesitates to make lengthy eye contact with him, choosing instead to study the weather-beaten seats and scarred floorboards of the little craft in mock interest. She catches a glimpse of his personal belongings in a small canvas bag between his feet. Steven notices her interest and stops rowing for a moment. Sticking his hand into the bag, he pulls out two, brown-colored cigarettes and some French chocolate. Holding several pieces of chocolate in his outstretched hand, he says,

"Here, have some. It is French chocolate and very good."

For the next few moments, Antonella's mind dances wildly between trusting this man and taking the chocolate or being careful and refusing to try some. She notices the candy is wrapped in delicate, colorful paper, making it very tempting. An instant later, she takes a piece of the chocolate and says,

"Grazie, tante, Steven." While Antonella savors the delicious chocolate, Steven lights one of the two cigarettes he has retrieved from his bag and hands it to her. At first, she raises her hand, shaking it from side to side, saying,

"No, no. I have never smoked a cigarette before."

Steven continues to encourage her to try it and, soon, her curious nature overcomes her better judgment. Taking the lit cigarette between her fingers, she warily looks at it, trying to decide what to do next. Steven lights the other cigarette and says,

"Like this, Antonella," and takes a long, slow puff on his cigarette. She tentatively takes the cigarette between her lips and lightly draws on it. She does not inhale at first, only swirling the smoke inside her mouth and then blowing it out upwards, hoping to appear more experienced than she is. Steven laughs and says,

"No, no, you must inhale," demonstrating the technique by deeply inhaling another mouthful of smoke. Antonella sees the ease with which he smokes his cigarette and attempts to inhale a large puff of her own. Her reaction is predictable and unpleasant. She begins to cough and choke from the smoke in her lungs, and her face reddens while she gasps for air. In a harsh, raspy voice, she tells him,

"I...I can't breathe. I don't want any more." But Steven persists, instructing her to take smaller amounts. He shows her how to do it and, after a few more puffs, the discomfort begins to lessen.

Antonella's first experience with cigarettes and sailors produces a euphoric excitement she finds fascinating. The attention of the attractive foreigner suddenly makes her feel more like an adult than a young girl. After the surf guides the small boat onto the beach, she jumps out and says,

"Good bye Steven. Thank you for the chocolate and the ride in your boat."

She dashes across the beach in the direction of the modesty huts and the boy who has been watching her bag, but before she disappears from sight, Steven shouts,

"Please come back tomorrow. We can go out on the boat again."

Antonella hears him shout to her but understands nothing he is saying. But she too, begins planning to return to the beach the next day, in hopes of meeting the British sailor once again. Arriving at the huts, her young, love-struck admirer sees her and rushes up to deliver her beach bag. She kisses him once again and hastily steps into the changing hut to put on her dress. She's had an exciting time and, while returning home, wonders why Lucia fears the sailors so. Her encounter today convinces her that Lucia is wrong, and she cannot wait to tell her all about the amazing adventure.

When Antonella enters the apartment, Assunta sees that her hair is damp and knows she has not been with a client, as she had said. She becomes furious and begins to shout,

"Antonella, how did your hair become wet when visiting with a client?" Antonella replies,

"Senora Minelli was not at home when I arrived there. She lives very close to the beach, you know. It was very hot today, and I went swimming to cool off."

Her excuse does not fool her mother. Assunta is both angry and disturbed that her youngest daughter ignores the dangers that reside in the harbor. She pleads with Antonella, saying,

"You must not swim near the large ships. The men on those ships are all thieves and criminals. They will rob you and hurt you if you get too close to them." Antonella tells her mother,

"Mama, I promise I will not swim so far from shore again." But even as she speaks the words, she schemes for ways to break that promise. She remains fascinated by the British sailor and cannot resist the temptation to meet him again.

Leaving her mother in the kitchen, she enters the bedroom she shares with Lucia and prepares to take a bath. Antonella carefully adjusts the two porcelain tub handles until the water temperature feels comfortable. The tub is slowly filling as Lucia returns home. She joins Antonella in the bedroom and finds her sitting on the edge of the tub in nothing but her underclothing. As Antonella splashes her hand in the fresh, bath water, Lucia suspects she has been swimming alone. There is no other reason for her to bathe at this time of the day. Lucia's concern for her sister's safety overshadows the risk of another argument with her, and she asks,

"You have been swimming alone today, haven't you? I know you have, so don't lie to me."

At the same moment Lucia asks that question, Antonella jumps up, removes her underclothing and climbs into the tub. Lounging comfortably, she stares at no particular place on the ceiling, as if she were dreaming. Then with a light and whimsical tone in her voice, she says,

"I met a very handsome stranger today. He came up to me in a little row boat while I was swimming."

"Is he from Napoli?" asks Lucia with raised interest.

"Oh no. His name is Steven and he speaks only English. I think he is from Britain."

"He is from one of the ships, isn't he?" she asks angrily.

"Yes, but he is very nice. He gave me French chocolates. They were very delicious."

Then, with a mischievous grin on her face, Antonella confesses,

"I even tried smoking cigarettes today. It was so exciting." Lucia sees no humor in what she's just heard from her younger sister.

Lucia shares her mother's worry over Antonella. She fears this naive young girl with the body of a goddess will continue to take reckless chances in Bagnoli unless she is severely warned. Lucia stands next to the tub with her hands placed on her hips and says,

"Antonella, terrible things can happen to young women found swimming in the main harbor. Some have been raped and murdered by foreign sailors. Others have been kidnapped and forced into

prostitution. Is that what you want to happen to you?" Antonella scoffs at her sister, saying,

"Lucia, do you think those old wives tales are true? They are so foolish sounding. I do not believe one word of them."

Lucia, feeling frustrated and helpless, warns Antonella,

"I will tell Giancarlo if you continue to see the foreign sailor. I most certainly will."

But Antonella simply ignores her sister, sinking beneath the warm water of her bath in unconcerned defiance. Since the death of her father, she feels no need to seek the approval of any man for her actions, including that of her brother. She has become accustomed to taking care of herself and intends to continue doing so.

Ignoring Lucia's warnings, Antonella returns to the beach several days later. She eagerly scans the immediate area looking for the little dory and the English sailor, but they are nowhere to be found. She continues on to the modesty huts to change into her swimsuit again. Giovanni, her young admirer, sees her and runs to assist her once again. This time, however, he has a message for her.

"Antonella, an English-speaking sailor has been asking about you today," he reveals.

"Where did he go? Do you know?" she asked. Pointing toward the end of the beach, he says,

"His small boat is tied to the pier over there, but he is no longer in it." Excited by the news, she dives into the water and starts to swim in the direction of the distant pier.

After a short swim, she can see the small boat bobbing up and down in the rolling waves but, as the young boy said, there is no one aboard. Nearing the boat, she clings to its hull and pulls herself sufficiently out of the water to look inside. She sees no evidence of his being there and decides to swim back to the beach. Turning away from the dory, she suddenly hears her name being called from the pier,

"Antonella, Antonella, wait, don't go!"

She stops and turns to face the pier once more. There she sees the Englishman, running along the pier and waving with one hand, while trying to hold a heavy bag of provisions with the other. Arriving at the boat, he is breathless from the struggle with his bag of supplies. He drops them into the bobbing craft and places his hands on his knees as he tries to catch his breath. Amused by his flattering effort to greet her, she says,

"Boun giorno, Steven," using the only English word she knows. Once again able to breathe, he extends his hand out to her and says,

"Here, I'll help you climb aboard." After he assists her into the bouncing dory, they exchange nervous smiles while trying to talk to each other. Steven resorts to pulling cigarettes from his shirt pocket.

"Do you want to smoke?" he asks while lighting a cigarette for himself. This time, Antonella is able to smoke the cigarette with much less difficulty than during her first attempt. Wanting to act like someone older than herself, she holds the cigarette between her first two fingers and puffs on it in a rapid-fire technique, blowing the billowing smoke up into the air in long, streaming columns. She then points in the direction of the large ships anchored nearby and asks,

"Da che delle molte navi siete?"

Steven guesses by her gestures she is asking which ship is his. He turns, faces a large transport anchored near the pier and points in its direction, saying,

"There. The Channel Star. The one with the British flag flying. That's my ship. Do you understand?"

"Yes, I understand. Your ship is very close." she answers.

The large ships that visit Napoli have fascinated Antonella all her life, and they still intrigue her. Her curiosity and interest are obvious, and Steven can sense it. While motioning at the large vessel, he asks,

"Do you want to come aboard my ship and visit for a while?" Through a combination of his English, her Italian, and endless hand-gesturing, Antonella finally understands his invitation and agrees to join him aboard the ship.

As Steven releases the dock lines from the mooring cleats, Antonella can feel an exhilaration from this adventure beginning to build. The cadence of the squeaking oarlocks and the sea splashing against the wooden hull of the tiny boat place her temporarily at ease. Never having been on a large harbor ship before, she looks forward to seeing one up close.

Steven is the ship's watch officer and has responsibility for the ship's security during its stay in Napoli. All other crewmen from the Channel Star are ashore during the day, and the large ship's vast decks are deserted. Steven is aware there will be no one else aboard but says nothing to Antonella. Her naiveté will soon betray her.

Arriving alongside the Channel Star, Steven secures the dory to the gangplank with the dock lines. He motions for Antonella to remain seated, telling her,

"You wait here. I will carry the bag up to the main deck and return. Do you know what I am saying?"

Antonella nods in agreement, saying,

"Si, io capisco."

Sitting motionless in the dory, she is in awe of the enormous size of the hulking old ship. Having spent her life watching them from the beach, she is not aware of their great length and height…longer than two city blocks in Bagnoli and higher than the apartment building in which she lives. She feels highly intimidated by this floating city. Steven returns and motions for her hand, pulling her onto the gangplank. He points up the long metal stairway leading to the main deck and encourages Antonella to climb up in front of him. She starts up the unstable ascent when she unexpectedly feels Steven's hand on her waist, as if guiding her upwards. She turns her head and looks over her shoulder momentarily but feels no threat from his touch and continues climbing upward. Upon reaching the main deck of the towering transport, Antonella is astonished by the beautiful view of Napoli. The city and sea present a spectacle of pink corals and mystic greens splashed wildly together onto a life-sized artist's canvas. With a blue summer sky as a backdrop, the view is breathtaking. Expressing her exuberance, she says,

"Look at how beautiful Napoli is. I have never known it to be so wondrous."

She scampers across the deck to enjoy the panoramic view from several different locations, but she remains oblivious to Steven's increasing physical contact. He places his hands on her back and shoulders while standing behind her and pointing out ships from other countries. As he becomes more aggressive, Antonella suddenly feels a flash of discomfort. She pulls away and keeps a safer distance between them. His physical contact subsides for a short time, but then he asks,

"Would you like to see where the *Capitan* steers from?" mimicking someone with both hands on a large wheel. He points up to a deck lined with many windows, up yet another stairway.

"No…No thank you. This is…this is…," she tries to tell him. But before she can finish her remark, he grabs her by the hand and leads her to the pilothouse. Steven's behavior becomes more callous and demanding. He holds onto her hand firmly and, with an increasing threat in his voice, tells her,

"Go up. It will be fine. Go…don't you know what I mean?"

Antonella is feeling very uncertain about staying aboard the ship any longer, but she is not allowed a choice to stay or leave.

Feeling like an invited guest, she obliges him and makes her way up the next stairway. Once onto the pilothouse deck, Steven opens the locked door to the control room and leads Antonella into the strange-looking world of steel and glass. He begins to show Antonella the controls, explaining in slow, animated English,

"This is where the Capitan steers from, and this handle controls the horn."

She understands nothing he is saying, but his articulated hand signals are somewhat clear. She places her hands around the horn's control and asks,

"Can I pull this?" making a gesture of her own, imitating a jerking motion.

Steven nods in agreement, and she pulls the control as hard as she is able. It emits a loud, ear-piercing boom that frightens her greatly. Steven laughs at her startled reaction and, after her shock recedes, Antonella also laughs at her reaction to the blaring sound. The humorous moment camouflages Steven's abrupt mood change. He grasps her by the wrist and pulls her further into the ship's interior. Antonella becomes very frightened and, as before, tries to pull away.

"I want to go now. I must leave," she pleads, but to no avail. Directly behind the pilothouse is the pilot's berth room and, after entering, Steven closes the door behind them, trapping her inside with him.

His eyes, once kind and gentle-looking, now cast a fierce and chilling glare at her. His mouth is agape, his tongue flicking in and out of his mouth like that of a python. He has positioned himself in a very intimidating posture between her and the door. He springs forward, grabs her wrists and pins her against the rearmost wall of the cramped little room. He tries to kiss her but she thrashes her head from side to side. She feels the wetness from his tongue on her lips and cheeks, and at last she screams,

"No, no, please stop. This is not why I came here."

"Its all right, my pretty little lady. Relax and enjoy yourself," he replies in a groveling voice. He does not stop and his hands begin fondling her all over. She succumbs to total panic while trying to fight off the advances of this man she had trusted. Her screams go unheard aboard the deserted ship and, as she struggles to free herself, Steven pulls her bathing suit top down around her waist. With her breasts revealed to a man for the first time, she gasps as he pushes her down onto a bunk, where he continues to kiss and fondle her exposed body. Now crying and in fear for her life, she makes one last attempt to free herself by violently kicking at Steven and landing a severe blow to his groin with her powerful legs. He recoils in agonizing pain, drops to his knees and curls up on the floor of the cabin, holding himself between his legs.

Antonella seizes the opportunity. She leaps over her fallen attacker, runs to the cabin door and pulls it open. Disoriented by the ship's confusing structure, she speeds in the wrong direction before turning back toward the pilothouse deck. Her years of swimming have made her strong and fast, and all she can think about is running as hard as she can and getting off the Channel Star. She runs down the first stairway, and for a moment, loses her bearings once more. Even greater panic sets in when she cannot remember how to get off the ship.

She spins and darts in several directions, vainly looking for the way to the main deck. She finds a familiar-looking stairway and leaps down it, taking several steps at every stride, until she reaches the bottom. With tears streaming down her face, she races along the main deck until she at last finds the main stairway leading to the dory. When she reaches the lower gangplank, her instinctive reaction is to dive into the sea and swim to safety. But, first, she unties the little boat and casts it away from the Channel Star, preventing Steven from following her. Diving into the water, she swims as hard and as fast as she is able and finds herself a safe distance from the great ship in a matter of minutes.

After reaching the shore, she runs to the young boy holding her beach bag. Still terrified, she forgets the top half of her bathing suit remains gathered around her waist. The boy clutching her bag can see the terror in her face. He says nothing and hands Antonella's bag to her, so she can put on her dress. She is trembling so badly while sitting in the changing hut, she cannot button the back of her dress. She waits for several minutes, hoping to calm down before she must return home, but the trembling will not subside. Still badly shaken by the events aboard the transport ship and desperately wanting to go home, she steps from the changing hut and asks Giovanni if he will button her dress for her. He would do anything for Antonella, and as he fastens the buttons, he asks,

"Antonella, what happened? Are you in danger?"

"I am not hurt Giovanni. But please promise to say nothing of this to anyone," she replies in a weak quivering voice.

Antonella runs home, makes her way into the small apartment and goes directly to her room. Fortunately, there is no one home at the time. She continues to tremble with fear from the near rape. Her trust in men is thoroughly shattered, and life will be very different for her after today. She lies on her bed, pulls a blanket over her and curls up into a little ball, weeping. She feels alone and vulnerable for the first time since Pirrone's death. Before drifting off to sleep, she murmurs,

"Papa, sono così spiacen," apologizing to her father for what almost took place aboard the British ship.

CHAPTER 5

It is now 1940 and Mario has reached his mid-twenties. He pays little attention to the war in Europe and never thinks about Hitler and Mussolini. His machinist's job provides him enough money to live from day to day and have a little left over to try his luck with the dice. Lena, and other women like her, have become a regular part of his uncomplicated world. He's not found love with any of them, and his ambivalence brings a sense of loneliness that constantly haunts him. His only solace is with John and Joe. They also remain unmarried, but each has a woman he is seeing regularly. Mario suspects it is only a matter of time before they will get married. The thought of them no longer living together as a family saddens him. And to make matters worse, Giuseppi has been strongly suggesting that they all should be married by now and providing him with grandchildren. Mario knows his brothers are listening.

It is another typical Friday night, and John and Mario rush from the plant immediately after their shift is over. The usual after-work crap game has never gotten started, and Mario is anxious to find some action. They end up in a small bar not far from their home, and after a few drinks, Mario tries to persuade his brother to go with him to a club in Toledo he has heard of recently. Mario knows John is not in the mood for one of his adventures, but he is relentless in his tactics, saying,

"Come on, John. You ain't got shit ta do tonight. Besides, I hear they got a band that plays jus like Jimmy Dorsey, and the women there are supposed to be gorgeous."

John is all too familiar with Mario's pleadings and says,

"I got a date if I want it. Why the hell would I want to drive sixty fuckin miles to Toledo to find another? Besides, I know all ya wanna do is find a goddamn crap table somewhere."

"Yeah, well, so what? Look, if ya go, I promise we kin leave right away if it ain't any good," replies Mario.

Toledo is a rowdy city situated on the banks of the Maumee River. Its burlesque houses and dingy eateries attract a surly crowd of customers. When fueled by an abundance of cheap booze, their main interests on the weekends are arguments and bar fights. In the end, Mario is sure John wouldn't risk letting him go there alone. Even though they are both grown men, the years John spent watching out for him are not easily cast aside. John reluctantly agrees to join Mario, saying,

"OK, goddamn it, I'll go, but just this once. Don't ever pull this shit again, ya hear?"

Mario's face lights up in a huge smile. He immediately orders another round of Crown Royal and water, slaps John on the back and shouts,

"Ya see, I knew ya wanted ta go. Who knows, maybe we can find ya a hot little woman ta make ya forget your problems." John stares down into his fresh drink, slowly shaking his head from side to side. With a half-hearted laugh, he says,

"Mario, the only problem I have right now is you." Mario knows that whenever John gives up arguing that way, he's won him over and they are certain to have a good time together.

Mario argues with John over many things. When they were younger, their confrontations included an occasional fistfight. Giuseppi was frequently forced to intervene, threatening to throw them out of his house if their battles didn't end. Fortunately, their physical attacks on one another ended, but they continue to argue as only brothers can. Throughout all their battles, however, exists an unbreakable bond of trust and love of family. And even though they will occasionally scream at each other, no one but Giuseppi dares to interfere.

Upon returning home, John and Mario find Giuseppi sitting at the dining room table reading the day's newspaper. He doesn't look up when they enter the room. With his elbows resting on the table and his forehead in his hands, he leans over the paper in deep thought.

He peers through his wire-framed reading glasses at the story before him, unaware of their presence. They can see something is troubling him, prompting John to ask,

"What'sa matter, Pa? Ya look upset about something."

"Itsa thees damn a war in Europe. Mussolini isa helpa da Nazis and *Italia* isa gonna fighta the British. Itsa gonna be very bad for our *familia* ina Sicily," he responds in a solemn voice. Mario tries to lessen his concern, saying,

"Maybe they're in a safe place, Pa. Besides, there ain't no fightin in Sicily, right?"

Giuseppi waves an old, tattered envelope at Mario and says,

"Thees isa the lasta letter I get froma my cousin, Enrico. He say alla the younga men are gone froma the city. Itsa no good, Mario. Itsa no good." John also tries to console his father, saying,

"Pa, you know the damn Europeans look for reasons to get into wars. Shit, they been doin that forever. This'll all be over in a little while; you'll see."

Giuseppi knows better, however. He remembers the First World War and is aware of how easily the horror of war spreads. He says nothing, but he is frightened about the potential of the United States to get dragged into the conflict. John, Mario, and Joe are all at the prime age for military service, and Giuseppi clearly understands that. As is his nature, he does not easily express these most private of feelings, but his obvious worry over the war is an unexpected surprise to his sons. He is not sure they realize what is really troubling him, but with the world on the brink of madness, his emotions are becoming more difficult to hide.

Mario looks at John and shrugs his shoulders. He waits for a reaction from him, but there is little either of them can say to lessen Giuseppi's concerns, so they simply leave him sitting in the dining room. After washing, shaving, and changing their clothes, they decide to get some dinner before going out for the night. Without warning, Mario stops in the middle of the living room, turns to John and says,

"Wait, I got another idea."

"Now what?" John laments. Mario suddenly storms into Joe's bedroom, grabs him by the arm, and pulls him out of the door with him, laughing and shouting,

"Let's go, Joe. Me and John are gonna go out and get somethin' to eat, then get a coupla drinks, and you're goin with us."

"Where the hell are ya goin? I already got plans," argues Joe.

"Not any more. Get your ass up and movin," hollers Mario, flaunting a mischievous grin. Mario gives Joe little choice in the matter, as he and John are not about to take no for an answer. After he puts on some dressier clothes, they charge out of the house and pile into the Ford sedan.

"Ya didn't tell me where the hell we're going yet," Joe says once again. John starts to chuckle, looks at Mario and asks,

"You wanna tell em, or should I?"

"Go ahead. You tell him. I can't duck if he takes a swing at me," jokes Mario.

"We're gonna get some dinner at the Little Café, drive ta Toledo and find a nightclub Mario heard about."

Joe rolls his head back, stares at the ceiling of the car for a moment and says,

"Shit! I knew this was a bad idea."

Mario is excited to be going out with his brothers again. It replenishs his sense of belonging that seems to disappear as they each find their own way in life. He starts the car, guns the engine, and they roar away from the house in raucous laughter. The three men love eating at the Little Café, and after a harrowing ride with Mario at the wheel, they arrive there in just minutes. Upon entering the restaurant, they hear a voice speaking to them in Italian. It is coming from behind the bar.

"Oh my God! The three Carlucci brothers," he shouts.

Enzo Talamonti is not only the bartender and owner, but he is also an old neighborhood friend of the Carlucci's. He is ecstatic to see the brothers together tonight. He runs up to John, gives him a big hug and a kiss on the cheek, and says,

"Giano, how coma you no eat here no more? You gotta beautiful girl somaplace to cooka for you now?"

John grins and says,

"Enzo, no woman I know can cook better than you. Even a pretty one."

He greets Mario and Joe with the same traditional hug and respectful kiss. Enzo is always happy to see the Carlucci's. Many years earlier, Giuseppi loaned him money to start his restaurant, and he has been more like a member of the family than a business partner ever since.

He seats them at a nice table near the bar and scurries away to find tableware and some of his legendary wine. The Little Café is a classic-looking Italian tratorria, much like those found all over Italy. The main dining room is small, with only eight to ten tables, but there are trellis-covered alcoves in each of the corners, which offer more private seating. Enzo has covered the tables with traditional red and white checkered table clothes and lights them by candles set into Chianti bottles covered with bright layers of aged wax. He has hung colorful paintings depicting scenes of his favorite cities in Italy on the heavily plastered walls. Enzo's restaurant is the best in the city. His wife, mother and daughter cook, while he and his son serve. The meals are authentic Sicilian and prepared with family-like care. And even though Enzo has no liquor license, he serves the best homemade Chianti outside of Palermo.

Enzo returns to the table a few minutes later with a large, yellow porcelain pitcher and four matching cups and saucers. The pitcher is full of his delicious red wine, and he pours each of them a cupful. He laughs in a devilish chuckle and says,

"The cops, they no can a figure out why I hava such a happy customers alla the time, but they never checka my yellow cups." Then he raises his cup and toasts,

"Salute, e familia Carlucci." The boys join him in his toast by clinking cups and returning his kindness, saying,

"Salute, Enzo." They share in the joy of the moment and, while Enzo sits and drinks with them, he asks,

"How isa you Papa?" He is curious after not seeing Giuseppi for several months. With a suddenly serious tone in his voice, John replies,

"He's fine, but this war in Europe has him worried." Enzo nods his head in reluctant agreement, saying,

"Ah, yes. Thees isa no good. My broder, he lieves ina Rome and I'ma worry too." Discussing the war in Europe makes the mood noticeably uncomfortable, and the subject is dropped as rapidly as it is brought up. Enzo takes their dinner orders and dashes off to the kitchen while John, Mario, and Joe talk about their plans for the evening. Joe starts to grill Mario,

"Look, I wanna know about this joint we're goin to."

He doesn't go nightclubbing very often and, although he thinks he'll be safe with them, he can't be sure. Joe has a steady girlfriend, and he knows if she is to find out about this little outing, she'll get very angry. Before Mario can answer Joe's question, Enzo returns with their dinners. Mario is famished from his long day at the plant and starts eating as soon as the food arrives. Between bites, he says to Joe,

"I'll be happy ta call your girlfriend and tell er you're goin out with us tonight."

Mario knows how to bait Joe into frenzy, and with that comment, Joe reacts with predictable excitement, saying,

"Just shut the fuck up about where we're goin tonight. The last thing I need is for you ta start makin excuses for me to her."

Mario and John laugh hysterically at their brother's nervousness during their entire dinner. Joe has always been the target of his older brother's gags and tonight is no different. After finishing their dinners, they drink more of Enzo's wine. Rosetta, Enzo's wife, arrives at the table with a platter of freshly made cannolis and a pot of strong, Sicilian coffee. Placing them on the table, she says,

"Here, you enjoy. I justa make a them for you boys. *E delicioso.*"

They thank Rosetta for her kindness and feast upon the wonderful pastries and coffee. After finishing their dessert, they pay Enzo for the excellent dinner and prepare to leave. As they rise from the table, Enzo reminds them,

"You musta bring Giuseppi witha you nexta time, *capisce*? You tella him I cooka his favorite *rigatoni*." They promise they will, thanking him once again for the wonderful meal. Enzo shakes their hands one final time, and they depart the eatery.

Mario jumps into the car behind the steering wheel again, while John and Joe climb into the front and back seats and speed away from the Little Café, heading for Toledo. Mario thinks all the questions are at last over, but Joe begins quizzing him again, saying,

"What's the name of this place we're goin to?" Mario tilts his head in the direction of the rear view mirror, giving him a better look at Joe's face as he says,

"The joint's called the Green Door, and it's someplace on Summit Street near the riverfront docks."

"Where the hell did ya hear about this place?" Joe shoots back. The questions begin to irritate Mario, but he tries to answer them without losing his temper, saying,

"A coupla guys from the plant went there and say it's worth the trip. That's all they said." As the car rumbles down U.S. 24 for Toledo, John and Joe won't let up and continue to interrogate Mario about the destination. John asks,

"What's so hot about this place?"

"Yeah, I'd like to know that too," Joe chimes in. Mario's short temper has finally reached its limit. Fed up with all the annoying questions, he shouts back,

"Why the fuck are you two so suspicious?" Joe is pretty sure what Mario is up to and challenges him, saying,

"I'll betcha fifty bucks right now that you'll find a crap game in less'an an hour after we find this Green Door." John howls with laughter at Joe's bet and, before long, they are all laughing over it.

Mario won't take the bet. After driving for over an hour through endless miles of cropland, they pass a string of cheap rental cabins, and they know they've arrived in Toledo. Following a brief, unscheduled tour of the river district, they eventually find the area where the club is located. Driving up and down several seedy-looking streets, John spots a small sign hanging over a dimly lit doorway. With disgust, he says,

"Is that it?"

Mario stops the car, backs up to the doorway, and stares at the broken-down building. The old, faded sign reads "The Green Door," but the doorway looks more like the entrance to an old warehouse than a nightclub. Joe doesn't like what he sees and immediately starts to complain, saying,

"What kind of a fuckin' dump did ya bring us to?"

"For Christ's sake, Joe, wouldja shut up for a few minutes?" barks Mario. He slowly drives through the dilapidated neighborhood until he finds somewhere to park. After easing the car into a curbside space not far from the entrance to the club, he turns off the engine, throws his arm over the seat back, and turns to face his brothers. After all the criticism he's been taking, he clears his throat in nervous anticipation and says,

"Let's go inside and take a look. Like I said, if we don't like what we see, we can leave." Mario waits for them to say something. Joe looks to John to make a decision and says,

"Well, whadda ya think?"

86

"Let's go. We're here, ain't we?" he answers reluctantly. The three of them head for the dingy-looking doorway.

Mario pulls open the heavy, metal door and enters the club first. An older, heavy-set woman who appears to be a hostess immediately greets him. She has mousy brown hair that is wild and dirty-looking, and the dress she is wearing appears at least two sizes too small for her. Her translucent purple eye make-up is smeared across her eyelids in wide, blotchy patches, and her lipstick seems to cover most of her lower face. She welcomes them in a thick, southern drawl, saying,

"Evenin boys. Welcome to the Green Door. Y'all are new here, ain'tcha?"

"Yeah, it's our first time here. Where's the bar?" Mario inquires.

"Y'all jus follow this ole hallway, and it'll take you right to it, hon," she says while pointing in the right direction with her finger. John looks at Mario and quips,

"Gorgeous women, my ass," remembering Mario's claim earlier in the evening.

They follow the long hallway to its end, where Mario can hear a noisy crowd of people and a band playing a bad version of *Chattanooga Choo Choo*. John is right behind Mario and jokingly says,

"Somethin smells pretty fuckin bad right here. Ya sure this ain't the men's john?"

Mario ignores John's taunts and keeps moving further into the club. At the end of the hallway, the place opens up into a larger bar area with an adjacent dance floor, complete with a stage for the band. There are at least several hundred people drinking, dancing or simply sitting around inside the club, and Mario begins to feel a lot better about coming here. The noise from clinking glasses and beer bottles, the band playing in front of a non-attentive crowd, and the drone of aimless conversation are all familiar sounds to Mario. He and his brothers gather around a small, wooden table, order three Crown Royal and waters, and study the bustling crowd.

A long, mahogany bar is located off to one side of the dance floor. There are no visible seats or bar stools, and the foot traffic is hectic. Mario looks through the thick, blue haze from hundreds of cigars and cigarettes and notices a series of doors along the rear wall of the building. He can see customers from the bar working their way to one of the doors, where they are then permitted to enter. He has a pretty good idea what is behind those doors, and all he has to do is figure out a way to get in there.

While sipping his drink, Mario makes eye contact with an attractive-looking woman sitting among a small group of people only a few tables away. She does not seem the least bit intimidated by his attention and returns his stare with a warm, receptive smile. After a few moments of this visual exchange of interest, the woman rises and casually passes his table, casting a suggestive look at Mario on her way by. John, eager to get Mario hooked up with a steady woman, indiscreetly points her out and says,

"Did ya see that look? Are ya goin ta jus sit here or try and find out what she's up to?" Joe pushes at Mario from behind, practically knocking him from his chair. Mario needs little of his brother's pestering to encourage him to go after her. He gets up and begins to follow her. When she stops at the bar to order a drink, Mario stands next to her and asks,

"I wonder if I could buy you that drink ya just ordered?" She smiles graciously, extends her hand to meet his, and says,

"Why, yes, you can. Thank you very much. My name is Mia Collins." Mario wraps her hand in his and replies,

"It's very nice to meet you, Mia. My name is Mario. Mario Carlucci." She shakes his hand and says,

"Well Mario, it's a pleasure to meet you, too. This must be the first time you've been here. I don't remember ever seeing you before." Mario pulls out a pack of Pall Malls, lights one for himself, and offers one to Mia. After lighting her cigarette, he says,

"Yeah, this is my first time here. Some guys from work told me about it. How about you?"

"Well, I come here occasionally with a few friends," she admits.

"What can you tell me about this place?" Mario asks.

"What do you want to know?" she inquires with a suggestive smirk on her face.

Mia is an extremely attractive woman. With short blond hair and bright blue eyes, she has an innocent but mysterious look about her. She has a trim waist, well-proportioned breasts, and long, shapely legs, which are readily visible through the long slit up the side of her slinky gown. She dresses in expensive-looking clothing and jewelry and doesn't look as if she belongs in a club like the Green Door. Their conversation remains friendly and casual. To his surprise, Mario discovers she is from Detroit and usually accompanies friends on trips to visit this club. Mario asks,

"Are your friends all from Detroit, too?"

"Oh no, not all of them. Some live here in Toledo," she answers. Mario decides to hint at his interest in gambling, hoping Mia will know something about the doors in the back. He says,

"I usually look for a crap game on Friday nights in Detroit, but tonight no one was playing, so I ended up here."

"Do you like to shoot craps?" she asks with heightened interest. That question is precisely what Mario has been counting on, and he promptly replies,

"Yeah, I do. I hear there is some action in this place." Mia smiles as if she has a secret she no longer wants to keep and says,

"There is if you know the right people." Mario understands her subtle offering, smiles at her, and asks,

"Do you know the right people?" Mia remains secretive and simply answers,

"Maybe."

Mario assumes Mia is just being cautious about revealing too much information to a total stranger. Not wanting to be mistaken for the police, he continues sharing small talk with her. He can see she is slowly starting to trust him. He believes that if he remains patient, she will get him invited to the back rooms. They talk for several more minutes, comparing their favorite nightclubs in Detroit and exploring each other's interests. Then Mario asks,

"Would you like to join me at my table for a little while?"

"Sure, I'll follow you," she answers.

Mario knows John and Joe have been watching him from the moment he followed Mia to the bar. As he escorts her to the table, he sees them adjusting their ties and smoothing their hair back with their hands. When he arrives, each of them have large smiles pasted on their faces, awaiting an introduction.

"Mia, this is John and Joe," Mario begins.

They stand, shake her hand, and say hello. Joe pulls in a chair from another table and invites her to sit down. After taking a seat, she momentarily studies each of their faces and then asks,

"Are the three of you related?"

"Yeah, we're brothers. John's the oldest and Joe's the youngest. I guess you can tell, huh?" Mario replies. Mia giggles a little and says,

"Oh yes. It's so obvious." Her smile suddenly changes to an expression of mild surprise, and she asks,

"Carlucci's? From Detroit? Are you related to Giuseppi Carlucci?" The mention of Giuseppi's name stuns Mario and his brothers, and they exchange wordless stares while trying to decide how to answer her question. John, ever the negotiator, innocently asks,

"How do you know Giuseppi Carlucci?" answering her question with a question. Mia laughs and explains,

"My uncle's Antonio Bomarito. I've heard him mention Giuseppi Carlucci's name many times. Usually while complaining about losing a lot of money to him at cards."

Admitting she was Antonio Bomarito's niece changes everything for Mario. What, only moments earlier, had been a chance meeting between two strangers in a bar, has unexpectedly become more of a family gathering, linked by two, old Sicilian friends. Mia's relationship to Antonio Bomarito eases the concerns Mario and his brothers have for saying too much about their father's business. They talk about Giuseppi's card games and the long friendship he has with Antonio. John even mentions the stolen car incident, saying,

"We think Antonio helped ta get our car back after it was stolen a coupla years back, even though our old man never admitted it." Mia snickers softly, saying,

"Was that your car? I've heard Uncle Tony talk about that a few times. You do you know what happened, don't you?" She sees the puzzled looks caused by her question, and then Mario admits,

"All we know is the car was found the next day, but nobody said anything about Antonio bein involved." Mia laughs even harder as she tells them what her uncle had done.

"Uncle Tony, that's what we call him, knew a ring of car thieves hung out in a rough neighborhood near the steel mills. You know the River Rouge area, don't you? When Giuseppi called and asked him to help find your car, he drove to River Rouge and went into the Delray Bar. That's where the punks, that's what Uncle Tony called them, like to eat lunch all the time." Judging by their astonished reactions, it is apparent to Mia that John, Mario and Joe have never heard any of this before. They listen intently as she continues, saying,

"When Uncle Tony walked into the Delray Bar, a few people inside must have recognized him because he said it got real quiet. This is the best part. Then he reached inside his coat with both hands and pulled out two big guns from his belt and laid em right on top of the bar so everyone could see. Uncle Tony told the bartender that someone had made a terrible mistake and that his good friend's new car had been stolen. He said he wanted it back right away or he'd be back the next night." Mario shakes his head from side to side, looks at John and Joe, and they all begin to laugh at what they've just heard. John adds,

"Goddamn, no wonder the car wasn't wrecked when we got it back. Ain't that the funniest damn story."

Mono V. D'Angelo

They continue to laugh and joke about the entire incident, wishing they could have been in the Delray Bar when Bomarito pulled his guns. In the midst of all the fun, Mario begins to realize there is much more to Mia than he'd first thought. She seems well connected, and for the moment, very fascinated by him and his brothers. He is already thinking of how to take advantage of her friendship.

Mia notices her friends waving for her to return, and she excuses herself a short time later, saying,

"I have to rejoin my friends. They probably think I've been kidnapped or something. But if you plan to be here for a while, I'll be back later."

"Sure, we're not goin anyplace soon," Mario answers.

Half an hour later, she returns as promised. Only now, a tall, well-dressed man accompanies her. She begins to make introductions.

"This is Peter O'Haloran; he owns this place. Peter, this is John, Mario and Joe Carlucci. They're from Detroit and their father and my Uncle Tony are old friends from Sicily. Isn't it a small world?" she says. Following introductions, they shake hands and gather around the small table, as Peter orders a round of drinks, saying "Welcome to Toledo. Any friends of Mia's are welcome here." Mia then asks Peter,

"Peter, tell them how you came to own this place. It's such an intriguing story."

He appears reluctant at first, but complies with her request, saying,

"I was able to buy a liquor license from the local politicians. This town loves corruption, and as long as I treat em right, they pretty much leave me alone."

After a little more small talk, he casts a glance at Mario and says,

"Mia tells me you might be interested in a little dice action?" Not wanting to appear too anxious, Mario nonchalantly answers,

"I like to try my luck when I get a chance. Anything goin on around here?" Mario waits for an answer. Peter looks over his shoulders, making sure no one else is listening and then confesses,

"Most of the time, I never allow strangers to gamble here, but since you guys know Antonio, I'll make an exception tonight. Follow me."

After inviting them to the private club, he leads them along the edge of the crowded dance floor to one of the unmarked doors located at the rear of the main room. Peter reaches into his pocket, retrieves a set of keys, and searches for the one that fits into the lock. As he bends over, his suit coat falls open, and Mario notices the butt end of a gun sticking out from under his belt. He says nothing, but it is clear there will be no room for trouble here tonight.

When Mario and his brothers enter the private room, they enter the illegal world of gambling operated by Peter O'Haloran. The gaudy red drapes hung over every wall are in stark contrast to the well-worn wooden floor. There are small bars in every corner, and a variety of leather sofas and chairs scattered all about. Moving slowly among the many tables, Mario can see virtually every type of gambling that anyone could be interested in. People are playing roulette, craps, and blackjack, along with an assortment of other card games. Mario is impressed by the size of the place. He has never seen so much action before. He cringes when Joe reminds him,

"This is the easiest fifty bucks I ever made," referring to the bet made in the car. Peter and Mia look momentarily confused until Joe explains with a chuckle,

"John and I bet em fifty bucks he'd find a crap game tonight, and we were right." Mario is a little embarrassed by Joe's declaration, but everyone finds it as amusing as Joe does, including Peter. Soon, Peter indicates he has some business to attend to and says he will have to leave them on their own. He excuses himself and says,

"Go and enjoy yourselves for as long as you like. Mia knows her way around the place, so you're in good hands. Drinks are on me." After purchasing chips, Mia guides Mario to her favorite table on the floor. The croupier greets her with a cordial smile, saying,

"Hiya, Mia. Nice ta see ya again. Where ya been lately?

"No place special, Charlie, just waiting for my luck to change. You been taking far too much of my money." Seeing her surrounded by three handsome men, the croupier asks,

"Who are your friends?"

"This is Mario, John, and Joe. They're from Detroit, and this is their first time here. Now you be nice to em, okay?" she responds with a wink.

Mario is not surprised by Mia's friendliness with the croupier. She is given royal treatment by everyone, and he is convinced that her uncle is the reason. He welcomes her effort to make him feel comfortable, and he looks forward to playing. Mario starts to feel the adrenaline pumping as the excitement begins to build. While studying the other players at the table, he tries to find some telltale betting patterns he can take advantage of. After a few minutes, he places his first wager, betting against the shooter, and winning twenty-five dollars. Mia places her arm around his neck and gives him a light kiss on the cheek, saying,

"You know, winning your first bet is always a sign of good luck."

Mario knows that is a lot of bullshit, but he does feel lucky. Mia is right, however, and he begins placing winning bets for the next several hours. He keeps betting against the point, only to see one shooter after another roll losing sevens and elevens. His instincts are uncanny as he successfully lays bets with mind-reader like skills. When he gets on a run like this, he is hard to beat. John, Joe, and Mia cannot resist following Mario's lead. They have all won some money using his tactics. It is a good night, with Joe winning over five hundred dollars, the most any of them have won. He insists on leaving a winner and excitedly announces,

"Goddamn, this is great. I ain't never won this much money before. That's it for me. I'm done."

Mario doesn't want to quit, thinking this is easy money, but he knows better than to leave the club with a lot of O'Haloran's money on this, his first visit. He knows Antonio Bomarito is the only reason he is being allowed to play. In spite of O'Haloran's friendly behavior, Mario remembers the gun in his belt. Not wanting to risk a confrontation, it seems like a good time to leave. He announces,

"Joe's got the right idea. Let's get outta here before Peter gets pissed off at us for winning so much of his money." They cash in their chips and have one last drink. Mario starts to say goodnight to Mia when she hands him a small slip of paper and says,

"That's my address. Let's be sure to get together again soon. I had a lot of fun tonight." She gives him a gentle kiss on the lips and reminds him once more,

"Now don't forget about me. I'm serious." Mario looks at the address and says,

"Don't worry; I won't forget."

On their way out, John and Joe don't waste any time reminding Mario who Mia's uncle is. They tell him he should be careful about getting too involved with her. But he pays little attention to their opinions. He is already thinking about what might come from this new-found friendship with Mia. She certainly seems to know her way around Detroit and Toledo, and she obviously likes him. He finds her to be equally fascinating and is certain she can open a few doors for him. The thought of sleeping with her certainly appeals to him as well.

CHAPTER 6

Following the successful night at the Green Door in Toledo, Mario is anxious to meet with Mia once again and get better acquainted. He waits about a week, however, to determine if Giuseppi has received any news of his chance meeting with Antonio Bomarito's niece. He hears nothing, so he makes plans to contact Mia and invite her to go nightclubbing.

Early one evening, he drives around trying to locate the address she had given him. Before long, he finds himself in an exclusive neighborhood known as Palmer Park. The streets are lined with large estates with well-manicured lawns and expensive cars. The area is consistent with Mario's image of Mia having nice things and lots of money. In spite of the luxurious neighborhood she lives in, Mario isn't intimidated by her apparent wealth. He continues to drive down the street. After a short distance, he finds an elegant, three-story house with an address matching the one on the small scrap of paper Mia gave him. After pulling the car over to the curb, he turns off the engine and sits in the darkness for a moment, his brother's warning still echoing in his head. He considers himself too savvy to let any woman, even one like Mia, lead him into any trouble he can't get out of. This ego driven overconfidence is the first link in a chain of events that is to change his life forever.

Stepping from the car, he double-checks the address and approaches the alcove at the front of the house. Raising the brass knocker, he gently taps it several times against the large wooden door. He waits for a few minutes, but no one responds, so he knocks again, only a little harder. This time, he can hear footsteps. Several seconds later, the door swings open and there stands a teenaged boy. They stare at each other in silence for a brief moment, then Mario blurts out,

"Hello, I'm lookin' for a Mia Collins. Does she live here?"

"Yeah, she lives here. She's my sister. Who are you?" the boy inquires.

"My name's Mario. I'm a friend of hers," Mario continues.

"Come on in. I'll go tell 'er you're here," he answers. He turns and leaves to find Mia. From the foyer, Mario surveys the inside of the mansion. Never having been inside such a grand home before, he finds the layout fascinating. He can see a mahogany-lined hallway with numerous doors on each side. It leads to a tall, circular staircase at the opposite end, which disappears into the upper level of the house. There are several large crystal chandeliers suspended from the ceiling, and along both sides of the hallway hang a variety of expensive-looking paintings. Mia suddenly appears and startles him back into the moment.

"Well, hello Mario. What a pleasant surprise," she exclaims while extending her hand out to greet him.

"I'm sorry for showin' up without callin' or anything, but all ya gave me was your address," he reminds her. She smiles and says,

"That's perfectly all right. If I give someone my address and they come to my house, I like to believe they are much more interested because they have to make an effort to find me. Please come in. Would you like a drink?"

"Sure, I'd love one," he responds.

"Well then, follow me," she says.

She leads him down the long hallway he has just been studying and through one of the side doors. It opens into a small reading room with a bar on one side and shelves full of books along the opposite wall. After they enter, Mia closes the door behind them, admitting with some slight embarrassment,

"Edward, that's my little brother, the boy you just met. He gets somewhat nosy whenever I have guests over. If I close the door, he knows it means I don't want to be disturbed." Mia steps behind the bar and asks,

"Crown Royal and water, right?"

Mario is pleasantly surprised that she remembered his drink and says,

"That'll be fine, thanks." She makes two drinks, hands one to him.

"So, what brings you here tonight, Mr. Carlucci?"

"I guess I just wanted to find out if the address you gave me was real, and besides, I really did want to see you again," he replies with a nervous laugh. She flashes a wide grin at him and says,

"As you can see, the address was very real. I'm happy to know you're still interested."

The initial uneasiness of meeting once again rapidly melts away, and they begin to talk more freely to each other. Mia tells Mario that this house belongs to her parents. She also reveals that her mother is Antonio Bomarito's sister and her father owns a successful trucking company. Mario is relieved to find out that Mia's father is not in the same business as her uncle.

"How are John and Joe?" she inquires.

"They're doin' good, especially Joe. He still can't believe he won so much money in Toledo. He never plays craps very much." They laugh when Mia compliments Mario, saying,

"You made us all winners that night. You sure had that table figured out. I've never seen anyone make so many good bets in one evening."

Mono V. D'Angelo

While they continue talking about their success in Toledo, Mario guesses now might be a good time to explore the possibilities of finding another game with her.

"Do you know of any good action locally?" he finally asks.

"I have friends who will usually get me into several places if I want to gamble, but I've been going to a couple of private clubs on my own lately, so I'm quite sure I can get in without anyone's help. When would you like to go?" she asks without any hesitation.

"Anytime you feel like it," Mario shoots back. They agree to meet at an upscale nightclub located near the downtown theater district the following Saturday and then go on to find a crap game. Mia says she can be at the club at 9:00 PM. After making the date, Mario tells her,

"I'll look forward to seeing you Saturday, then. We'll have a good time." They discuss the details of their date a little longer, and then he says,

"Maybe now's a good time for me ta leave, so your little brother won't get into trouble." She is amused by his little joke.

"You don't have to hurry off so soon, you know."

Mario thanks her for the offer to stay, but he wants to leave before he meets her parents. He thinks meeting them at this time might be awkward, and he wants to avoid any questions that might come up regarding his father and Mia's uncle. After leading him to the front door, she positions herself directly in front of him.

"Thank you again for coming by tonight. I'm looking forward to seeing you next Saturday." She leans forward and gives him an affectionate kiss. Mario reacts by wrapping his arms around her. Mia welcomes his embrace and, while they linger in the foyer, a small spark of excitement ignites between them. Mario eases away and says,

"I gotta go. This'll keep till Saturday, don't ya think?"

On the Saturday Mario is to see Mia, John is relaxing at home eating lunch and reading yesterday's paper. Mario notices he is sitting alone at the kitchen table and decides to join him. Grabbing a few slices of bread and cold cuts, he makes a sandwich and plops down in the chair directly across from him. After a few bites of the sandwich, he says,

"I gotta date with Mia tonight. Did I tell ya?" Each of them know, of course, that Mario has said nothing of his date, but John plays along.

"Oh yeah? Where ya going?" Mario is certain that if he tells John of his real plans to go shoot craps with her, he'll catch another "big brother knows better" lecture from him, so he says,

"Probably out for a few drinks. After that, I'm not sure." John says nothing to persuade him from seeing her again, but his coolness regarding the date sends Mario a message. John simply says,

"Well, don't get your ass inta some jam ya can't get out of. You know what I'm talking about."

John is not sure Mario actually understands his meaning. He hopes his advice will stick with him for once in his life. John realizes that Mia is one of the most interesting women Mario has ever met and that he is excited about seeing her again. He doesn't trust Mia, however, and is more than a little suspicious of her intentions. He knows she can be with any man she wants and certainly with one who has much more money than Mario will ever have. She is an attractive woman with big money connections, and she is backed by one of the most notorious mobsters in the city. John believes that Mario thinks he can take advantage of her ties to some local gambling, but Mia is not only beautiful, she is also smart. She is far more educated than any woman Mario has known in the past, and John suspects she has plans of her own. He says all he dares as they finish their lunch together, and his only comment is,

"Have fun."

Mario has planned to meet Mia at the 52nd Showbar, a premier nightclub in the heart of the city. He dresses in a crisp, double-breasted suit and a white shirt, complete with ivory cufflinks and a wide, colorful tie. Wearing a new fedora, wing-tip spectators, and carrying a pocket full of cash, he's prepared to see the classy Mia once again. Unsure of where his date with her might take him, he thinks it's better to be overdressed, just in case he winds up somewhere elegant. After entering the club, he checks his hat at the coatroom and finds his way into the bar. With no idea of exactly how to find Mia, he orders a drink and waits to see if she will show up. It is a little past 9:00 PM, and the many tables and booths inside the main ballroom are filled with patrons awaiting the start of the evening's entertainment. A large orchestra and showgirls in revealing costumes will soon have the crowd charged with excitement. Mia has not yet arrived, but he expects her to be late. About forty-five minutes later, he hears a woman calling his name above the noisy clamor.

"Mario, over here," she shouts.

Turning in the direction of the voice, he sees Mia moving through the crowded dance floor. She looks beautiful, as he expected she would. She is dressed in yet another expensive dress and adorned with several strings of pearls. Many eyes watch her glide through the maze of people in fancy gowns and formal tuxedos. She rushes up to him and gives him a short kiss on the cheek.

"How are you? Have you been waiting long?" she inquires.

"I've been here long enough ta need another drink. Can I buy ya one?" Mario quips.

"Of course you can," she responds with a bright smile. Mario orders two Crown Royals and water and asks,

"Did you just get here?"

"No, I've been here for a short time, but I was talking to some friends of mine about finding a game tonight," Mia responds. Mario smiles.

"And were you able to find some action?" Mia takes an intentional slow sip from her drink, stares into Mario's eyes with a playful expression on her face and says,

"Yes, my dear. I've been invited to an old mansion on East Grand Boulevard. It's near the Medical Center, and there are usually lots of doctors with scads of money there. Do you want to go?" Mario downs his drink, takes Mia's arm, and with a charming smile, says,

"Hell, yes. Let's go."

"Well, don't I at least get to finish my drink?" she responds with a chuckle.

Mario is beginning to feel lucky, and a high-stakes crap game is just what he was hoping to find tonight. While they work their way through the crowded nightclub for the coatroom, several of Mia's friends spot her and ask if she will be returning. Laughing in excited anticipation, she says,

"That depends on how much money we win tonight. Isn't that right, Mario?"

Her comments fire up Mario's enthusiasm. Feeling more like a high roller than just a factory machinist, he grabs Mia by the waist and arrogantly heads for the exit. They fight their way out of the bustling nightclub and walk the short distance to Mario's car, arm in arm. He opens her door and is about to help her in, when she turns and throws her arms around his neck, saying,

"This is going to be so much fun. I'm very anxious to play with you again, tonight."

"I sure hope those doctors bring a lotta money. I'm really feelin' lucky tonight," he confidently replies.

Mario opens the car door for her and, while she eases into the front seat, the hem of her gown slides well above her knees. He is reminded just how sexy Mia is. She notices his attention, but she does nothing to try to hide her legs from him. He closes her door once she is seated, jumps into the driver's side, and prepares to leave. No sooner has he slammed his car door shut, when Mia reaches over, places her hand behind his neck, and gives him a hard, suggestive kiss. Their passion for one another continues to heighten after exchanging more erotic kisses. Finally she backs away from him, saying,

"There will be plenty of time for this later. Let's go before we change our minds."

The idea of them changing their minds amuses Mario. He chuckles and says,

"Sure. Let's go. It's gonna be a long night with a lot to celebrate." He starts the car and drives away from the 52nd Showbar, thinking how well this is all working out.

Mario is unfamiliar with the part of the city in which the gambling house is located. As he nears the medical district, Mia directs him down a dimly-lit street.

"There! Right there it is, Mario. The one with the porch light on," she exclaims. She points to a weathered, old home in the middle of the block. Mario ducks his head slightly, giving him a better look through the passenger's window at the large, brick residence. It looks no different than any other blind pig he's ever been to, causing him to wonder if Mia may have exaggerated her description of the joint just a little. But she seems to know her way around the seedy neighborhood, so he decides to go along for the time being. She tells Mario,

"Why don't you park around the corner? We can walk to the house from there. You know, just in case there might be any trouble."

Parking a safe distance from the blind pig is an experienced gambler's trick. Someone has taught Mia well. He follows her suggestion without asking her how she knows of such things. As they hurry from the car, his heart begins beating like a jackhammer at the thought of trying his luck at a high-stakes crap game. They carefully negotiate the creaky porch steps leading to the door, but before he knocks, Mario notices someone peering at them through a small window. The door opens slightly, but he can only see a dark, shadowy figure between the door edge and the badly gouged door jam. Then, a gravely sounding voice rudely asks,

"Dis' is private property. What's ya'll want?" Mia steps from behind Mario and moves directly under the pale white light over the doorway. She cheerfully responds,

"Hi Donnie. It's me, Mia."

Suddenly, the door slams shut. Mario can hear someone fumbling with the lock chain, only to have the door fling wide-open seconds later. Standing there is one of the most menacing-looking black men Mario has ever seen. He estimates the doorman is well over six foot tall and has to weigh a couple of hundred pounds. He has no hair and his face is adorned with a long, vicious looking scar that starts near his eyebrow and extends to below his ear lobe. Mia gives him a big hug and asks,

"Donnie, it's nice to see you again. How've you been?"

"Oh, I's been doin' jus fine lil' darlin'. How's bout you?" he answers with a throaty chuckle.

"You know me, Donnie. I'm always looking for a little fun," she replies. Donnie laughs at her.

"Mia, you has mo damn fun den anybody I knows." Mia casually slips her arm under Mario's.

"Donnie, this is my friend, Mario Carlucci. Can we come in tonight?"

"Hell yeah, you kin. You know you's always welcome as long as I'm on da door. But I's telling ya, der ain't much of a crowd tonight." Then he directs his attention to Mario. As Donnie studies him for a moment, Mario cautiously extends his hand out to him, saying,

"How ya doin, Donnie? It's good ta meet ya."

While Donnie takes Mario's hand into his huge, bearish palm, he stares at him with a suspicious glare. With a sudden seriousness in his voice, he asks,

"You ain't carryin' are ya?"

Mario says no, pulling open his suit coat to show he has no weapon.

"Well, I jus gotta axe, you know. It's ma job," he apologizes. After Mario assures him he has no gun, Donnie gives him a huge grin and says,

"I know Mia won't be a bringin' nobody in here who be causin' trouble. Ain't dat right, darlin?" Mia giggled and says,

"Donnie, you know I wouldn't do something like that to you."

After she thanks him again, Donnie holds open the door and they enter the old house.

This place is not unlike other blind pigs Mario has been in. It is, perhaps, a little cleaner and better furnished, but the thick clouds of cigarette smoke and excited screams of winners and losers are exactly the same. While wandering through the many different rooms, he can see the usual variety of gaming tables. After a short tour of the place, Mia leads him to a small window, guarded in heavy, steel bars. She tells Mario,

"This is the cashier's window. We can buy our chips here and then go find a table."

Mario has brought all the cash he has, nearly nine hundred dollars, with him, thinking it will be enough to get him started. He buys five hundred dollars worth of chips for himself, as does Mia. Once they have their chips, they sit at a bar and Mario orders each of them a Crown Royal and water. He takes several, slow sips from his cocktail, while using the opportunity to survey the bar area and study the clientele.

It is clearly an upscale crowd. Everyone is well dressed; a number of men even wear tuxedos. The few women there appear elegant and sophisticated, and even the staff wears formal attire. He is grateful for his decision to overdress for the evening. Mario enjoys the privileged feeling of being in a private, and obviously well protected, gambling hall. After they finish their drinks, Mia grabs his hand and says,

"Let's go. I know a perfect table to start at."

She escorts him up a flight of stairs to the upper level of the house. It is as large as the lower level, and there are many more people there than he's seen on the first floor. He follows Mia into a noisy, smoke-filled room, which houses four heavily populated crap tables. Compared to the rest of the joint, this room is crowded. Mario wonders what Donnie considers a small crowd, given the many people jammed around the tables.

During the many crap games he's played in the back rooms of the plant, this is the type of place all the men fantasize about. The beautiful women, the big money, and the fancy clothes are dreams that will never come true for many of these men. Even he never thought he'd have a chance to play in a game such as this. But here he is, ready to play some high stakes craps with doctors and lawyers, and all while in the company of one of the most attractive women in the place. His heart is racing, but he knows he needs to keep himself under control. After years of watching his father play emotionless cards, the one thing he has learned from Giuseppi is how to remain calm whenever he gambles. That is his advantage, and he is ready to put it to good use. He takes a deep breath and asks Mia,

"Do you have a favorite table?"

"I sure do. Come on with me," she replies instantly. Grabbing his hand once more, she takes him to a table tucked away in a far corner of the room, saying,

"This is the one I always start on. It seems to bring me luck."

Mario studies the players surrounding the table for a few more moments and then says,

"Okay, let's play."

Sticking to his usual routine, Mario watches for patterns and lucky runs while placing several small, insignificant bets. He plays conservatively for about thirty minutes, and Mia follows his lead without question. They both manage to stay even on the board, but Mia soon becomes impatient with the small bets and keeps trying to up the ante. After he places yet another small wager, she leans in his direction and whispers,

"Come on, Mario, let's get serious. You can beat these guys. Let's lay some real bets." He looks her into her eyes and finds her intensity an unexpected turn on. With a beaming smile on his face, he tells her,

"Relax, Mia. Ya gotta trust me on this. We're gonna win here tonight. I can feel it."

Mario, indeed, begins to win, and he gradually increases his wagers after playing with the house's money. With a little luck, he can be amazingly successful on a table, and tonight he finds a streak of luck that will last for several hours. He sorts the lucky or good players from the rest and keeps betting the weaker ones almost perfectly. Mia watches her winnings continue to mount and religiously follows every move Mario tells her to make. Becoming more excited with every winning pass, she jumps up and down, screams with delight, and hugs and kisses him repeatedly. He can't help but think about the boys in the plant and what they would say if they could see him tonight.

Mario continues to win more than he loses and, after several hours, he recognizes the need to take a break. Too many people are watching him closely, and several of the big losers are becoming angry and suspicious of his good fortune. He remembers the lessons learned from his father a few years earlier about winning quietly, and he knows what he has to do. Mario takes Mia into his arms, as if to kiss her, but softly whispers,

"I think we'd better knock off for a while. Some of these guys are getting pretty upset." Her eyes fly wide open, and her jaw tightens with a surprised reaction. She completely disagrees and looks at him in disbelief, saying,

"You're not serious are you? We're killing them here. Why in the world do you want to stop now?" Mario tries to explain his reasons to her.

"Look, I wanna come back here again sometime. If I have a big day my first time here, these guys will remember it. I can't play my game when too many people are watchin' me. Trust me; we'll be back."

He's barely convinces her, but they pick up their chips and head for the cashier's window. After cashing out, they sit on a small, out-of-the way sofa, where Mario counts his winnings. He is surprised and excited to discover he's won over two thousand dollars. Mia has won big too, and they start for the bar to celebrate their good fortune.

Before arriving at one of the small barrooms on the main floor, Mario notices a stranger coming right at them. He is dressed in a tuxedo and accompanied by a rough-looking character Mario can only assume is a bouncer. Mario has no idea who this guy is, but he apparently knows Mia quite well. With a forced smile on his face, he asks,

"Hello, Mia. Did you do any good tonight?"

"Oh yes. Mario and I did very well tonight."

"You must introduce me to your lucky partner."

"Of course, how rude of me. Mario Carlucci, meet Paul Felston. Paul is the manager of this place." Mario shakes hands with the manager.

"Nice to meet you, Paul. You got a nice place here." Mario suspects this friendly introduction is no chance meeting, not after having won so much money tonight. Felson's voice drips with insincerity when he says,

"Congratulations on doing so well tonight, Mario. I hope we can see you here again sometime." Mia looks at Mario for a reaction, but she sees none. She then turns to Felston and says,

"Of course we'll be back, Paul. Where else can we find such a charming host?"

Mario knows that Mia has missed the subtle hint in Felston's comments and body language. They are *expected* to return and give the house a chance to recoup some of their losses. He knows what Felston is suggesting, and he politely tells him what he wants to hear.

"Yeah, I agree with Mia. I'm lookin forward to comin' back here again, too."

Mario realizes Mia's influence is the only reason Felston is treating him with such disingenuous courtesy, and he starts to feel uncomfortable around him. He decides to play very cautiously from now on, knowing that Felston will be watching his every move.

After escaping Felston's annoying presence, Mario at last allows himself to get excited over his good fortune. Upon entering the bar, he orders two more whiskey and waters and raises his glass in a cheerful toast,

"Here's to one helluva lucky night. Let's hope there's many more ta come."

Mia lifts her glass, lightly taps his, and says,

"You really got em' tonight baby. That was great."

She moves in close to him and gives him a long, congratulatory kiss. Mario grabs her by her waist again and kisses her back. Their success on the crap table has increased their attraction for each other. Mia slowly rubs his shoulders and says,

"Maybe it is a good time to leave."

Her intentions are not lost on Mario, but before leaving, he wants to be sure she understands what Felston meant by his comments.

"You know Felston was a little pissed off, don't you?" For all her beauty and intelligence, she has not caught on to what has just taken place. Puzzled by Mario's remark, she asks,

"Why do you think that? He's always been nice to me." Mario continues to explain why they need to leave.

"It's simple. I won too much of his money tonight. Ya don't think he stopped us by accident, do ya? That big goon standing behind him was a kinda warnin'. He wants a chance to win some of his dough back. But not tonight! Let's go back to the 52nd and celebrate." Mia agrees and kisses him once again. This time, Mia presses her body tightly against his and Mario gets a feeling his run of good luck is not over yet. On their way out, Mario pulls two fifty-dollar bills from his winnings. Upon reaching the front door, he greets Donnie by stuffing the money into his huge hand.

"We had a good time tonight, Donnie. I can't wait to come back again."

Donnie is someone Mario wants to befriend. He hopes the hundred dollars he's just given him will be a cheap insurance policy against any problems at the blind pig. When Donnie sees the size of the tip, he momentarily freezes and stares at the money. Slowly raising his head, he looks at Mario.

"Dat's a lotta cash, Boss. You musta done good, huh?" Mario gives him a friendly smile.

"Donnie, if ya didn't let me in, I wouldn't a won nothing. I just wanted to say thanks." Donnie thanks him for the money several times. Because of the tip, Mario feels confident he won't forget him any time soon. Donnie opens the heavy front door.

"You two have a nice night now, ya hear? I be sure ta get ya in da next time ya come by." As they leave the old house, Mario looks forward to the rest of an already interesting night.

After returning to the car, Mario helps Mia in and then hops in behind the steering wheel. He starts the engine and prepares to return to the 52nd Showbar. But as they are leaving the medical district, Mia asks,

"Mario, can we make another stop? It's not far from here."

Although puzzled by her unexpected request, he follows her directions until they arrive in front of an old apartment building. Because of all the money they are carrying, wandering around strange neighborhoods at this time of night makes him overly skittish. Before getting out of the car, he asks,

"What's going on, Mia? Where are we?"

"It's okay. I just have a little surprise for you, that's all." He is still uncomfortable going into a place he knows nothing about, and he tells Mia,

"I don't like this. Before I go anywhere else, you gotta tell me where we are."

John's warning suddenly pops into his mind, and it is all that he can think about for the moment. Mia looks at him with a smirk.

"I keep a small apartment here for my personal needs. There is nothing to get nervous about. It's perfectly safe." After spending the evening together, he doubts she would intentionally lead him into any trouble, and Mario agrees to follow her.

The apartment building is located in an older, run-down part of town near the ballpark. Mario rarely visits the area, but he knows the neighborhood is a mixture of many ethnic and racial groups. Standing at the front entrance, Mario is surprised to hear a few muted conversations taking place at such a late hour. As they climb a flight of stairs, he hears someone speaking Italian and finds it strangely comforting. The main hallway is poorly lit, with only two overhead lights in working order. But the lack of light does not hide the building's many signs of age. There are numerous holes in the walls, and most of the apartment doors have been sloppily painted over in attempts to hide the many nicks and gouges beaten into them from years of abuse.

Mia stops in front of apartment twenty-four, takes a key from her purse, and unlocks the door. Mario follows her into the darkened room and closes the door behind him. Mia clicks on a small table lamp. Its pale, white glare casts a degrading glow on the collection of old furniture, creating a mosaic of black shadows over ragged and torn textures. He looks around the room as Mia removes her coat and tosses it onto a chair.

Even though the apartment is old, it is clean and orderly. A small kitchen area occupies one corner, and there are two doors and a short hallway entrance clustered in the other. Mia flips off her shoes and heads for the tiny icebox.

"Do you want a drink?" she asks.

"Sure, that'd be great," he replies, while still giving the apartment the once over.

"If you need to use the bathroom, it's located behind the door on the left, just off the entrance." Mario walks to the bathroom, flicks on the light, and relieves himself. As he rinses his hands in the small porcelain sink, he can't help noticing the well-stocked supply of expensive towels, soaps, and perfumes. It is just like Mia to keep such nice things in a dump like this, he thinks. He returns to the living room just as Mia arrives with their drinks. She hands him his drink, raises her glass in a mock toast and says,

"See, I told you we would have plenty of time to be together tonight." Her sultry voice excites Mario. He clinks her glass with his and takes a long drink.

"You're fulla surprises I wasn't ready for." Her eyes twinkle, and with a beaming smile, she asks,

"So, do you like surprises, Mr. Carlucci?"

Mario considers her question more of an invitation. He takes her drink, places it on the table, and pulls her against himself. In the glow of the small table lamp, they exchange warm, slow kisses. She feels firm and sensuous to his touch. Their yearning for each other has reached its pinnacle, and they enjoy the passion flourishing between them. Their touching increases to a feverish intensity when Mia suddenly stops, takes Mario by the hand, and whispers,

"Come with me." She accompanies him down the short hallway and into the bedroom. There, she lights several candles and begins to undress him. After removing his coat and shirt, she turns her back to him and asks,

"Can you unzip me, my dear?"

Mario slowly eases the zipper downward, revealing Mia's bare back. While kissing her neck, he slides his hands under her gown and caresses her breasts. Excited by his touch, she lets the gown slide from her shoulders, allowing it to drop to the floor and completely reveal herself to him for the first time. Her body is as beautiful as

Mario imagined it would be. They grapple with one another in frenzied passion while exchanging ravenous kisses. Mia unbuckles Mario's belt, removes his pants, and falls onto the bed with him. Their lovemaking is wild and aggressive, fueled by the same rush of excitement they experienced at the crap table that evening.

Mario's relationship with Mia continues to revolve around gambling and sex. He tells his brother about his success at the blind pig, but John is not impressed. In one last attempt to make his point about Mia, John says,

"If Mia can walk right inta a place like that, ya know damn well her uncle is involved. I think you're askin for trouble, Mario."

Mario has said nothing to their father about his relationship with Antonio Bomarito's niece, and he knows John is pissed off about that as well. Both John and Joe have announced plans to marry their girlfriends, and they no longer have time to bail him out of a jam. On the heels of John's constant warnings, Mario decides it is best to just stop talking about Mia, knowing he'll only provoke an argument.

Mario eventually falls victim to a serious run of bad luck and hasn't won big on Felston's crap tables for several months. He will sometimes break even, but he usually goes home a loser. On one particularly bad night, he and Mia have dropped a bundle of cash. He knows Felston is watching his every move, and he is frustrated over losing so badly. Mario has experienced losing streaks in the past, but they have never involved so much money. Mia is unaware of Mario's anxiety. All she wants to do is keep playing and, when they run out of money, she offers a solution.

"Why don't you ask for a house loan? They do it all the time here." Mario growls back at her, saying,

"I ain't one of those rich doctors who hang out here. I don't have nothin to cover a loan."

"I can take care of that for you. I borrow money here all the time," Mia says. Mario isn't sure what Mia is proposing, but out of desperation, he follows her to the cashier's window. She turns and asks,

"How much do you want to borrow?"

It is still unclear how she is going to secure the money, but remembering John's warning, he suspects her uncle will be involved. Standing before the cashier's window, Mario can see Felston at the rear of the cashier's cage. When Mia asks for a thousand dollars for herself and another thousand for Mario, the cashier spins around on his stool and looks to him for his approval. Staring at Mario through the bars on the window, Felston says,

"Mr. Carlucci, I don't believe you have any credit with us. I can't lend you any money." Felston's sinister half smile convinces Mario his loan will be denied, and he prepares to leave when Mia says,

"It's okay, Paul. My uncle will stand good on this money for both of us."

Felston's face reddens with anger, and Mario is sure Mia has done this before. After Felston reluctantly agrees to the loan, Mario is asked to sign a debit slip and is handed his money. His brother's suspicions have just been confirmed. Mia's uncle allows her to influence a man like Felston, and her family's wealth supports her gambling habit. Borrowing money on Antonio Bomarito's credit will be a big problem if he doesn't repay the loan quickly. But Mario's addiction to the dice and his passion for Mia drag him even deeper into a quagmire of bad decisions. Like any gambler, he is sure his luck will change at any moment, and he returns to the dice tables on the second floor. For Mario, this is no longer just another crap game. He will play scared for the first time in his life, and that is something he isn't very good at.

Mario loses one bet after another. No matter what he tries, his strategy backfires. Within a few hours, he and Mia lose the entire two thousand dollars they have just borrowed. Between them, they have lost nearly three thousand dollars, the most he's ever blown gambling. He yanks Mia aside and tells her,

"I can't play any more. We gotta get outta here before I get into deeper shit than I am already." With no luck and only a few dollars left, he realizes his skills alone will not be enough to turn things around. It is time to quit, but Mia isn't ready to stop yet.

"Come on baby. Let's go get some more money. It's still early. We can get it back," she pleads. The long losing streak has pushed Mario's temper to its limit, and he shouts at her,

"Look Mia, there's no fuckin way I'm goin to keep shootin here. It's just not my night. Now let's go."

She barely reacts to his ultimatum. She becomes distant and unconcerned about his predicament and has no intention of leaving. Since he sees she has her mind made up and finds her uncaring attitude humiliating, he storms from the place without her. Heading for the front door, he sees Donnie standing inside the foyer. When he approaches, Donnie wants to say something to him.

"Mr. Carlucci, I knows what happened here tonight, and I jus wanta warn you bout deese guys. Dey don't fuck around if you owes dem money. You watch yo back, hear?"

He takes little comfort in Donnie's warning, but he is happy that Donnie is one less problem he'll have to deal with. His generous tips have bought Donnie's loyalty, but he doesn't want him to know how worried he is. He simply replies,

"Thanks for the tip Donnie; everything's going to be all right."

But Mario knows everything isn't going to be all right. He is in a lot of trouble. Two thousand dollars is a lot of money, and he doesn't know how he is going to repay Felston. He realizes his biggest problem was allowing Mia to connect his debt to her uncle. It will be only a matter of time before Antonio Bomarito finds out and tells Giuseppi. For the moment, he can't begin to explain to his father how he's gotten into such a huge mess, but there will be little time to think about it.

CHAPTER 7

Antonella's harrowing experience with the British sailor has made her wary of any strange man who approaches her. While her beauty brings her many invitations from several young men in Napoli to go to the theater or dinner, she is reluctant to accept. She elects to remain safely at home with her sister and mother in the months following the attempted rape. Though they know nothing of her narrow escape from the Channel Star, they can see a marked difference in her behavior. No longer does she go to the beach alone, and even her manner of dress has changed. Her exotic dresses remain hidden away in an old suitcase, replaced by less fashionable clothing that is more traditional. She knows that her mother and sister see the change in her behavior, but they have little time to question her because of disturbing news from Giancarlo.

Giancarlo has not returned home for many months. His letters have stopped arriving weekly, as they once did. They have become rare and special events to Antonella and her family, as rumors that Italy has joined the war in Europe run rampant throughout Bagnoli. There are rumors of terrifying German attacks on England, Poland and France. It is said that Mussolini has declared war on Italy's neighbors and has joined Hitler in a misguided attempt to implement his social changes. Fascism and Nazism are words Antonella and her family do not understand. She wishes her brother were home to look after them but knows his return is doubtful. As the rumors and newspapers tell of nothing but the war, a letter from Giancarlo miraculously arrives after nearly five months of silence. Antonella and Lucia join Assunta at their small kitchen table. She tears the letter open and begins to read it aloud.

> *Dearest Mother and Sisters,*
>
> *I apologize for not writing to you. As you will see, my life is very different now. Several months ago, I flew my first combat mission during the Abyssinian War. I have also participated in Italian air raids on England, and I know I will not be returning home again until the war is over. My thoughts are constantly with you, for I have seen the terror we all may face. I have dropped bombs on unsuspecting cities and have seen the terrible destruction they cause. I am sickened by the thought of killing innocent people. I do not sleep well any more. I am committed to my career in the military, and as an officer, I feel compelled to honor that commitment to our country. I am a good pilot, and Italy needs the best men available to support its war*

effort. I have recently been promoted to Colonel and given command of my own squadron after only a few months of that promotion. I had one day hoped to command my own squadron, but now that we are at war, I find the job of killing people unbearable. I miss you all dearly. I sometimes think about Sunday mass and our outings along the seashore with Father. Those days seem so long ago now, almost as if they were someone else's memories. I wish we could go back and enjoy them again. Sadly, our lives are changed forever by this brutal war. I love you all. Please be safe, and I will try to help you in any way that I can.

With all my love,
Giancarlo

Assunta places the letter on the table and lays her hands on top of it, as if trying to touch her son once more. Antonella and Lucia feel the sense of loss his letter has created and begin to cry. The possibility that Giancarlo may never return weighs heavy on Antonella's heart, and she asks her mother,

"How is this possible, Mama? Why must Giancarlo do these terrible things?"

Assunta tries not to cry. The letter places the burden for the family's safety upon her, and she wants to be strong while responding to Antonella's unanswerable question. She says,

"Giancarlo must repay his debt to the military. He has to do what he is told, even these horrible things in his letter. We must pray for him every day."

129

Antonella understands very little of why Italia is in this war. What she knows is that Giancarlo is flying combat missions and lives in constant danger of being killed. Antonella, Lucia, and Assunta begin to live with a never-ending terror that haunts every family of every man who has ever gone to war. They will miss him dearly in the dark days to come.

After the war in Europe engulfs Italy, Antonella's flourishing career becomes an early victim. The many wealthy customers she once had are far more concerned over the fate of their city. During these troubled times, Napoli's natural gulf and strategic shipping facilities are a greater worry to all who live there. Antonella hears the grim rumors circulating throughout Bagnoli that the harbor will become a main shipping port for Mussolini and the Nazis. It is the threat of Nazis coming to Napoli that sends shockwaves of fear rippling through the city. Any of Antonella's clients who can afford to leave Napoli do so, knowing its busy harbor will be a primary staging center for the Axis armies. The ensuing panic among Napoli's citizens results in serious shortages of food, fuel, and even clean water. As a result of the shortages, a black market emerges in Napoli, and anyone can find whatever he wants there, if he has money.

Petty theft is everywhere in Napoli. Since it is a port city, many rationed or scarce goods find their way to the black market after being stolen from the main harbor docks. The very streets upon which Antonella and her family loved to walk are now crowded with panic-stricken people in search of coal, firewood, or food. Following the collapse of her business, Antonella and her family are forced to give up their comfortable apartment in Pozzouli and return to an area of Bagnoli where Assunta had first lived with Pirrone. They know of a small, run-down building with an apartment located on the second floor. Antonella and Lucia join with their mother to meet Theresa Minnelli, an old friend of the family. Theresa owns the building and is waiting for them when they arrive. She hugs Assunta and kisses her cheek.

"Assunta, I am so sorry for your misfortune. Are you and your daughters well?"

Assunta heaves a deep sigh and replies,

"Yes, Theresa. We are well. It is nice of you to ask, but we struggle as everyone does these days. Thank you for helping us. We are very grateful."

"Pirrone was very kind to our family when my husband died. I am happy to be able to help you as long as I can. I feel bad that I cannot do more. The apartment is very small, but the building is strong and safe. Come, I will show you."

She leads them up a stairway, opens the heavy door, and enters the apartment. Its two windows overlook the street below and permit ample light to shine through. The main sitting room is also the kitchen. It is equipped with a small, wood-burning stove that is heavily blackened from many years of use. A small bedroom is located through one doorway, and a toilet and sink are behind another. Antonella detects an odor of dead fish and asks,

"Senora Minnelli, what is that foul smell in here?"

"Ah, for that I am so sorry. But the last tenant was a fisherman, and he cleaned many fish in here. I'm sure, with a little scrubbing, the smell will go away."

Antonella, Lucia, and Assunta look at each other in hopeless resignation. There are no other choices for them, and this is now their home. Assunta takes Theresa's hands into her own.

"We will do just fine in here, Theresa. Thank you again for your kindness."

The war has brought both financial and physical hardship to many people across Italy, including Assunta. She has tried to adjust to life without Pirrone's support, but no matter how hard she works, there is never enough money to pay for the over-priced goods in the black market. With the economy in Napoli worsening, her only sources of income are the meager wages she earns as a mid-wife. In spite of the war, babies are still being born in Napoli and, on many occasions, Assunta is paid in foodstuffs for her services. She willingly accepts food or any other staple to help feed her family as she continues to struggle to survive. Now that Antonella and Lucia can no longer find work, Assunta is determined to keep them from joining the swelling ranks of despondent women who have turned to prostitution to survive. Assunta receives small amounts of money from Giancarlo periodically, but the deteriorating government services make mail delivery untrustworthy, and she believes much of the money he sends is stolen before it can be delivered. Increasing rumors of the Nazis occupying the north of Italy circulate throughout the city, spreading the fear of invasion or occupation even further. Assunta is deeply worried over the frightening reports of German troops in Italia. She goes about her business, day by day, while awaiting the reality she knows will one day arrive.

With most of Italy in chaos, Assunta becomes consumed with protecting her daughters. Her role in life is one cultivated from a traditional Italian family, one dominated by a strong husband. Without Pironne and Giancarlo, she feels utterly lost. Because she has never been totally responsible for her family's safety, she lacks the confidence to guide them through this crisis. She has never thought of herself as a courageous woman and worries whether she has the strength to see her daughters through this frightening experience.

Unable to work or safely leave the tiny apartment, Antonella and Lucia become even more reliant on each other. They speak openly and honestly with each other and begin to question what will become of their lives. Many evenings, after Assunta has fallen asleep, they sit cross-legged atop the bed they share and talk late into the night. In the amber glow of a solitary oil lamp, Antonella asks,

"Lucia, do you believe we will ever be married and have families of our own?"

"Yes, of course we will. The war will not last forever; you will see." Antonella gazes wistfully into a shadowy corner of the bedroom. With a slight smile on her face, she says,

"My husband will be tall and very handsome. And he will be very rich. I just know he will." Lucia giggles at her sister's fantasy and joins her in escaping reality for a little while.

"My husband will be handsome, too. And we will have three beautiful children, two girls and a boy." Antonella takes Lucia's hands into hers and joyfully responds,

"And so shall I...and then we can all meet on Sundays and enjoy walking along the Via Pozzouli and have lunch at the trattorias again...It will be so wonderful."

They giggle from embarrassment while talking of making love with their husbands and, for several hours at least, they can forget the never-ending monotony that is their daily routine.

Antonella and Lucia treasure their brief escapes from reality, but the harsh circumstances that cripple Napoli inevitably come back into their conversations. Accurate information about the war is rare, and they constantly pray for Giancarlo to return home to help them. Reports from Rome describing executions, rapes, and other unbelievable atrocities being committed by the Germans are rampant. Many times Antonella finds Lucia crying from sheer desperation. With tears streaming from her eyes, she whispers,

"Our lives will never be normal again, Antonella. We will all die in this horrible war." Antonella is saddened by Lucia's remarks

134

and tries to comfort her. Cradling her in her arms while slowly rocking her back and forth, she says,

"We will not die, Lucia. You must stop thinking that. This war will end soon, and we will both be happily married someday. You will see."

Antonella's fiery personality has remained locked inside of her since her near rape, but it begins to re-emerge in a display of quiet bravery as she tries to ease Lucia's fears. While she is as frightened as her sister, she worries more for Lucia than herself. Their bond of love and loyalty to each other will become stronger each day as the terror of real, bloody warfare is only months away.

As the weeks pass into months, new rumors regarding the Nazis are circulating daily. It is confirmed that they now occupy Rome and are moving to the south to fortify Sicily. Assunta knows Napoli will certainly fall under German control, and she waits in fear of that dreadful day. Frequently finding it difficult to sleep, she stares into the darkness late at night, worrying over Giancarlo's well being or wondering where her family will find their next meal.

One such night, she can feel a slight trembling in the apartment strong enough to rattle her dishes and pans. The trembling is much like the earthquake tremors that sporadically rumble through the region. Tonight, however, the usually brief vibrations continue to escalate. The muffled roar of buses or trucks soon accompanies the rumbling. There is a strong odor of exhaust fumes that drifts into the apartment, and Assunta's heart begins to beat more rapidly. Curious about the unexpected commotion, she climbs from her tiny cot and moves next to the windows overlooking the street. She lifts the edge of the curtain just enough to peer out to the street undetected. She is shocked by what she sees.

What she had earlier thought were buses or trucks are, in fact, battle tanks. The armored column stretches as far as she can see. The hulking war machines bear black and white crosses on their sides, the well-known insignia belonging to the Panzer Division of the Nazi Army, and each is guided by a pilot bellowing out instructions in German. Atop each Panzer sit heavily armed soldiers, followed by countless others on foot. Standing there in disbelief, she watches the endless parade of tanks, soldiers, and equipment pour into the city.

Antonella and Lucia are also awakened by the commotion. Lucia sits upright in her bed. Startled and curious over the strange sounds and smells, she asks,

"Antonella, are you awake? Do you hear those noises? What do you think they are?"

"I don't know. Let's find Mamma." Still in their nightgowns, they quietly make their way into the room with their mother and ask,

"What is it, Mamma? What do you see?" She turns to face them. Her hands are pressed tightly against her face, and they can see she is crying. In a low voice, she whispers,

"Il Nazis è qui."

Antonella and Lucia join her at the window. They stare down at the street in silence, realizing the war has finally arrived in Napoli.

In the weeks following the Germans' arrival, Napoli is besieged by panic and fear. The city is an armed fortress, and its citizens are forced to abide by the new military policies dictated by the Nazis. Curfews, barbed wire barricades, and armed patrols are but a few of the harsh changes Napoli must bear. Assunta hears more terrible rumors of the Nazis' disregard for Italian citizens. Although Italy is thought to be an ally of the German Army, the Nazis reportedly treat each Italian city they enter as occupied territory and its citizens as prisoners of war. Stories of public executions, mass murder and even slavery are whispered throughout Napoli. The heinous tales keep most citizens a safe distance from the Germans, while creating a city of prisoners confined to their own homes.

Assunta, like her neighbors, is consumed by the threat to her family's safety. Her primary goal is to protect her beautiful, young daughters from the dangers found all around them. Of all the terrible rumors circulating throughout Napoli, the most frightening to her are those involving the vicious Cossacks supporting Hitler. The Cossacks are tribal Russians who hate the dictator, Joseph Stalin. They will fight along side anyone who will help defeat him. Ruthless and nomadic, they are considered fierce fighters who place little value on life, a trait the Germans use to their advantage. In exchange for their ferocious behavior, the Nazis turn their backs as the Cossacks rape and plunder any town they enter. It is said they will torture and kill young women with their swords, often mutilating them beyond recognition if their perverse demands are not met. Of all Assunta fears in the terrifying new world around her, the thought of Cossacks finding Lucia and Antonella is beyond comprehension.

The Nazis consider the harbor in Napoli a key component to the successful defense of an anticipated allied invasion of Italy. In the months that follow, more troops, war machines and supplies pour into the port facilities, as thousands of German soldiers prepare to move southward to Sicily. Their presence is vast and overwhelming. They take over all hotels and harbor buildings and use them as command centers. The very beaches Antonella and Lucia loved to visit as young girls are now littered with large gun compounds, landmines, and razor wire. The Germans have converted Napoli into a critical center of activity for their war effort, while at the same time making it a prime bombing target. Many in Napoli understand what will happen if the Nazis suffer defeat in the Italian Theater. The fear of allied bombing raids drives most local residents from the harbor district and into the safer, mountainous regions outside of Napoli. Many, like Assunta and her daughters, cannot move. They have little money and will live in certain poverty if they venture into the surrounding hills. Assunta knows Senora Minnelli's little apartment provides more shelter and comfort than a barn or abandoned shack in the mountains. So, along with thousands of other less fortunate Napolitans, they will have to endure the deadly risk of living amidst the German army.

Assunta serves a meager meal every evening in an attempt to maintain some normalcy in their lives, but life is far from normal for them. Knowing of the dangers in every part of the city, she warns Lucia and Antonella of the perils they face. In a somber and foreboding mood, she says,

"You must not leave the apartment. There are many dangerous men in Napoli now. The Cossacks are animals that rape and kill young girls. They have done many terrible things all across Italia." Lucia and Antonella have never heard their mother sound so terrified. Lucia begins to cry once again. Her voice quivers as she says,

"Oh my God, Mamma. Wha...what will happen to us? I'm so scared. I want Giancarlo to come home...why...why can't he come home?" As fear overcomes Lucia, Antonella wraps her arm around her shoulder and tells Assunta,

"We will not go out of the apartment, Mama. We promise."

Late at night, they hear the scurrying of rats overhead, and Assunta believes there may be another level above the apartment. She searches the ceiling and locates a loose tile. Assunta moves a chest of drawers directly beneath it, climbs up on top of it, and discovers it is a removable panel. Behind it, she discovers a small, well-hidden, attic above the room that Antonella and Lucia share. It is a dark, musty-smelling little space, but it would serve as an ideal hiding place. She immediately arranges the little furniture they have to serve as steps, which will provide quick access if they need it. She eventually stores a jug of water, a small jar of boiled potatoes, and several blankets there. She even thinks to include a bucket for use as a toilet, in case they must remain hidden for long periods of time. She has taken every precaution she can think of to insure her family's safety and, while still vigilant, she is comforted to know there is one last place her children can go should something happen to her. With her daughters confined to the apartment, she searches for food and work daily. To reduce the risk of any unwanted attention, she wears black dresses and shawls to appear as old as possible. Childbirths have become less frequent, forcing her to devote most of her energy to finding food or fuel. While walking the streets during her daily outings, she carefully studies the German soldiers she encounters. Being able to move among them relatively unnoticed, she listens for any languages other than German, but hears none. All of the soldiers are wearing standard German uniforms, and she feels better knowing there are no mercenary Cossacks in Napoli.

During the months of German occupation, Napoli continues to be a critical command center for the Nazis. Thousands of troops with tons of equipment disembark from the many transport ships that crowd the harbor and move southward to Sicily. Many more combat forces are permanently located in Napoli. Due to the large number of soldiers in every corner of the city, there are few places anyone can go without encountering them.

In spite of mounting anxiety and claustrophobic conditions, Antonella and Lucia heed their mother's warning and rarely leave the apartment. Their lives become more deplorable each day. Food is scarce, with locally caught fish the only reliable source of nourishment. Fuel, be it coal or wood, is nearly impossible to find, and even bathing becomes a luxury. The constant fear of the world outside of their tiny apartment takes its emotional toll on Antonella and Lucia. Lucia often cries over the wretched living conditions the war forces upon them. Frustrated and angry, she can no longer keep her emotions bottled up inside her. After eating the last portion of boiled fish served for the daily meal, she hurls her bowl against the masonry wall, exploding it into hundreds of tiny shards. She screams out in a sobbing rage,

"Why can't they just leave? I...I can't stand this any long...longer. We may as well be dead. What is there to live for?"

She runs into the bedroom and falls onto the bed, her head burrowed into her arms. She weeps in deep, powerful gasps. Even Antonella's tolerance of their misery reaches its end, and she joins her sister in fits of uncontrollable sadness over their plight. Sitting on the edge of the bed with Lucia, she angrily condemns their situation, saying *"What have we done wrong? Why is our life becoming so terrible? Oh my God, please let it end."*

The cycle of tears, anger and then depression repeats itself time and again. When Assunta is home, she becomes the target of their outbursts. Antonella begins to make demands, saying,

"Mama, we cannot stay here any longer. We must get out of here or we will go crazy. If you are able to move about, why can't we?" Assunta tries to calm Antonella.

"I can go out because I look like an old woman. Do you see the way I am dressed? No matter how a young woman dresses, she will not be safe. The soldiers, they know. Please, I beg you...you must stay in here no matter what happens."

They have the same argument many times, and Assunta manages to convince her daughters that she is right, but the agony remains. The mental anguish they suffer begins to affect Assunta physically. She has lost weight and appears to be aging right before her daughter's eyes. Her once dark hair is now streaked with gray from worry, and her face no longer has the sparkle it once did. Her eyes are ringed in dark shadows, making her appear tired and weak.

Although her spirit has been badly damaged, it is not yet broken. Her will to live is fueled by the single-minded goal of seeing her daughters through this hell that is stealing so much of their lives. Like her daughters, she wants it all to end. She misses her son and desperately wishes he were home; she wants to know whether he is safe, or even alive, and longs to have him help the family through this tragic time. Every day is a mental struggle as well as a physical one, and she begins to wonder how long she can continue. She fears death only because she would no longer be able to watch over her daughters. But it is for this singular reason she will somehow survive this brutal experience.

The occupation of Napoli gradually changes the patterns of life in the city. Its citizens can only watch as the Nazis fill every trattoria and hotel. The extreme caution regarding the Nazi danger is eventually eroded away by the complacency of many, including Antonella and Lucia. Antonella begins to pressure Assunta.

"Mama, the streets are crowded with our neighbors. If we go out, we can help you find the food we need. We will be safe if we do not go too far from the apartment."

Assunta finds it difficult to argue with her.

"If I allow it, you must promise me you will not wander away from our neighborhood. And if you see any soldiers, you must stay away from them." They respond enthusiastically.

"Of course, Mama, we promise. We will be very careful. Maybe you can rest while Lucia and I look for food today."

After months of confinement, Lucia and Antonella enjoy the opportunity to leave the apartment. While on their way to an open-air fish market located near by, they see Theresa Minnelli and stop to speak with her. Her eyes are half closed and her hair is not combed. She looks very tired and depressed but greets them with an affectionate hug and asks,

"How are you, girls? I have not seen you for such a long time. How is your mother doing?"

"Mama is home resting, Senora Minnelli. She has been working very hard these days," relies Lucia.

"She is a lucky woman to have such good children to take care of her during these horrible times."

"We are off to find some fish to eat, so we cannot talk too long. Mama does not want us near the Germans, and we must hurry back to the apartment," says Antonella.

Theresa's face draws taut at the mention of the Germans. She leans closer to them.

"She is right. You two should go about your business and return to the apartment right away. It's not safe in Bagnoli any more." They exchange hugs once again, and Antonella says,

"Goodbye Senora Minnelli. We will tell Mama you asked about her."

It is only a few, short blocks to the fish market, but Antonella and Lucia look down every street they cross and waste no time in getting there. Today they are fortunate and find several small mackerel they can afford. After wrapping the fish in some newspaper, they return home without incident, pleased over having done something to help their mother.

Despite her uneasiness over Antonella and Lucia leaving the security of the apartment, she welcomes the luxury of the few extra hours of sleep it affords her. The rest enables her to regain some of her strength, making her daily excursions physically less demanding. Early one morning, Lucia seems surprisingly cheerful and Assunta asks,

"Lucia, you are very happy today. Is there any special reason for that?" Lucia joins her mother at the table.

"I have been thinking, Mama. Why don't the three of us go out today? It will be nice to leave the apartment together. We can go to the fish market and find something to eat. Do you want to go?" The smile on Lucia's face gives Assunta a brief moment of pleasure.

"That is a wonderful idea, Lucia. It will be nice to go to the market with you and Antonella. It seems there are fewer Germans in Bagnoli lately, and I rarely see any of them near the market place. We can leave in a few hours. If we wait until the fishermen return to the beach, perhaps we can find something fresh." Lucia excitedly dashes off to tell Antonella the good news.

The day is warm and clear, bringing more people on the street than usual. With her daughters by her side, Assunta is reminded of the memorable outings to the beach with Pirrone only a few years earlier. Her life has changed dramatically in that time, and this day with her children seems to restore a little sanity to her otherwise insane world. She does not become careless, however. As they move through the streets, she remains alert to the presence of soldiers or any danger that may threaten them. Assunta is grateful this short journey has not required them to hide from any Germans. Then, as if from nowhere, a large military truck roars past them, careening wildly down the street. It carries six or seven soldiers standing in its open cargo bed, and as it races by, Assunta sees them staring at her and her daughters.

The men in the back of the truck begin shouting to the driver, and he abruptly stops several hundred yards ahead of her. Assunta wastes no time, saying,

"Oh my God. They have stopped. Hurry back to the apartment...go...you must go right now. But don't run. That will only make them more curious." Lucia says,

"Mama, you must come with us. You cannot stay here alone. Please Mama, come with us now." Assunta's attention remains focused on the truck and the soldiers.

"No, they will not harm me. You must go immediately and hide in the little attic above your room."

Lucia takes Antonella's hand, and they begin to turn back toward the apartment. She tells Antonella,

"Do not look back, Antonella. We must keep going, no matter what happens."

"Lucia, I am so afraid...I...I...just want to go home as fast as I can," replies Antonella.

They are frightened and begin to panic. Antonella forgets her mother's instructions, and her walk quickly escalates into a run. Lucia begins to chase after her while calling out,

"No, No, Antonella. Don't run. Remember what Mama told us to do." But Antonella will not stop, and Lucia must run to keep up with her. They do not stop until they return to the apartment.

By now, several of the soldiers jump from the truck and begin walking toward Assunta. She is not sure what they will do, but she is certain they are interested in her daughters. Even from a distance, she can see they are dressed much differently than the German soldiers she is used to seeing. Their coats are a brightly-colored burgundy, with large gold buttons adorning the lapels and pockets. Their pants are black, with satin stripes on each side, and they are all wearing tall, woolen caps rather than the standard military helmets most of the German soldiers wear. Studying them even more closely, she sees something that freezes her in a moment of total terror. Swords, they are all carrying long, frightening swords. Her greatest fear of the war has just become a reality; there are Cossacks in Napoli, and they have seen her daughters.

Her heart races while her breathing becomes shallow and labored. When she turns to escape, she can hear them speaking both German and a language she believes to be Russian. She wants to run, but she is afraid that they will chase after her and somehow find Lucia and Antonella. Instead, she walks with brisk, purposeful steps directly at the oncoming Cossacks. Her trembling legs will barely support her as the Russians stop and shout at her. She does not understand what they are saying and shrugs her shoulders as she tells them,

"Sono spiacente ma non capisco."

They become angry at her answer and look up and down the now empty street, but Lucia and Antonella are safely hidden from view. One of the Cossacks pushes her out of his way, slamming her into a nearby building as they all return to the truck. She stands motionless, clutching her shawl, and does not move until they drive off. Only after she is certain they are gone does she cautiously return to the apartment.

Arriving there, she races up the stairs and enters the apartment, frantically locking the door behind her. She finds Antonella and Lucia pacing around the main room. They are elated when they discover Assunta is unharmed. Antonella wipes tears from her eyes and says,

"Mama, what did the soldiers want? Did they hurt you?" Assunta places her hands onto her chest and draws several deep breaths while trying to calm herself. She pauses for a moment.

"The men in the truck...I...I am afraid they...they are Cossacks. I know they saw you. Dear God...I could see their awful swords. I know they are Russian because I heard them speak." Antonella and Lucia are terror-stricken by the news. Antonella asks,

"What will we do? Are we to hide in the attic tonight?"

"Yes. You will be safe there until they are gone. Go...go there now and I will give you some fresh water and what little food we have."

"You must come with us, Mama. Please don't leave us alone again," pleads Lucia.

"I will be safe. I must stay here and be sure they are gone before you can come down from that attic," says Assunta.

Antonella and Lucia say nothing more as they move into their bedroom. They climb atop the furniture and crawl into the dark, dusty little hiding space. Assunta hands them an additional jug of water and a partial loaf of bread. She encourages them to hurry, saying,

"Please go quickly. The soldiers may be able to find us. We cannot wait."

With Antonella and Lucia hidden safely in the attic, she slides the chest of drawers against a wall to reduce the risk of discovery. Once she is satisfied with the appearance of the bedroom, she looks up at her daughters through the opening in the ceiling.

"I love you both very much. I am so very sorry that you must hide in that awful place, but it is the only thing we can do. Now, put the tile over the opening, and no matter what you hear, do not remove it unless I ask you to." Lucia and Antonella begin crying as they see tears in her eyes. Antonella momentarily chokes back her anguish and asks,

"Mama, will you be all right? We...we love you too." Assunta can only nod her head as Lucia and Antonella fit the tile in place. They all wonder if they will ever see each other again.

Assunta sits in a chair near the window for hours, looking down on the street for any signs of danger. She tries to remain alert, but stress and exhaustion finally overcome her, and she eventually falls asleep. She is suddenly jarred awake by loud yelling and shouting coming from below the window. It is the same Russian tongue she heard the Cossacks use during her first encounter with them, and she realizes they are only steps away. Her heart pounds

149

and her mind races. How did they find this apartment? Do they know her daughters are here? She tries not to panic.

Even though gripped by fear, she is still able to lock the apartment door and bolt the windows. She carefully searches through the apartment one more time, looking for anything that suggests someone else lives there. Having done all that she can, Assunta sits frozen in helplessness as she hears the cadence of heavy footsteps climbing the stairway. Her eyes are riveted on the door handle as it begins to twist from side to side. Once locked, the sturdy door is not easily opened, and soon the door handle lies still.

The menacing presence does not leave, however. Moments later, a rifle butt crashes through the window, exploding slivers of glass across the entire room. The wood and steel mace repeatedly shatter the window until all the glass is broken out. Afterwards, the only sounds Assunta hears are the broken pieces of glass crackling underfoot. Then, without warning, the black-booted intruder steps through the window and onto the floor before her. The soldier slowly looks around the room, finally directing his stare at Assunta. His fearsome glare paralyzes her. Too terrified to speak or move, she remains seated in the tiny chair while looking directly into the face of a living nightmare.

He wears the same uniform and carries the same terrifying sword as the Cossacks she had met on the street. Standing there in the middle of her apartment, he is more gruesome looking than she could ever imagine. His foul odor is nauseating. Many of his teeth are either missing or decayed, and his face and hands are rife with open sores. An unshaven, grizzly-looking face and wild, ochre-colored eyes worsen his demonic appearance. The thought of her children falling victim to this monster drives her courage. With the most defiant voice she is able to exhibit, she demands,

"Che cosa desiderate? Non ho niente."

She can see he does not understand her, but she maintains eye contact while trying to capture all of his attention. Her arrogance angers him, and he begins to scream at her in violent, unintelligible German,

"Gibt es irgendwelche jungen Frauen hier?" He waves his arms about wildly and points to the tiny bedroom. She is not certain he speaks of her daughters, but she continues to try and divert his attention, nonetheless.

"I cannot understand you. I speak only Italian." His anger builds, and he charges at her. With one hand on the handle of his sword, he grabs her with the other and pulls her from the chair. Twisting her arm upward, he brutally holds her within inches of his face. He again screams,

"Gibt es irgendwelche jungen Frauen hier?"

Assunta tries to look away, but he will not allow her to turn her head. His hand begins to slide the massive sword from its sheath in an up and down pulsing motion, as if to threaten her even more. She believes she is about to be killed and begins to silently pray. Her trembling becomes even more violent, and she almost faints from fear. The Cossack suddenly releases her and, as she stands before him, he studies her as if she were a piece of livestock. He begins tearing off some of her clothing, but stops and pushes her back into the chair. He looks about the tiny apartment once again and enters the bedroom leading to the hidden attic.

Antonella and Lucia have heard the loud voices and breaking glass but are unsure of their origins. They can hear the heavy footsteps and monstrous growling only a few feet from where they hide. Antonella looks to Lucia, places her finger over her lips, and gently whispers,

"Shhhhh...we must be quiet."

They are almost too terrified to move, and it is all Antonella can do just to blow out the candle to reduce the smell of melting wax. Narrow beams of sunlight leak in through holes in the old roof, providing a feint, dust-filled haze to see by. They hold each other in desperate fear for their lives and the life of their mother.

Lucia begins to lightly weep, certain that their mother has been murdered. Antonella gently places her hand over her sister's mouth to keep her as quiet as possible. With no means of escape, they breathe quietly while trying to avoid detection. The intense fear is so pervasive, Lucia wets herself. There is nothing they can do but bury their heads against each other's shoulder and remain perfectly motionless. Antonella is certain the Russian Cossack can hear her pounding heart as her own fear intensifies.

Afraid the Russian will discover her daughters hiding above his head, Assunta attempts to attract his attention. She bravely stands in the doorway of the bedroom and asks,

"What is it you want? I have nothing of value." Her pleading does little more than provoke a series of guttural sounds as he continues to search the small apartment. Without warning, he whirls around in a maniacal rage and rushes toward Assunta. His face is distorted by an angry, violent expression. With distain and utter menace, he once again stands only inches from her face and screams,

"Sie pathetic alte Frau, vergeude ich meine Zeit hier."

Infuriated at not finding any valuables or young women, he pulls the steel saber from its sheath. Assunta expects to die at the hands of this ghastly beast, and she begins to anoint herself with the sign of the cross. Before she can finish the blessing, the Cossack pummels the side of her head with the heavy metal handle of the saber. The brutal impact knocks her to the floor. She can feel the warmth from her own blood flowing across her forehead as she awaits certain death to claim her. But the deathblow never comes. The Cossack mysteriously storms out of the apartment as quickly as he had come. After hearing him stomp down the stairs, she breaks down in tearful relief as she whispers,

"Thank you dear God. Thank you."

Lucia and Antonella have heard the Cossack's screams but can only wait and hope that their mother is alive. Although they fear the worst, they do not remove the tile from the ceiling opening.

Overwhelmed by raw fear and unrelenting panic, they weep in whispers at the thought of their mother being butchered by the Russian. Lucia asks,

"What shall we do? Oh my God, Antonella. What if Mama is dead...I'm so afraid. What will happen to us?"

"I don't know, Lucia. I don't know," she replies.

They sit in agonizing silence for several more hours, but then hear someone moving in the bedroom below. With a slight, whispering voice, Assunta calls to them.

"Lucia. Antonella. Are you safe? Can you hear me?"

"It's Mama. It's Mama. Help me remove the tile, Lucia."

With the tile removed, they look down at their mother covered in blood, and Lucia gasps,

"Mama, what happened? We...we were so scared. We thought you were dead. Are you hurt badly?"

"It is only a cut on my head. It is not serious, but we are not safe in our own home, and you must stay hidden up there until the danger has passed."

For the next several days, Assunta repeatedly looks for signs of any soldiers, but they have apparently moved elsewhere. She cautiously allows her daughters to come down from the hiding place but keeps it ready at all times in case the threat returns to Bagnoli.

Assunta's brush with death marks the beginning of greater threats and unspeakable horrors that will remain a part of her family's life for many more months.

CHAPTER 8

The late call awakens Giuseppi. He rolls over in bed, clicks on the table lamp, and squints at the black and white face on the small alarm clock. It's a few minutes before midnight, and he wonders who would be calling at this time. He climbs from his bed and makes his way to the dining room. The phone rings incessantly, the caller not easily discouraged by the lengthy wait. He lifts the handset and says,

"Hello?" Astonished to hear Antonio Bomarito's voice, he asks,

"Antonio! Why you call atta thees late hour?"

"I hava somathing to tella you. It'sa you son, Mario. He's inna big trouble. Do you know he'sa been out shooting craps witha my niece?" he answers sharply. Giuseppi hears uneasiness in his old gambling friend's voice. He cautiously responds,

"No, Antonio. I know nothing abouta the women Mario sees."

155

"He'sa taking my niece, Mia, to soma high price blinda pig, and he'sa losta lot of money," Antonio continues to rant. Giuseppi has witnessed Antonio's temper in the past and can hear it in his voice now. He tries to apologize.

"Antonio. I'ma sorry ifa Mario has embarrassa you family. Somatimes, he'sa no think about thesa things and..." Antonio rudely interrupts him before Giuseppi can finish his thought.

"Giuseppi, that'sa not why he'sa inna trouble. I don'ta give a goddamn if he fuck'sa my niece or losa all his money. Mario, borrowed money onna my name to make a soma bets, anna he can notta pay it back. He use a my name withouta telling me, Guiseppi. That'sa something noboby does a to me. People, they getta hurt doinga stupid things like a that. You know that, Giuseppi."

The disturbing news fully awakens Giuseppi from his sleepy daze. He can feel his pulse quicken. The stress of his own anger brings about a cold sweat as he seeks a way to appease his violent friend.

"Antonio, thanka you for telling me alla these. Whatta can I do to maka theesa trouble go away?" he respectfully asks. There is a brief pause before Antonio responds. Then, in a harsh, threatening voice, he replies,

"Ifa somaone taka my money lika Mario did, they gonna end uppa inna fuckin alley somaplace. But we are old friends, Giuseppi. Old friends respect each other. I'ma goin to giva you soma time to worka this out. You hava until the end of thees week to getta me my two thousand dollars. And you maka sure Mario, he knowsa his gambling isa over, *capisc?*"

"*Grazie*, Antonio. I'ma gonna make sure Mario knows whatta you say." Antonio slams the phone down without saying another word. After hanging up, Giuseppi paces around the house in a seething rage. He is furious over Mario's stupidity and dumbfounded over why he let this happen. He will get little sleep for the rest of the night while waiting for Mario to return home.

It has been over a week since Mario borrowed the money from the blind pig, but he has not been able to pay it back. He decides to sell his car, but it's only worth about nine hundred dollars. With a buyer lined up, he hopes to borrow the rest from his brothers. Unsure how much time he has before someone starts looking for him, he wants to get out of this mess before his father finds out. It's early in the morning, and he's returning home from being out with Lena again. After parking the car in front of the house, he lets himself in, quietly continues up the stairs to his bedroom and undresses. Mario crawls into bed, and the glare of the ceiling lamp unexpectedly lights up the room and startles him. Mario rubs his eyes and looks up at the door. Giuseppi is standing there with an angry scowl on his face and his hands braced on his hips.

"I wanna you to coma downstairs right now," he growls.

Mario sees that he is irate. Certain that Giuseppi knows about his predicament, Mario pulls on a pair of trousers while wondering what the old man's been told. Giuseppi is sitting in his usual place at the dining room table, and he angrily motions for Mario to sit across from him.

Seeing how flushed and agitated Giuseppi is, Mario tries to explain what has happened. Before he can speak, however, Giuseppi says,

"Justa shut upa for a goddamn a minute anna listen to me." The old man nervously runs his hands through his thin hair while staring down at the table in deep thought. After a moment of silent anger, he looks up at Mario.

"Antonio Bomarito calla me at midanight. He'sa mad asa hell. He says you owe hima money? Whatta fuck isa going on, Mario?" Even as a grown man, Mario is still intimidated by the old man's anger. He squirms in his chair while trying to answer his father's question. He finally begins.

"It's true Pa. I...I owe em money from a crap game a few days ago."

"How mucha you owe hima?" Giuseppi demands to know.

"Two thousand dollars." Giuseppi shakes his head in disgust, and then asks,

"What'sa these bullashit about Antonio's niece. Do you know he'sa niece?"

"Yeah. I met her in Toledo a few months ago, and we been goin out for a while. She got me the money at the blind pig. I...I thought I could win there. I beat those guys before. I just had a bad night, that's all."

Giuseppi's frustration mounts as he listens to Mario's story. Without warning, he stands up and leans over, placing his palms down on the table directly in front of Mario. With his face only inches from Mario's, he screams,

"Whatta hell isa wrong with a you? You cannotta embarrass a man lika Antonio Bomarito by screwing hisa niece anna stealing hisa money. You're lucky you are notta dead or inna goddamn a hospital by now." Giuseppi's face is the color of faint crimson, and veins pulse across his temples as he continues to vent his fury on Mario. With his hands on his hips, he paces around the dining room, shouting,

"Where inna da hell are you gonna finda two thousand dollars?" Mario nervously wrings his hands together as he explains his plan to repay Bomarito.

"I got it all figured out, Pa. I gotta a buyer for the Ford. Now that John's got his own car, I can sell it. I can get about nine hundred for it, and I'll borrow some from John and Joe. They always have some extra money. They know I'm good for it," he answers. After his hostile outburst, Giuseppi cannot help feeling a little sorry for Mario, and his fit of anger begins to slowly pass. But he knows his other sons cannot help him.

"Mario, John and Joe, they are gonna be married soon. They cannot giva you that mucha money." Mario had been counting on his brothers' help to get out of this jam, but Giuseppi's warning worries him.

159

"Pa, are you sure? They always got some extra money saved up."

"They don'ta have enough money for the weddings. They wanna soma money froma me. Weddings, they costa lot of money, Mario." Mario's dilemma worsens as his scheme to borrow from his brothers disintegrates. In desperation, he reluctantly asks his father,

"Pa, can you help me out? I'll pay ya back right away. I promise."

"I don't hava eleven hundred dollars righta now, Mario. That'sa lot of money. Alla I can do isa ask Antonio ifa he will giva you some more time to pay hima back."

Their argument is over for the moment, and Mario thanks him for whatever he can do. He knows his problem has greatly embarrassed his father in the eyes of Antonio Bomarito. He's let the old man down and, even if given additional time to repay the debt, his father's damaged friendship with Bomarito will not be restored until the money is paid back in full. Without his family's aid, Mario feels totally alone for the first time in his life. It will not be the last.

Mario sells the Ford sedan and sends Antonio Bomarito the entire nine hundred dollars from its sale. The money has bought him a few more weeks to find the remaining cash. He tries to borrow money from a few friends in the plant, but he cannot come up with enough to pay what he owes. If something doesn't turn up soon, he'll be in serious trouble, the kind that can get him hurt badly. Mario knows that Giuseppi has stretched his friendship with Bomarito as far as he dares and that there is little more the old man can do.

A cold, north wind swirls clouds of fresh snow into scattered piles around the neighborhood. It is early December, and winter has tightened its grip on the city. Giuseppi hates going out during the cold months, but he treks off to the local newsstand to buy a paper every day. Mario's troubles are not his only concern. He searches the pages from beginning to end, looking for any information about the war in Europe. Stories from the foreign press report that the Nazis control all of Italy, including Sicily, and the old man worries about his family there. The newspaper tells of conflicts in Europe and Africa, as well as China and Japan. Giuseppi is sure America will eventually be forced into the war to assist its allies, and the thought terrifies him. His sons are all eligible to go to war, and that fact is never far from his thoughts.

It is December 8, 1941, and Giuseppi arrives at the newsstand early in the morning. The paperboy sees him coming and shouts out to him,

"Hi ya, Mr. Carlucci. Not too cold out this mornin, huh?"

"It'sa stilla too goddamn colda for me, Louie. You gotta my paper today?"

"Sure do. Kept it hidden for ya. With President Roosevelt speakin on the radio this morning, everybody and der uncle wants a paper today."

"Whatta you talking about, Louie?"

"You mean you ain't heard? Der sayin he's got something really important to talk about. It's supposed ta start in about an hour from now. Ya got time to get home and listen."

Giuseppi thanks the paperboy for the information and rushes home. He looks at the front page of the paper while hurrying along. The headline reads, "CONGRESS DECLARES WAR." His worse fear has come to pass. When he arrives home, he removes his coat and boots and immediately calls out to his sons,

"John. Coma here right away, and bringa you brothers. Hurry." They dash into the living room and find Giuseppi adjusting the dials on the RCA radio.

"Pa, what's goin on? Is there something wrong?" John asks.

"It'sa President Roosevelt. He'sa gonna make an importanta speech. We all musta listen. Sit down, all of you. It's abouta the war. The Japanese, they attacka Pearl Harbor." He continues to adjust the dials until he hears an announcer say,

"Ladies and gentlemen, the President of the United States." The four men sit in silence as the President begins to speak,

"To the Congress of the United States.

Yesterday, December 7, 1941—a date which will live in infamy—the United States was suddenly and deliberately attacked by naval and air forces of the Empire of Japan.

The United States was at peace with that nation and, at the solicitation of Japan, was still in conversation with the government and its emperor looking toward the maintenance of peace in the

Pacific." As the president reveals the details of the attack, John mutters,

"Jesus Christ. The Japs attacked us. I can't believe it."

The president continues,

"The attack yesterday on the Hawaiian islands has caused severe damage to American naval and military forces. Very many American lives have been lost. In addition, American ships have been reported torpedoed on the high seas between San Francisco and Honolulu."

Giuseppi and his sons listen to the entire speech, but it is the concluding statement made by the president that sends the most chilling message,

"I ask that the Congress declare that, since the unprovoked and dastardly attack by Japan on Sunday, December 7, a state of war has existed between the United States and the Japanese empire."

After the speech, Giuseppi and his sons sit in somber silence for a few moments. He knows from the reports published in the newspapers that the United States will also declare war on the Germans and Italians, thereby plunging the country into the center of the world conflict. His worst fears have become a reality, and anxiety rapidly tightens his insides into a quivering bundle of nerves. He has not felt this uneasy since leaving Sicily as a young boy. The possibility of all his sons going off to war causes him to regret not having been a better father to them. He keeps his guilt and fear concealed from them while he listens to their reaction to the news.

"The miserable cowards. How can the bastards think they can get away with somethin like that?" says Joe.

"We got the biggest fuckin navy in the world. The Japs are gonna get their ass kicked in a few weeks, you watch," Mario exclaims.

"I'll bet there are guys lined up at the recruitin office right now, ready ta join up," Joe says. John thinks of the more immediate impact of a war and says,

"I wonder what's gonna happen at the plant? Ain't nobody gonna be able to buy cars anymore. Shit, we'll be lucky to buy any gas in a few months."

"I'll tell ya one thing. Ain't no Japanese gonna take over this country as long as I can hold a gun," adds Mario. Their patriotism surprises Giuseppi, but he cannot bear to listen to such things. As he leaves the room, John asks his father,

"You feel okay, Pa? Without stopping, he answers,

"Yes. I'ma tired, that'sa all. I wanna lay down for a little while."

In the privacy of his bedroom, he thinks of the horror war brings to families. Will his sons survive? Will they come home wounded or injured for life? He remembers images of men scarred by the First World War, and imagining his own sons having to live through such hell deeply disturbs him. He came to this country to find a better life for his family, but all that he has accomplished could be lost if his sons must go to war. Even now, he feels a terrible sense of loneliness beginning to creep into his life.

With the country at war, the world the Carlucci's live in changes dramatically. Gasoline and tires become scarce, things such as imported foods and beverages are no longer available, and many of their friends talk of enlisting in the military or are awaiting their draft notices. The plant where John and Mario work prepares for a major reorganizing in the first few months of the war. Early one afternoon, John is called into a large meeting at the plant. In attendance are all the plant mangers, production supervisors, and union stewards. Harold Burton, the senior manager, addresses the group.

"Gentlemen, we have been awarded a contract to build half-tracks and personal carriers for the army. This is Colonel Ralph Tuscott. He'll give you the details." The Army officer stands before the plant staff and begins to explain the plan.

"Thank you all for coming. This plant has been selected to build war vehicles. We have been discussing this with your management for several months and are now ready to change the plant over. All of you have been chosen to play key roles in that effort. Your managers say you are the best men to get this important job going. We will begin immediately. Our troops are in urgent need of this equipment, as I speak, so we cannot waste any time. You will all be given exemptions from military service in order to keep this work going. There will be more details later today, but for now, that's the plan. Good luck to you all."

John is stunned by the news. Being exempt from military service to build Jeeps is like a small miracle. His fear of going to war had upset his plans to get married, but he cannot wait to surprise his fiancée with the remarkable news. Even in elation, however, a strange mixture of guilt and relief overcomes him as a result of the extraordinary turn of events. He says nothing to anyone and considers himself lucky to be among the men chosen to run the plant. For the moment, he is anxious to get home and tell his family the good news.

Giuseppi finds himself spending more time with his sons, usually over an evening meal he prepares. Knowing the time left to spend with them is short, he delights in cooking large, sumptuous meals every chance he gets. The large dining room table is set with plates and wine glasses, and when his sons return home in the evening, he often serves large bowls of pasta and platters of sausage. They cluster around the table, pass the bowls to each other and, between bites, share any breaking news from the neighborhood.

"I hear Tommy Esposito joined the Marines today. Did you guys hear anything like that?" Joe asks.

"He joined the Marines? I hear ya gotta be a mean son-of-a-bitch to make it in that outfit," Mario adds.

"Someone said he wants ta be a fighter pilot. Shit, he was never smart enough ta get through school. How the hell is he gonna fly a fighter plane?" Joe asks in wonder. John cannot wait any longer to tell them the news from the plants and says,

"You ain't gonna believe what happened to me today. The plant is gonna start makin Jeeps and half-tracks for the Army, and I've been chosen to help get the production started."

"Holy shit, when is that gonna start?" asks Mario.

"Right away. There're shuttin down the lines tomorrow. But that's not all they said. A Colonel Tuscott said we are exempt from the military cause our job is more important here. Can ya believe it?" Giuseppi stops eating and looks up at John. Wanting to be sure he heard him correctly, he asks,

"You meana you don'ta hava to go inna the Army, John?"

"Yeah, that right, Pa. I have ta stay here and help build the Jeeps. I still can't believe it," John replies in astonishment. Mario immediately asks,

"Does that mean anyone workin there will be exempt? Do ya think I will?"

"No. I don't think so. They said only the guys picked ta run the lines will be exempt," John answers. Mario's disappointed by John's answer, but remains supportive, saying,

"Well, at least one of us will get a break outta this. That's good John, real good."

John can see Giuseppi is thrilled by the news. The old man raises his wine glass in a toast.

"John, that'sa wonderful news. Maybe your brothers can hava the same a kind of a luck. I hope a so."

Mono V. D'Angelo

John's good fortune brings Giuseppi and his sons closer together, making the evening dinners increasingly important. With friends and neighbors entering the military almost daily, they understand that Mario and Joe can soon be drafted, and in the time they have left, Giuseppi tries to become the type of father he never was.

The dinners continue and the list of friends and acquaintances that have either been drafted or enlisted increases every week. The scope and brutality of the war becomes a regular topic of conversation. Giuseppi reads the newspapers religiously. During their dinners, he often discusses what he reads.

"The British anda Germans, they fight in Africa, anda the Japs holda alla the islands inna the Southa Pacific. Lot's of a our Marines, they fight there. The Russians, they fighta the Germans. The whole world isa fighting. I'ma afraid theesa war, itsa not gonna end very soon."

After listening to Giuseppi comments, Joe's excited over some good news he's received.

"Some of my customers in the store were tellin me if ya join up, ya got a better chance of endin up someplace ya choose instead of where ever they send ya, so I went to see a recruiter and tried to enlist today." Everyone is surprised by the unexpected announcement. Mario asks,

"Joe. Whatta ya mean ya tried to enlist? Did ya or didn't ya?"

"Let me finish, will ya. When I filled out the paperwork, the recruiter noticed my medical history. He started to ask me all kinda questions about my health and said I needed to take a physical. He didn't think I could join up because of my heart condition."

"Joe, didda you take a the physical?" Giuseppi asks.

"Yeah, they sent me over ta see the doctors, who checked me out and said I can't pass the physical. So I can't enlist or be drafted."

Giuseppi, John, and Mario are shocked but relieved over Joe's news. Once again, Giuseppi cannot believe that another of his sons will remain home, safe from the war. While grateful for Joe's good fortune, it seems that Mario is the only one of his children destined to fight in this bloody war.

Mario's job has become a part of the military production line. He now machines parts for the Jeeps that will soon be built in the huge plant. At the end of his long shift, he is thirsty for a few beers and stops at the local bar he and John sometimes frequent. He drinks alone, however, as John's new responsibilities keep him in the plant at all hours of the day and night. The bar is not as crowded as it once was, and he sits at the old, drink-stained counter top wondering how many of its customers have ended up in the service. Between taking swigs off of the long-necked bottle, he unconscientiously peels away small pieces of the label while reading over the front page of a newspaper left on the bar. The headlines tell of increased conflicts around the world as the war rages in Europe. Unexpectedly, a voice calls out to him from the doorway.

"Mario, is dat you?" someone asks. Turning to see who it is, he finds Donnie, the bouncer from Felston's blind pig, standing behind him. Mario is surprised to see him, but he knows why he's here.

"How are ya, Donnie?"

"I ain't doin too good right now, you know? Mista Felston and Mista Bomarito, dey told me ta find ya and beat yo ass if ya don't get them da money you owes em."

"So, is that what you're gonna do? Beat my ass?" Mario asks.

"Naw, Mario, you knows I ain't gonna do dat. I jus gonna tell em I cain't find ya. But dey got udder guys who will kick yo ass, so ya better gits dem der money soon."

"Thanks for the advice, Donnie. I'm tryin to find the rest of the dough, but I ain't havin much luck."

Donnie rocks his head from side to side, discouraged over what Mario says. He likes Mario and doesn't want him to get hurt, but warning him is all that he can do. He shakes his hand and says,

"I gots ta go. You watch out fo yoself, ya hear?"

Donnie leaves and Mario sits thinking. He's grateful for the generous tips given to Donnie, but he realizes that not even the war will deter Antonio Bomarito from collecting his money. The nine hundred dollars given to him apparently will buy no more time, and Mario has exhausted all possibilities of finding the rest of the money he owes the mobster. Under the circumstances, he begins to consider enlisting in the Army as a means to escape the debt. He assumes he will be drafted soon, regardless of what he does, and while he waits for his draft notice to arrive, Antonio's goons are still a threat to him. He pays his bar tab and heads for home with a plan that will change his life.

Mario lies in his bed later that night, but he is not asleep. He is waiting for John to return home from the plant. From his upper level bedroom, he hears the front door open and is sure it's his brother. Climbing out of bed, he looks out the window for John's car. It's parked in front of their house. Mario slips on his trousers and joins John in the kitchen. It's been another fourteen-hour day for John, and Mario can tell he's tired and hungry. While his brother prepares some of Giuseppi's leftovers for himself, Mario asks,

"John, ya got a few minutes ta talk?"

"Yeah, sure. But I'm worn out, so if I doze off, just smack me," John jokes.

"I gotta do something ta get Bomarito off my back. I found out today he's got people looking for me…they wanna kick my ass if I don't come up with the dough I owe." John stops what he's doing. Although his brother's problem is becoming very serious, he reminds him,

"Mario, I want ta help you, but I don't have a lot of money ta give ya."

"I know, I know. But this is what I wanna do. Listen," Mario says. He clears his throat and fidgets in his chair as he begins to reveal his plan to John.

"I figure I'm gonna get drafted any time now. And I...well...I just think I might as well...uh...get it over with and...uh...enlist in the Army. That way Bomarito's guys won't mess around with me anymore. Whatta ya think?"

John has a difficult time answering his brother's question. Mario has just asked him to condone an idea that will send him to war. He rubs his hand over his chin with slow, forceful strokes, trying to relieve some of his nervousness. He's unsure of what to say. After a few moments of awkward silence, he responds.

"Jesus Christ, Mario. I don't know what ta tell you. Yeah, I guess you're right. Bomarito will leave ya alone, but joinin the Army right away?...If ya wanna wait for the draft, I'll watch your back. You know that. But I...I...can't make that decision for ya."

"I ain't gonna get no exemptions like you and Joe got, so I'm goin no matter what. What difference does it make if it's now or a month from now?"

"Sounds like you got your mind already made up." John often acts more like a father than an older brother to Mario, but he won't make this decision for him. If his brother does not return from the war, that decision would haunt him for the rest of his life. He can feel his eyes getting watery and his chin starting to quiver as he realizes that Mario will be the only family member to have to fight this war. He tells Mario,

"I hate this goddamn war, but I'm proud of ya for doin this."

"Don't say anything ta Pa about this yet. I wanna tell em after I get this all worked out." John stands up, gives Mario a mock headlock as a gesture of affection and says,

"Don't worry. I won't. Come on, let's go get some sleep." For Mario, there will be little sleep tonight, as he ponders what he is about to do.

A few days later, Mario borrows John's car and drives to an Army enlistment office located in City Hall. The large, granite-lined corridor is lined with men waiting to enlist. He wanders around until he sees a small sign hanging over a doorway. It reads "Recruitment Office—U.S. Army." Men are going in and coming out in revolving door fashion. Mario asks one of them,

"Hey buddy, what's goin on here. Is this the place to enlist?"

"Yup. Jus go in an give em your name, and they'll come out an git ya when they're ready. But don't be in a big hurry," chuckles the stranger.

Mario finds a place in the line, and he slowly works his way into the office. Once he's inside, several uniformed soldiers sitting behind a skinny table ask for names and addresses. Mario gives one of them the information, and he's told to wait out in the corridor and someone will come for him soon. He locates an unclaimed marble column and leans against it, waiting and watching. There are a lot of young men trying to join up. Some don't even appear to be of legal age. There are also older men with touches of gray hair visible beneath their hats. Every few minutes, one of the uniformed clerks steps out into the waiting area and shouts out someone's name.

"Panatti, Carl Panatti."

"Paul MacMurty."

"Andrew Jones."

The men seem to come from all over the city, and Mario is amazed at how many are eager to join up. A few moments later, the clerk returns once again and calls his name,

"Carlucci. Mario Carlucci?"

Mario raises his hand and is led into a small interview office. He studies the enlistment posters hanging on each wall. The Marines, the Navy, as well as the Army are well represented. The door to the office swings open and a tall, uniformed soldier enters the room.

"Hello. My name is Sergeant Frank Willis. I'm one of the Army recruiters here. You are Mario Carlucci, correct?"

"Yes, I am," responds Mario.

"Okay, Mario. I'm going to ask you a few basic questions. Then if I get the answers I need, we can make this quick. Do you have a criminal record?"

"No, I don't."

"Got any serious health problem, tuberculosis, bad feet, things like that?"

"No, I'm pretty healthy."

"Are you employed right now, and if you are, what do you do?"

"Yeah, I'm a machinist in one of the plants down near the Rouge complex,"

"A machinist, huh? That's real good, Carlucci. The Army needs that kind of talent. It takes a lot of hardware to fight a war, and we never have enough people who can keep that shit running."

Mario is not sure why the recruiter is so interested in his machinist skills, but in less than twenty-five minutes, the Sergeant hands him an enlistment form and says,

"Can you read and write?"

"Sure."

"You'd be surprised how many guys come in here who can't. Fill this out completely and sign it at the bottom. Just open the door when you're finished." He promptly leaves, and Mario stares at the document. Its title reads, "Property of the United States Army."

With the stroke of a pen, he too, will become property of the U.S. Army. A chill shoots up and down Mario's spine while he examines the three-page questionnaire before him. It is like a window through which to view the rest of his life, but he can't see through it. He rakes his hand over his head, bewildered by the uncertainty of his future. His factory life seems mundane and simple when compared to this chance to do something truly important. He feels a sense of patriotism welling up inside of him. He thinks of where this adventure will take him. Will he end up in Europe? Or some hell-hole of a little island in the South Pacific? He wonders how many of these men here today will never come home. Will he kill or be killed?

The reason he's decided to enlist suddenly seems so trivial as he contemplates all the frightening and amazing experiences that are before him. He realizes this is the most important thing he's ever done in his life. He picks up the pen, fills out the paper work, and proudly signs the form.

Mario drives around for a few hours before returning home. He drives by his father's seafood store and a few of his favorite clubs. He does not stop, however. He wants to see anything that is his life and store these images away in his memory for some unforeseen use in the months to come. He's not sure how to tell his father what he's done, so he rehearses a speech to give him, but it never comes out the same way twice.

He parks the car in its familiar place along the curb and goes into the house. Having lived here all his life, he has always taken it for granted. But today is different. The aroma of garlic and tomato sauce bubbling in the kitchen, his father clanging pots and pans as he cooks, and the feelings of warmth and safety the house provides all seem so much more vivid now. His hands and legs begin to shake slightly, and he can feel a slight sweat beading up on his forehead. His insides churn and his breathing is short.

He sits in the living room for a moment, having second thoughts. He hears his father working in the kitchen. He wipes his forehead with the sleeve of his shirt, pulls his hair away from his face, and prepares to tell him the news. As he enters the large, well-lit kitchen, he finds Giuseppi standing in front of the stove. His rehearsed speech forgotten because of his nerves, he simply stands there before his father, unable to say anything. The old man looks up and says,

"Mario. Where hava you beena alla day? John, he'sa look for he'sa car."

Mario says nothing. His face is pale and his eyes are drawn and tired. His somber expression and visible shaking foretell of something seriously wrong. Giuseppi asks,

"Mario. Whattsa matter?" Mario takes a few deep breaths and then says,

"Pa. I...I got something to, uh, tell ya. I...uh. I joined up today. I...uh, enlisted...in the Army." Giuseppi has known this day would come, but he is still surprised by the news.

"How coma you no tella me before?

"I don't know. I, uh, guess I didn't want to bother ya any more. You know, be...because of the mess I made of your friendship with Bomarito and everything."

Giuseppi becomes upset with himself for allowing his friendship with the ruthless Bomarito to appear so important to Mario. He can practically feel his son's fear, and yet Mario did not tell him of the most important decision of his life until after it had been made. The two men stare at each other for a few quiet moments, and the reality of his son going to war overpowers Giuseppi. He slowly puts down the cooking utensils and instinctively wipes his hands on the short, food-stained apron he wears. He can see tears in Mario eyes. He places his hand on his son's back.

"Sit down here atta the table, Mario." They sit across from one another at the little kitchen table and try to repair their family differences while they still have time.

"I'm sorry for all the trouble I caused you, Pa."

"That'sa not important any more. I know I'ma not a very good father, so we both arra to blame for our problems. But...I'ma very proud...of a your courage...to do this." Having never been emotionally honest or open with any of his sons before the war, he wants to be sure Mario knows how he feels. Giuseppi leans forward and rests his elbows on the table.

"Mario. You are my son an...anna I know I never tella you this but...I...I'ma very worried abouta you. Promise a me you willa come home when a thisa goddamn war issa over. Promise a me...Mario." Mario wipes his eyes and says,

"I promise, Pa. I promise."

CHAPTER 9

Daily reports in the newspapers tell of increasing battles and conflicts. The war rages in the Philippines as the Japanese accelerate their march through the South Pacific. The Navy has fought a major battle in a place called Midway, and fears of a Japanese attack upon the west coast of the country force the internment of many Japanese citizens living there. Germany has begun bombing England, and the conflict spreads across the entire continent of Europe. As the war intensifies, the need for service men is critical and, within days of his enlistment, Mario receives orders to report for basic training immediately. There are hasty goodbyes with his brothers and father, after which John drives him to the enlistment office. Together, they wind their way through the maze of men waiting to be assigned to one of the buses preparing to depart for training camp. John is not permitted to go beyond the office door.

"Look, you take care, ya hear? I'll see ya when ya get home on leave."

"Yeah, I'll call ya when I get a chance. Besides, I need a little rest from the plant anyway." John gives him a hug and leaves Mario standing among the throng of men waiting to board the buses.

He will be transported to the Ft. Custer induction center. It's located only a few hours from Detroit, and Mario hopes he'll be able to go through basic training but still get home on an occasional leave. He receives his enlistment instructions and climbs aboard one of the waiting buses for the short ride to the camp. Each bus carries all the men who will be housed together for the duration of their training. There's a lot of joking and laughing as the men get to know one another. Mario meets men from Chicago, Cincinnati, Ft. Wayne and many other cities in the region, as well as Detroit. Shortly afterwards, the bus arrives at the camp and stops at the front of a narrow barracks building. The driver shouts out,

"Ok, guys this is it. Everyone off." As the men file out, a short well-built man in a crisp, clean uniform greets them. He begins shouting out instructions.

"All right, all right. Line up in front of this building right here and pay attention. I'm Sergeant Zekeil Bosely, your drill instructor. It's my job to turn you guys into soldiers. We only got ten weeks to get that done, so there's a lot of work to do. You guys see that building over there with the long line in front of it? Get your asses into that line, pick up your gear and get back here without any side trips. Find a bunk inside and wait for me before you do anything else."

The drill instructor, or D.I. as he likes to be called, is nothing but business. Basic training is all about discipline, and the D.I. preaches discipline to the squad of new recruits. They are up at four o'clock every morning and start a daily routine of four-mile marches, hours of calisthenics and weapons training. The work is physical, demanding and relentless. For six weeks, Mario does nothing but train, eat and sleep. Letters and phone calls home are not permitted, and no one is allowed to leave the camp.

The brutal regimen gradually becomes more tolerable, and the recruits begin to form friendships. For some, the training is a first time away from home. For others, it is an opportunity to get away from something in their past. Mario becomes friendly with several recruits, usually having meals with them. Billy Magee is from Dayton, and Tom Cousino is from Milwaukee. After their evening meal, they often spend the last few hours of the day talking about the lives they've left behind.

"Hey Mario, you got a girlfriend back home?" asks Billy.

"No one special. How about you?"

"Oh yeah. My girlfriend and I are gonna get married when I get back. I been goin out with her for over three years. We went to the same school."

"Come on, Billy. Do ya think she's still gonna be waitin around for your ass ta get home from this fuckin war? Do ya?" chides Tom.

"Sure she will. She already told me she will." Tom begins laughing at Billy's gullible nature and teases him unmercifully.

"Shit, Billy. You ain't even left the country yet, and I'll bet she's probably fuckin some new guy right now."

Mario feels sorry for Billy. Sometimes he hears him crying late at night and can tell he's afraid. Tom's jokes are cruel and upsetting, so he tries to intervene.

"Come on, Tom. Ease up on him, will ya? You know that's just a lot a bullshit, don't ya Billy?"

For six long weeks, Mario's life consists of nothing but the daily grind of the camp and a few humorous moments with his new friends, but on a Thursday afternoon, the D.I. makes a long awaited announcement to the squad.

"You guys are doin real good. In fact, you're ahead of the training schedule, so I'm giving ya a weekend pass off the base. There's gonna be a few buses headin back into Detroit tomorrow afternoon. But if ya leave the base, make goddamn sure you're back here by reveille Monday morning." The squad bursts into a loud cheer, and they all make plans to leave the base at long last.

Mario is excited to be going home. He packs a small bag and is one of the first to board the bus for town on Friday afternoon. The two-hour ride seems to take twice as long as it did when he traveled to the camp. After arriving at the station located near the recruiting office, Mario scrambles off the bus in search of a phone booth. He locates one near the entrance to the terminal, drops in a nickel, and impatiently listens to the clicking noises as the call goes through. The phone rings several times before John answers.

"Hello." Mario instantly recognizes his voice and shouts into the handset,

"John. It's me, Mario."

"Mario? Holy shit! Where are you?"

"I just got into the bus station. You know, the one down the street from the city hall building. Can ya come and pick me up, or should I catch a cab?"

"You just sit tight. I'll be there in fifteen minutes. In the meantime, try not to get picked up by any women now that you're wearin a uniform." Mario laughs out loud at John's wisecrack.

"Just get your ass here. I'm starvin." John slams down the phone and runs through the house, shouting,

"Hey, Joe. Where are ya? You guys in the kitchen?"

"Yeah, in here. What the hell are ya shoutin about?" asks Joe. John charges into the kitchen and excitedly announces,

"It's Mario. He just called and said he's at the bus station. I'm gonna go pick em up. I know he's hungry, Pa, so why don't ya make em somethin to eat while I'm gone?"

"I will. You go anna pick him up anna I make a soma sandwiches. I got soma fresh salami and provolone. Go…hurry."

They're all thrilled to see Mario again, and anxious to know all about boot camp, especially if he's been assigned somewhere. John grabs his coat, charges out the door, and hops in his car for the brief ride to the bus station. He slowly cruises by the main terminal entrance, looking for Mario. The station is crowded with men in military uniforms, and spotting him is not easy. He stops near the boarding zone and peers out of the car's side windows, hoping to find him, when someone suddenly grabs the door and throws it open. Mario leans over, sticks his head into the car and jokes,

"It's about fuckin time. Christ, the war'll be over while I'm waitin here for you ta show up." Startled by Mario's sudden appearance, John laughs and screams,

"Get in here, damn it and quit complainin." Mario throws his bag in the back seat and jumps into the front. John shakes his hand vigorously and tells him,

"Welcome home, little brother. Ya look good. I guess the Army ain't so bad after all."

"Bull shit. I ain't worked so fuckin hard in my goddamn life." John laughs again and says,

"You can tell us all about it later. Let's get going. The old man's got some food waitin back at the house."

It feels good to be home after the grueling six weeks in boot camp, and Mario looks forward to visiting with his brothers and father. Parking in front of the house, they hurry inside. Joe greets Mario with a big hug, shakes his hands and looks him over.

"Wow. Ya look really great in that uniform, Mario. Wait'll some of your old girlfriends get a load of ya." Mario laughs at his brother's comment.

"Thanks Joe. But I ain't had much time for women lately. Where's Pa?"

"He's in the kitchen, where else? Christ, ya'd think he was feedin the whole army, with all the food he's makin. I hope you're hungry." They burst into the kitchen to surprise Giuseppi. He looks up, sees Mario and a breaks into a broad grin.

"Coma here. Letta me look atta you." Welcoming his son home in true Sicilian fashion, he first gives him a hug and then a light slap on the cheek. Taking him by the arm, he studies him carefully for a few seconds.

"You gaina soma weight. They mustta be feeding you ok, eh?"

"Well, it ain't like your cookin, Pa. That's for sure." Giuseppi gathers up four short drinking glasses for the wine and leads everyone into the dining room.

"You sit and enjoy soma wine. I go getta the food." On the table is a full gallon of wine from the Little Café. When Giuseppi returns with a plate full of sandwiches, he says,

"When I stoppa to tell Enzo you joina the Army, he giva me some wine. He say it'sa for you whenna you come home. So drink." Giuseppi pours the wine for everyone. They settle down to enjoy the meal and begin asking Mario about his experience in boot camp.

"What'd they have ya doin for six weeks?" asks Joe.

"Christ, they get ya up at 4:30 every fuckin mornin and just work your ass off until ya drop. I thought I was dead after my first four mile hike."

"How many guys are trainin in this camp?" asks John.

"I dunno, but they bring in new busloads every day. I'm barracked with guys from all over the place."

"Ya won't believe the plant these days. We can build hundreds of Jeeps and armored trucks every week. They're even hirin women," says John. John and Joe tell Mario about their marriage plans, and Guiseppi is already hinting at grandchildren.

"It'sa time we have soma *bambinos* around theesa place, eh, Mario?" The old man's not so subtle remark brings a smile to Mario's face, and he's almost glad he doesn't have to listen to that lecture every day. John just laughs it off and then asks a more serious question,

"Do ya know where you'll be assigned yet, Mario?"

"No, not yet. They won't tell me anything until basics are just about done. I got another four weeks to go."

"You gonna coma home a before you go?"

"I think so, Pa, at least for a coupla days."

Mario's future remains a major concern for the family, but they keep the questions regarding shipping out to a minimum. Giuseppi quickly changes the subject by grumbling in mock anger,

"I gotta go take care of the pasta and sausage before it'sa burn up."

The food and affection last well into the night, and Mario and his family make the short visit as complete as possible. After gorging himself on Giuseppi's delicious cooking, Mario announces,

"I'm goin to sleep. You can't believe how much I'm looking forward to sleepin in a room all by myself. If anyone bothers me before noon tomorrow, they're dead."

Everyone laughs at Mario's threat, and he says goodnight. It feels good to lie in his old bed again, to enjoy the aroma of clean bedding and experience the luxury of sleeping on more than one pillow. He's totally exhausted from the long day and drifts off to sleep immediately. During his short visit home, he does little more than make-up for the weeks of sleep deprivation he's suffered in boot camp. Before long, the weekend leave is over, and John is dropping him off at the bus station for his return trip to Ft. Custer.

Over the next four weeks, Mario is able to return home every weekend. He knows he'll be receiving his orders to ship out soon. While home, he tries to look up old friends from the plant, only to discover that many of them, like him, have joined up or been drafted. The war has turned the city into a different place, making him feel like a stranger. It is his final week of boot camp, and the squad has just finished its last long distance march. They sit exhausted in their barracks when the drill instructor gathers them together.

"Pay attention, guys. You're gonna get your orders today. The company C.O. will be here real soon and talk to each of you, one at a time. No one goes anywhere. Don't even bother to take a leak, got it?"

The squad buzzes with excitement and anticipation. Moments later, the C.O. enters the barracks, followed by a clerk carrying a large stack of envelopes. He pauses for a few minutes.

"Good afternoon, men. I'm Master Sergeant Colin O'Keef. I'll be calling you by name to meet with me in the office. I think Zeke has already told you the reason why. We'll go in alphabetical order. This won't take long." Mario is one of the first to be called. After he enters the office, Sergeant O'Keef says,

"Sit down, Carlucci. This is going to be pretty informal." He grabs an envelope from the top of the pile, peels it open and looks over Mario's assignment. He grins.

"Carlucci, looks like you caught a lucky break." Mario is puzzled by the Sergeant's comment.

"How's that Sarge?"

"You've been assigned as a Maintenance Specialist. You'll board a train and head to Ft. Dix. Once you're there, you'll hop on a transport ship bound for Tripoli. You're going to North Africa to help track down Rommel, the Desert Fox. You leave in three days, so get ready to pull out by then. Here are your written orders. Look em over carefully. Any questions?" Mario has a hundred questions but he knows he only has time to ask one.

"Sergeant O'Keef, I'm not sure what a Maintenance Specialist does. Can you tell me?"

"It's a good job, Carlucci. Because you're trained as a machinist, you'll be keeping things like tanks and trucks in running condition, so all the guys drivin em have to do is worry about stayin alive. Good luck, Carlucci. You're excused."

Mario leaves the office still a little confused. He isn't sure what his job will be, and the North African desert is not his idea of a lucky break, as Sergeant O'Keef put it. He returns to his bunk and reads over his assignment. Not long afterwards, Billy and Tom join him. Billy asks,

"Where are ya goin, Mario?"

"Fort Dix and then North Africa. How about you guys?" Billy looks a little frightened and says,

"I'm goin to tank school. Shit, I don't know nothing about tanks." Mario and Billy look at Tom and wait for him to reveal his next duty. He smiles and says,

"I asked for paratrooper's training, and I got it. I always wanted to fly in a plane."

The next morning, they prepare to go their separate ways. After packing duffel bags, they exchange home addresses and leave the barracks together for the last time. There, they shake hands, wish each other luck, and board separate buses that will carry them to their perilous futures.

189

Mario's bus arrives in the Detroit station at 3:00 AM. He decides to take a cab home rather than wake his family at this time of night. When the battered, green and white cab comes to a stop in front of the house, Mario asks the driver,

"How much do I owe ya, buddy?" The cabbie doesn't say anything. Instead, he stares at Mario through the rear view mirror.

"You shippin out?"

"Yeah, I'm leavin for North Africa in a coupla days. Guess I'll be seein a lot of action there fightin the Germans. Ya never told me what the fare was." The cabbie turns, looks over his shoulder at Mario.

"The fare's on me, soldier. Good luck to ya."

Mario thanks the driver for his kindness and steps out of the old cab. He climbs the few steps up to the porch and lets himself into the house. After dropping his duffle bag on the floor near the door, he quietly finds his way through the darkened house to the living room and collapses into a soft chair to wait for the morning's light. Even though dead tired, he won't get much sleep. With only two days left before shipping out, the possibility of never seeing his family again makes him edgy and restless. He wants to know where Tripoli is and what he's expected to do there. No matter how hard he tries, he can't shut the door on the endless string of questions that continuously invade his thoughts.

Mario hears someone shuffling around in the kitchen. Opening his eyes to the first hint of sunlight, he looks at the clock on the wall. It's 6:15, and he assumes the noise is from one of his brothers getting ready for work. He goes to the kitchen and finds John brewing a pot of coffee. John's back is turned toward him.

"Ya got an extra cup?" Surprised by someone's presence, John whirls around to see who it is and, upon finding Mario standing there, says,

"Jesus, Mario. You scared the shit out of me. When the hell did you get home?"

"I got in late. I think somewhere about three in the morning. I just been sittin in the living room, half asleep. Sorry about sneakin up on ya. I didn't mean to scare ya like that."

John pours some coffee into two cups and carries them to the kitchen table. While he sips his coffee, he sees Mario starring off into space as if he is preoccupied with something. John suspects there might be a problem.

"What's going on, Mario? You okay?" John's question draws Mario's attention back into the moment.

"I've been ordered to ship out for North Africa in two days. Have ya ever heard of a place called Tripoli? Hell, I don't even know where the fuck it is, for Christ's sake." John's been expecting Mario to ship out soon, but he's still stunned by the news. He waits to hear more, but Mario only stares into his half empty cup of coffee.

"Mario. Are you all right?"

"Yeah, sure. I guess I'm just tired, that's all."

"What else do you know? What the hell's in North Africa?"

"Shit, I don't know much more than that. They said I'm a maintenance specialist, and that I'll be working on tanks and trucks, but that's all they told me."

"Where do you go from here?"

"I'll take a train to New Jersey, and from there I'm gonna get on a transport ship." Mario laughs and says, "Then the sergeant says that I got a lucky break. I'm still tryin to figure that out. What's so fuckin' lucky about going to war in some shit-hole on the other side of the world?"

John tries to laugh at his brother's humor, but he can't. Mario's growing anxiety cannot be hidden by his own laughter. While talking more of North Africa, they hear the sounds of a toilet flushing and running water coming from Giuseppi's bathroom. John says,

"Sounds like the old man is up. I better make some more coffee."

He empties the stale coffee from the pot and freshens its contents just as Giuseppi enters the kitchen. Fumbling with the tie belt on his wool robe, the old man doesn't notice Mario sitting at the table. When he looks up and sees Mario, he hurries over to him, places one hand on his shoulder and shakes his hand. Full of smiles, he pats Mario on the back.

"Whatta nice a surprise, Mario. When a did you come home?"

"I've been home for a few hours, Pa. How ya feelin?" Giuseppi pours a fresh cup of coffee for himself and returns to the table. Cradling the cup between his hands, he takes a long sip, and temporarily ignores the question.

"John, he'sa maka good coffee, eh Mario?

"He sure does, Pa. It's a lot better than the shit I get in camp." Giuseppi returns to Mario's first question.

"I'ma feela fine. How long canna you stay home theesa time?" Mario glances over at John, as if seeking his approval to tell Giuseppi of his orders.

"I can't stay home for too long, Pa. I finally got my orders. I'm shippin out for North Africa in two days."

The news startles Giuesppi but does not surprise him. He places the coffee cup down on the table and gently rocks his head from side to side in displeasure. He looks across the table at Mario.

"You hava to leave inna two days? That's alla the time a you have?"

"I know it ain't much, Pa, but at least I get time to come home and have a nice dinner or something before I gotta go."

Giuseppi cannot bring himself to ask if Mario will see any combat. Although he's never been superstitious, a feeling from inside nags him not to say anything that could bring his son bad luck. The grim thought of Mario seeing combat is unnerving, and he tries to put it of out his mind by asking,

"Whatta time a do you hava to leave? You gonna taka the bus?"

"No, I'm takin a train. I gotta leave at 11:00 PM on Thursday." Giuseppi takes the opportunity to change the subject.

"Ifa you leave at eleven, I'ma gonna call Enzo and tella him we gonna hava dinner there before you go. Whatta you think, Mario?"

"That's a great idea, Pa. Who knows when I'll get another good meal again." The lack of sleep begins to catch up with him and he says,

"I'm gonna go lay down for a while. I'm feelin tired as hell right now. Wake me up in a few hours. I gotta get some things cleared up before I go." On his way up to his room, his curiosity forces him to ask Giuseppi,

"Have ya heard anything from Bomarito, Pa?"

"No. He'sa no come to my store too mucha anymore. He knowsa you joina the Army, but he'sa say nothing about the money, anna I say nothing. I think maybe he'sa justa gonna forget it."

The next forty-eight hours bring a seemingly endless list of last minute details that must be attended to. Mario returns to the plant, advises his foreman he's shipping out and visits with the few friends of his who are still working there. He spots Mike Thacker, an old gambling buddy from the back room crap games, standing in a break room.

"Hey Mike, how come you're still here? Stick a few women in the place and ya never wanna leave?" Mike's deep, throaty laugh can be heard over the roar of the plant noise. He screams at Mario.

194

"Goddamn, look at you. How ya doin, Mario? John told me you was shippin out real soon. I gotta get back to the floor here. This fuckin place ain't changed that much, ya know. But look, you take care of yourself and good luck to you." He shakes Mario's hand and rushes off into the plant. Looking around, Mario notes that the changes there are remarkable, and seeing women working on the floor is yet one more reminder of the war's impact on everyone's life.

After leaving the plant, Mario spends the rest of the day trying to visit old hang-outs and catch up with his past, but not much remains of his life as he knew it before he enlisted. He returns to the familiar surroundings of his father's home to enjoy his family's company on his last day at home. Later in the afternoon, Mario is reading the previous day's newspaper and having lunch when a heavy knock rattles the front door. Answering the door, he's surprised to find Donnie, the black doorman he'd befriended from the blind pig, standing there. Flashing a broad grin at Mario, he says,

"How's ya been, Mario? Man, you done lost some weight ain't ya?" Donnie's presence brightens Mario's mood.

"Yeah, about ten pounds. Those Army guys don't fuck around with ya. What are ya doin here, Donnie?"

"Some guys from da plant, dey told me you's home for a coupla days before ya ships out. Is dat true?"

"It's true. I'm leaving tomorrow night."

195

"You know, Mario, you is one guy who be treatin me good and, well, I jus wants to tell ya good luck and ta take care of yo'self." Unprepared for Donnie's kind gesture, Mario shakes his hand.

"Thanks Donnie. It's a nice surprise ta see ya here. I can use all the luck I can get."

"I gots ta get ta work, so I can't stay fo long, but I wants ya ta have dis. I hopes dey brings ya lottsa luck." Displaying his huge grin once again, he presses a small velvet bag into Mario's hand. Mario's surprised by Donnie's thoughtfulness and pulls open the drawstring on the little burgundy bag. Out of the bag pours a brand new pair of ivory dice. Mario breaks out into a wide grin and gives the huge black man a rousing bear hug.

"Donnie, this is real nice of ya ta do this. I'm sure I'll find plenty of ways to make em lucky for me."

Both men share a good laugh and shake hands one more time before Donnie leaves. Mario drops the dice back into the bag and jams it into the outer pocket of his duffel bag. The day has vanished, and the evening brings visits from a few relatives and neighbors. With frightening speed, the first of his final two days at home is gone. Mario tries to sleep but is unable to get much rest. He lies awake wondering if he'll ever get to enjoy this place again.

Mario spends the early part of his final day at home making sure his duffel bag is packed and ready to go. Many of his civilian clothes no longer fit, and he gives them to his brothers. The rest are carefully arranged in his closet as a personal symbol of hope for his safe return. The hours race by, and there's nothing left to do. Mario can hear Giuseppi running around the house and shouting,

"Let'sa go, I promisa Enzo that we gonna be at the restauranta by 5:00."

The mood is quiet and somber as they gather in the living room. While his father and brothers patiently wait, Mario takes one last stroll through the only home he's ever known. He memorizes the small nicks and scratches on the dining room table he's never paid attention to, the unique smells of the kitchen, and the small collection of photographs of his mother displayed in the living room. He knows it's his last chance to carry a small part of this house away with him.

Giuseppi, John and Joe say nothing, as they sense the finality that Mario is feeling. They can do nothing more than share concerned glances with each other while allowing him all the time he needs to walk out the door. After he rejoins them, little is said. John grabs Mario's bag, and they leave the house. When he climbs into Giuseppi's car, Mario stares out of the window in silence as the house disappears from view.

The Little Café is bustling with many customers when Mario and his family arrive. But as soon as Enzo sees them, he rushes up and greets them like family, giving each one a friendly hug and a handshake.

"All four Carluccis together. It'sa beautiful night. That'sa for sure. We hava biga crowd tonight, but I got a nice a table for you inna the corner." He escorts them to the large table already set with dinner plates, a pitcher of Chianti, and the traditional cups and saucers.

"Coma, sit and relax. Everyona, they gonna drink soma wine?" Enzo doesn't wait for an answer and fills the yellow porcelain cups sitting in front of everyone, including himself. He raises his cup and offers a simple toast to Mario.

"Salute, bouno fortuno, Mario."

Mario's skin tingles from a sudden rush of emotion as he watches his family join Enzo in his toast. Enzo's concern for him and his family leaves Mario a bit speechless. In a humbled response, he raises his cup to him in return.

"Thank you, Enzo. Thank you very much." Enzo calls out for his son to begin serving dinner, and then tells Mario,

"I maka soma delicious veal parmesan for you, Mario. I know you lika that."

In a matter of minutes, Enzo covers the table with bowls of salad, two kinds of pasta, and enough veal parmesan to feed ten people. He tops off the feast with cannolis and a basket of fresh fruit for dessert, and they eat until they can eat no more. Enzo never allows the wine pitcher to remain empty for very long, as the Carluccis enjoy Mario's last evening together. The time, however, passes quickly, and it's soon time to leave for the train station. Giuseppi asks Enzo for the dinner bill, but Enzo responds,

"Pleasa, Giuseppi. It'sa honor for me to hava you spend Mario's lasta night inna my café. I no want any money for that. You taka you son to the train station anna say goodbye to him, anna no worry about theesa dinner." Enzo's generosity moves Giuseppi, and he hugs him like a brother. Giuseppi's voice quivers slightly.

"Thanka you, Enzo. You are a good friend to my family." Before they leave, Enzo approaches Mario and places his hands on his shoulders. In a quiet and caring voice, he tells him,

"Pleasa, Mario. You musta be very careful. You gonna do thatta for me, yes? I promisa to cooka you another beautiful dinner whenna you coma home." Enzo's heartfelt concern touches Mario deeply, and he can barely keep his emotions from pouring out. He blinks to clear his eyes.

"I'll be careful, Enzo. I promise we'll have dinner together again. Thank you for...all of this." They leave the restaurant, and John and Joe gently place their hands on Mario's back as he wipes his eyes. They get into the car and drive to the train station.

No one speaks as Joe drives the last few miles to the train station. Mario and Giuseppi sit together in the rear seat of the car. Giuseppi feels anxious.

"You gotta everythinga you gonna need?" Mario knows his father's question is from the tension they're feeling and really needs no answer, but he calmly replies,

"I got everything I'm gonna need, Pa. I checked it all before we left."

Giuseppi looks at Mario for a moment and then turns to stare out the window without saying anything more. The moment he's been dreading since the war began is only minutes away, and it's still difficult for him to find words of comfort to share with his son. Mario looks out of the front windshield of the car to determine if they are near the train station yet, but he sees nothing.

"How far do we have to go, Joe?"

"We'll be there in a few minutes. Why? Ya in a hurry or something?" Joe's sarcasm helps to relieve some of the anxiety they are all feeling, and Mario chuckles,

"Naw, I just wanna get a good seat, that's all." Joe pulls the car into a parking space and shuts off the engine. He turns to face Mario in the back seat.

"Ya got time to change your mind if ya want." Mario grins at Joe's humor.

"Little late for that, I guess, huh?"

They get out of the car, and John opens the trunk to grab the duffel bag. Mario looks across the street and notices the many other soldiers and sailors waiting to catch their trains as well. His family is not alone in bidding farewell to loved ones. He sees what might be someone's wife or girl friend, mother and father, or brother and sister sharing final moments filled with tears. They work their way through the crowded station and locate his departure platform. The train is waiting when they arrive, and Mario looks at the large clock high on the wall above the platform. It's 10:30, and time is short. Mario needs to say goodbye to his brothers and father and board his car. Joe approaches Mario and puts his arms around him. Mario feels Joe trembling slightly.

"What are ya so nervous about? I'm gonna be all right."

"I know you will. I just didn't expect it would be so hard to watch ya go, that's all." Joe's eyes become watery, and his breathing is interrupted by short gasps for air. Mario tries to calm him down.

"Look, you take care of yourself. Don't forget ta keep doin what that doc told ya to do. I'll send ya's a letter when I can. You be sure to write an tell all about you're wedding."

Joe wants to remain calm and not upset Mario, but it's difficult for him to stop tears from running down his cheeks. John wraps his arm around Mario's neck, mimicking the childhood headlocks he once used on him, and whispers in his ear,

"Look, you just get yourself home in one piece. Do ya understand me?" Mario responds with a weak smile.

"Sorry, but its gonna take more than a little war to get rid of me." They hug each other tightly one last time. Before he lets him go, Mario tells John,

"I gotta go. Don't forget to tell me about your weddin, either. Take care of the old man, will ya?"

Mario looks over at his father and sees tears running down his face. The old man keeps wiping them away, as if embarrassed by the fact that he's crying. Mario grabs Giuseppi by the arms.

"It's gonna be okay, Pa. The sergeant told me I got a lucky break. He wouldn't say that if he didn't know something, right?"

"I hope so, Mario. But you be careful anyway. We gonna hava a bigga party when a you come home." They hug each other, and Giuseppi kisses his son on the cheek. Mario has never known this depth of emotion from his father before, and he whispers,

"I love ya, Pa." Giuseppi holds on to him tightly, reluctant to let him go.

"I gotta go, Pa. The train's gonna leave." Giuseppi releases his grip on Mario and reminds him,

"You write and tella me howa you are doing when a you hava time. You understand?"

Mario forces a smile.

"Sure, Pa. I will. I'll write whenever I get the chance."

Mario grabs his bag, shakes hands with his brothers one last time, and steps aboard the train car. He finds a seat near the window and watches his family wave to him as the train slowly pulls away from the platform. He stares at them as long as he can, but they are quickly lost in the night. Soon, there is nothing but darkness outside the train car, and the sense of loneliness that has followed him for so much of his life begins to smother him once again. He slumps down in his seat and tries to find a comfortable position in which to rest for the long ride to New Jersey. It's a little past eleven, and it will be a long time before he'll feel comfortable again.

CHAPTER 10

Mario shifts around in the well-worn seat of the old train car. Checking his watch, he discovers it's 1:00 in the morning. It's only been two hours since the train left the Detroit station, but it feels more like six. The soldier sitting next to him keeps falling asleep and annoys him by slumping over onto his shoulder. The heavy odor of beer coming from the man convinces Mario his snoring seat partner is more drunk than tired. He repeatedly pushes him upright and tries to find a more comfortable position.

The crowded train car carries, not only soldiers on their way to Fort Dix, but a small number of sailors and marines traveling to the large naval base in Norfolk, Virginia. A few spirited discussions erupt between members of the different branches of service, each man claiming to serve a more important function than the other. The debate wears on for hours, with only the most drunken passengers finding time to sleep in the noisy car.

For those first few hours, Mario does little more than stare into the darkness, slightly hypnotized by the rhythmic clicking of the tracks beneath the speeding train. The uncomfortable seat at last exhausts his patience, and he steps over his soused neighbor and into the narrow aisle. Weaving his way through the outstretched legs and misplaced bags, he finds his way to one of the latrines. After relieving himself, he stands in the open space between cars, lights a cigarette and enjoys the fresh air. Another soldier joins him on the small platform, and they greet each other with subtle head nods. After a few minutes, the soldier asks,

"Ya wouldn't have an extra smoke, would ya?" Mario doesn't mind sharing his cigarettes if it means not having to spend the next ten hours sitting next to his drunken neighbor. He reaches into his shirt pocket, pulls out a pack of Pall Malls, and shakes one halfway out of the pack. Extending his arm, he offers the cigarette to the soldier.

"Sure, take one. Where ya from?"

"Cleveland. You?" answers the man while lighting the cigarette.

"I'm from Detroit. Ya didn't find any food on this train, did ya?"

"Hell no. I just got done searchin the whole goddamn thing, and there ain't nothing ta eat. Man, I'm starving, too." Mario is even more grateful for the meal he had at Enzo's café. After taking a long puff on the cigarette, the soldier says, "Shit, listen ta me will ya. I didn't even say thanks for the smoke." Extending his hand out to Mario, he says,

"My name's Robert Blankford, but everyone calls me Bobbie."

"I'm Mario Carlucci. And don't worry about the cigarette, I got more."

"Good ta meet ya, Mario. Ya goin to Fort Dix, too?"

"Yeah. I'm supposed ta be shipping out for North Africa. How bout you? Ya know where you're goin yet?"

"I'm headin for England. Don't know why, though. Big ass secret, I guess."

While the two talk about their basic training, two more soldiers step into the small compartment and also light up cigarettes. Bobbie is the first to introduce himself.

"How you guys doing? My name's Bobbie, and this here's Mario." While shaking hands, the men respond,

"I'm Louie and this is Sam. You guys on yer way to Dix?"

Both Mario and Bobbie answer that they are. Sam then looks into the cars on either side of the open platform as if he were a thief about to snatch a purse, and he pulls a small whiskey bottle from his coat pocket. He takes a swig and his face twists in a painful grimace as he hands the bottle to Mario.

"Ya look like ya can use a belt, Mario. Go on, take a big one if ya want. I got another bottle in my duffel bag." Mario puts the bottle to his lips and gulps down a few mouthfuls of the liquor. The booze feels like a white-hot poker running down his throat. Mario coughs and laughs at the same time,

"Jesus Christ. What is that shit?"

"That's some good ole Kentucky moonshine. My old man makes the stuff. Got a real kick in the ass, don't it?" giggles Sam.

Mario hands the bottle to Bobbie, and they all watch and laugh as he suffers the same fate. Sam finds their reaction hysterically funny and drops his hands to his knees as he rolls over in laughter. Still gasping for air, he says,

"Man, I used ta give that home brew ta some of my girlfriends, and they practically jump outta their clothes wantin ta fuck." Bobbie, still trying to catch his breath, mumbles,

"They're fuckin lucky they ain't dead."

"Some of em looked like they was."

The four men pass the bottle around a few more times, and the powerful booze begins to have the desired effect. Louie, now noticeably drunk from many earlier doses of the lethal brew, begins to whine over the girlfriend he's left behind.

"Trudy, that's my gal...well, I mean, she used to be my gal. She told me she can't be my girlfriend no more cause she's afraid I won't be comin back. Ain't that some shit? She dumps me right after

I get fuckin drafted. You guys think there's any women where we're goin?"

"Louie, we ain't gonna see any women for a long, long time," advises Mario.

The four soldiers have a good laugh over Mario's warning to Louie and continue to pass the bottle around until it's empty. They stumble back into the packed passenger area to the sound of hard breathing and heavy snoring, and they are able to flop into their seats without waking anyone. The potent moonshine puts Mario at ease, and he slumps into his seat after crawling over his still-sleeping seat partner. He glances at his wristwatch and sees it's 4:30 in the morning. It's still too dark to see anything through the window, and he wonders where he is. The raucous noise from the numerous conversations finally gives way to a few quiet hours. Mario leans his head against the window glass and closes his eyes. He never slips into a deep, refreshing sleep, but the rest is a welcome relief.

He is startled from his half-asleep state by the train cars pounding together when the train's brakes are applied. He watches the passing landscape through the window of the slowing train and can see the brilliant light of the morning sun. The glare causes him to temporarily squint and look away. He reaches for a Pall Mall, lights up and turns his attention to the Trenton Station pulling into view. The train slows to a crawl while Mario takes a few deeps puffs on the smoke.

Watching the crowded platforms, he sees military activity everywhere. There are hundreds of newly arrived G.I.'s standing in long, tangled lines. They wait for directions to their next destination. Military police are everywhere, trying to bring some order to the chaos.

After the train comes to a complete stop, the sleepy atmosphere inside the car suddenly bursts into a frenzied mob scene. There is a great deal of pushing and shoving when everyone jams into the narrow aisle with bags in hand. Mario feels the combination of nervousness and fear shared by most of the men aboard the packed car. While filing out of the stale-smelling car, some men joke, saying the combat awaiting them overseas has found its way onto the train station, but not everybody is laughing. Mario pays little attention to the gallows humor and concentrates on getting off the stuffy car. Teams of military police immediately begin asking each man for his shipping orders. Once off the train, Mario finds himself in a makeshift line leading to several of the M.P.'s. When he stands before them, one of the M.P.'s asks,

"Let's see your papers, soldier." Mario hands him his documents, and the M.P. examines them for a moment. After crosschecking his army serial number against the master list of new arrivals, the M.P. tells Mario,

"Okay, Carlucci, pay attention. I'm only gonna tell ya this one time. Follow the platform to the exit at gate twelve, through the corridor, and then out to the parking lot. You're gonna see a long line of buses parked there. Find bus number 7560 and get on it. You don't go anywhere else, got it?"

"Yes sir. Bus number 7560. I'll find it. Thanks." Pushing his way through the turbulent crowd, Mario spots one of the men he met on the train earlier. Once close enough, he shouts out, "Hey Bobbie, wait a minute." Bobbie stops and looks to see who's called his name. He sees Mario and yells back to him,

"Mario. Do ya know where ya gotta go?"

"Yeah. I gotta get on one of those buses parked on the street over there. How about you?"

"Me too. I'm on bus 1315."

"Well, good luck to ya. Keep your head down and don't volunteer for anything," jokes Mario. Before Bobbie walks away, Mario pulls out his pack of Pall Malls and gives a couple of cigarettes to him.

"Here. Take a few of these with ya. Ya never know when you'll be able to get some more."

"Thanks. That's real kind of ya. You take care too, ya hear?" The two men shake hands once more and head for the long line of buses awaiting their one-way passengers.

With his duffel bag hoisted onto his back, Mario hikes alongside the parked buses and searches for the one numbered 7560. Judging by the many scrapes and dents gouged into them, Mario figures the buses are heavily used. Stopping before each one, he checks the small numbers displayed inside the front window.

Weather-beaten and badly faded, the numbers are often difficult to read. After the fourth stop, he locates what he thinks is his bus and climbs up the three short steps just inside the front door. There's no driver, and Mario asks the first soldier he sees,

"Is this bus number 7560?" The man nods his head.

"You got the right bus. Have a seat. The driver just went for a coffee." Mario thanks the man and slowly moves down the center aisle looking for a seat. The bus is about half full, and he finds a seat with some empty space in the overhead storage bin. After tossing his duffel bag into the already heavily used rack, he takes a seat next to another man.

"My name's Carlucci. Got any idea what's goin on here?"

"No. No...I...don't know too much right now. All th...the driver says is someone'll tell us what's goin on after all the seats are filled up." The man's response seems tense and nervous, and Mario figures he's just jittery waiting for whatever is going to happen next. They say nothing more as the bus fills to capacity.

Soon, the driver steps aboard and slides into his seat. He looks at the men through the large mirror over his head.

"We'll be leavin in just a few minutes...soon as Sergeant Thompson arrives." The atmosphere fills with the low murmur of questions among the men in anticipation of the sergeant's arrival.

Moments later, one last man hops into the bus. He is wearing a neatly tailored Army uniform and a billed dress cap. His sleeves are adorned with the six stripes of a Master Sergeant, and his chest is covered with ribbons and medals. Easily over six-feet tall, he appears to be fit and well conditioned. His eyes are clear, and the hair on his head is cropped short enough to appear as if he's shaved his head. Except for a serious scar located over his right eye, he reminds Mario of one of the enlistment posters he saw at the recruitment office in Detroit. Then, in a loud, commanding voice, the sergeant calls for everyone's attention.

"Okay, guys. Quiet down and listen up. My name is Master Sergeant Duane Thompson, and I'm your squad leader. You're going to Fort Dix for orientation and deployment. If you are not supposed to be on bus number 7560, then get off right now. Don't ask me any questions at this time because I can't tell you anything until we're inside the base." The sergeant leans over and tells the driver to get moving. Seconds later, the noisy diesel engine fires up, and the bus lurches away from the station for the thirty-minute ride to the base.

The ride from the train station to the fort winds through parts of Trenton, New Jersey. During the short trip, not much is said and Mario, like most of the men aboard, watches the passing neighborhoods with curious interest. Small corner markets, a Catholic church, and a local movie theater remind Mario of his home in Detroit. He even notices a few Italian restaurants and wonders if the food's as good as Enzo's. The bus driver grinds the gearshift into low, and Mario feels the noisy old coach beginning to slow down. The brakes sound out a loud, piercing squeal when the driver brings the vehicle to a stop.

"There it is. See it?" whisper some of the men after the entrance to the fort is recognized. Looking out of a side window, Mario sees a guardhouse and notices several armed men approaching the bus. The driver opens the doors, and Sergeant Thompson jumps out to greet them.

"I'm Sergeant Duane Thompson, and this is my new squad. You should have me listed on the new arrival manifest."

After they verify his identification and orders, the guards roll open the heavy gate and allow the bus to enter the camp. Everyone strains to catch a good look at the grounds while the bus slowly navigates the busy route. Mario can see row after row of side-boarded tents set up along both sides of the narrow road. Squads of soldiers are everywhere. A bivouac area is congested with men in training, and platoons of combat-ready soldiers march in all directions. Mario hears the report of heavy gunfire in the distance. Sergeant Thompson breaks the hypnotic spell of the passing landscape.

"Gentlemen, on your right you will see a barracks building. It will be your home while you are here. I know you guys have had a long day or two, but you won't get much time to rest. You'll have to get used to that. I want you to go inside, find a bunk and a locker, and settle in. I'll be filling you in on your assignment after I go check in with the C.O. You got a few hours to relax. I suggest you take advantage of it."

The bus stops in front of the long, narrow building. The two-story, wooden structure has six windows on each of its floors and is painted white, with a green roof. Mario recalls the half-barrel-shaped Nissen huts he was housed in at Fort Custer. They make this place feel like a fine hotel by comparison.

The men pile out of the bus and stagger into the building. On the main floor, they find two rows of six bunks and lockers straddling a wide center aisle. There are similar bunks on the upper floor. At the opposite end is a latrine and shower room. The men spread out, and each claims a bunk of his own. Most are dead tired, and they don't even unpack before lying down for a short sleep. Mario finds a bunk on the main floor and takes advantage of the precious little time to rest.

Sergeant Thompson returns to the barracks after a few hours and begins to provide information about what is going to happen next. He leans against a small table located just outside the showers and bellows,

"If anyone's still sleeping, someone be a good Samaritan and wake em up. I gotta lot to say, so everyone circle up and get comfortable. Fort Dix holds thousands of GI's at any given time. Most are preparing for deployment to the European theaters and will only stay for a few weeks. Others will be kept here for several months. It all depends on the assignment." Someone from the back of the group asks,

"What's our assignment, Sergeant?"

"Hold your horses, soldier. I'm just getting to that," jokes Sergeant Thompson.

He stands and begins to slowly roam among the men.

"Gentlemen, welcome to the Second Armored Division. You are now members of Company A, 760th Railway Diesel Shop Battalion. You've all been assigned to this company because of the valuable civilian skills you possess." Someone else shouts out,

"Whadda ya mean, Sergeant?"

"You're going be part of Operation Torch. That's an Allied invasion force heading for French North Africa. We're going to land somewhere between Casablanca and Algiers, but nobody knows exactly where just yet. After we get ashore, we'll move eastward toward Tripoli to support the British Eighth Army battling Erwin Rommel's Afrika Corp. If you guys read the papers, he's the guy they call the Desert Fox."

"When do we get going, Sergeant?" another man asks.

"We won't be shipping out real soon. This invasion is big, and it takes a lot of time to get 65,000 men across the ocean. You'll be stationed here for a few months until the brass says we're ready. Each of you will be assigned to a job and will start work immediately. We have a helluva lot to do before we leave. One last thing, you can't write to family or friends regarding this mission. All outgoing mail will be reviewed by base M.P.'s, so don't say something stupid. Any questions?"

"When do we find out what our jobs are?" one of the men asks.

"I'll be meeting with each one of you individually a little later today to go over orders and assignments. In the meantime, stay put and don't go wandering around."

Mario begins to unpack his belongings and stack them neatly in the small footlocker next to his bunk. The rest of the squad starts to do the same, with a few men offering up personal comments after the sergeant leaves.

"This joint is a helluva lot better then the last dump I stayed in. I don't care if we never leave," admits one soldier. Some of the others join in and begin offering detailed complaints of their own boot camp experiences.

Then Sergeant Thompson returns and begins to call men into his office in alphabetical order. Mario hears his name called within a few minutes. He enters the office and stands at attention until the sergeant says,

"You can relax, soldier. Have a seat." Mario pulls the chair away from the small table and sits across from his sergeant.

"Private Mario Carlucci, right?" the sergeant asks, looking up from his roster.

"Yes, sir. That's right."

"I know some of you guys been putting in some long hours. How ya feeling?"

"Fine, Sergeant, just a little tired and hungry now, that's all."

215

"We'll take care of that as soon as we're through getting everyone assigned. I see you're a machinist. That's good because we need that kind of talent here." Remembering the recruiter's comments, Mario asks,

"You're not the first sergeant to tell me that, but I'm still not sure what I'm supposed to do here."

"The Diesel Battalion keeps every piece of equipment with a motor in it in running condition. That includes tanks, trucks, jeeps, trains, and damn well anything else that can break down. You'll always operate well behind any front line action, due to the equipment needed for the job, so the odds of seeing any real combat are pretty slim. It's a lot of hard and important work, but it's a damn good job in a war."

Mario is stunned by the news. He finally understands what the recruiter and his D.I. meant when they called him lucky. A hundred thoughts skip through his mind, and his first reaction is to tell his brothers and father of the surprising news. The sergeant interrupts his brief daydream.

"You still with me, Carlucci?"

"Oh, sure, Sergeant. Sorry, but I'm, ah, just a little surprised by the news, that's all. So what do I do now?"

"You're going to report to the machine shop first thing in the morning. We have a lot of gear that needs to be made ready for North Africa, and there's not a lot of time to get all the work done. I'll take you there and get you going tomorrow. There are a few other guys who'll be working with you. I'm sure you'll get a chance to meet them later. Any questions?"

"I got no questions right now, Sergeant. But I guess I should say thanks. You can be sure I'll give ya my best work."

Returning to his bunk, Mario sits on the edge and listens to Sergeant Thompson call the names of the other men in the squad. Watching them parade past his bunk, he wonders who else will receive his assignment. He finishes unpacking his bag and lies on the bunk as the rest of the squad members receive their orders. He's able to relax and get a bit more of the shallow sleep that will become a regular part of his life for the next three years.

After Sergeant Thompson completes giving out assignments, he steps from his small office and announces,

"We'll be heading for the mess hall in a about an hour. If you're hungry, I recommend you wait here until then." The unit gathers in the center of the barracks. Some men stand, some sit on the edges of their bunks and begin to compare their fates.

"Anyone else gonna be a driver?" shouts one soldier.

"Naw, I'm a construction technician. I ain't even sure what that is yet," announces another.

It's not long before everyone begins describing his job. The jobs include cook, field support operator, and radio and communication specialist. Everyone wants to know if someone else shares the same duty. Mario joins in the discussion.

"Anyone else gonna be workin in the machine shop?"

"Yeah. I am. You must be one of the other guys Sarge was talking about," replies a soldier sitting two bunks over. Two others announce that they too have been assigned as machinists. The four men group together and begin to get acquainted. Mario introduces himself first,

"My name is Mario Carlucci. I'm from Detroit. Where you guys from?"

"Nice ta meet ya Mario. I'm Frank Erskin. Ya know where Arkansas is? Well, I'm from a little ole town there called Tylerville. Ain't much of a town, though. Only got one traffic light and Freddie's gas station."

He shakes Mario's hand enthusiastically. Frankie, as he likes to be called, is a skinny, wiry-looking man. He is the shortest of the four and has a simple, innocent-looking appearance. He seems in constant awe of everything and everyone. A heavy southern accent flavors everything he says, and he finds reasons to laugh at just about anything. He readily admits to being a hillbilly and likes to brag about it.

"I'm Henry Forrester...from Chicago," says another. Henry, or Hank, is as tall as Sergeant Thompson but not as muscular looking. He has blond, thinning hair and a slight beer belly of which he's quite proud. Having lived in a large city like Chicago, he seems far less impressed by the conditions in the camp than Frankie.

"Nice to meet you guys. I'm George Pinkerton. I lived in Des Moines, Iowa," announces the last of the four men. George is small in stature, but not as skinny as Frankie. His dark hair is very short, and he wears a pair of wire-rimmed glasses to correct his near sightedness.

"The mess hall is across the parade grounds. It's a short walk from here. Take a left on the road in front of the building, and you can't miss it," shouts Sergeant Thompson.

Mario, Frankie, George and Hank make the short walk together and spend their first night in Fort Dix getting to know one another. They sit together at a long table and begin to question one another during their first meal in camp. Frankie stuffs a spoonful of mashed potatoes in his mouth and, before he swallows, he asks Hank,

"What's it like livin in a big, ole city like Chicaga?"

"Hell, it's great. I don't have ta milk my own cows or grow my own food. We got people who do that for us." George and Mario nearly spit out mouthfuls of their dinner while laughing at Hank's teasing.

"What about you, Mario? What did you do in Detroit?" inquires Hank.

"I worked for my father for a while. He sells seafood. But later on, I went to work in an auto plant. That's where I learned to be a machinist." Mario chooses to say nothing about his father's other business or about his own circumstances. He asks,

"What did ya do in Chicago, Hank?"

"Aw, I drove a cab for a while and then worked in some private clubs. You know, tendin bar, runnin errands for the boss, that kind of shit." To Mario, Hank seems like the kind of guy who'd be willing to try anything for a good reason. Frankie looks over at George and says,

"Hey, George. You sure is awful quiet. Somethin wrong?"

"No, nothing's wrong. It's just more interesting to listen to you guys talk, that's all."

"Well, what in blue Jesus is so interestin bout all this shit?" asks Frankie. George chuckles,

"Chicago and Detroit sure have to be more interesting than Des Moines; that's all I mean. Hell, I used to work in a feed store, and I fixed broken tractors for a living. I went to Iowa State College for a year and a half but had to drop out cause I ran out of money."

"College? Man, I cain't hardly read, leave alone figure out college stuff. You must be a real smart guy," answers Frankie.

The three men find Frankie a constant source of amusement during the rest of the evening. They laugh out loud over his child-like wonder at everything he sees. After returning to the barracks, they continue to share more details of their lives during the rest of the evening. The four men are all to report to the vehicle repair center in the morning. It is there that they will begin a three-year odyssey destined to make them the best of friends.

Reveille sounds at five o'clock in the morning. Mario rolls out of bed and heads for the latrine and showers. Everyone in the barracks is up, so the facilities are swarming with naked men waiting for a sink or a toilet. Mario hates this part of the Army, but he has learned to put up with it and keep his thoughts to himself to avoid any trouble. Sergeant Thompson moves through the barracks, making sure each man knows where he is to report after breakfast. He locates Mario.

"Carlucci, will you tell Erskin, Pinkerton and Forrester that I want to see the four of you after chow? I'll be taking you over to the repair center and getting you guys started."

"Sure, Sergeant. No problem." Frankie, Hank, and George join Mario for breakfast, and he passes on the Sergeant's message. After they finish eating, they return to the barracks. They find Sergeant Thompson sitting in his office. When he notices them, he says,

"Come on in guys. I want to fill you in on the schedule today. The repair center is located in the third barracks compound just north of this building. It sits next to a fenced storage area...you'll see all the equipment sitting there. Ask for a Private McCauliff when you get there. He knows where everything is. You can take a break for lunch, but outside of that, only piss breaks are allowed. We got a lot of broken equipment that needs attention. Any questions?"

After the sergeant's no-nonsense orders, the men have no further questions and immediately hike over to the repair center. They enter through the large service door located at the side of the building, but find no one inside the place. A short tour reveals an impressive collection of machine tools and repair equipment. Large, portable floor jacks sit in every work bay, and a collection of new and old parts is scattered everywhere. The smell of motor oil saturates the air, and lights are far too few to be effective. Frankie picks up the barrel of a large machine gun and begins to examine it when suddenly a voice shouts out,

"Hey! Put that fuckin thing down before ya drop it or somethin." Frankie places the gun barrel back where he found it, wipes his hands on his shirt.

"You McCauliff?"

"That's right. Who the fuck are you guys?" Private McCauliff's an older soldier who's been training new men for several months now. His clothes are stained with grease and oil, and his fingernails are all tipped with black, crescent-shaped shadows. He looks angry about something.

"Sergeant Thompson sent us over here. He said to ask for you. That you will tell us where everything is," answers Hank.

"Does the Sergeant think all I got to do is wet-nurse a bunch of new fuckin recruits every month?"

"Are ya gonna help us or not?" asks Mario in a more threatening tone.

"Yeah, yeah. Sure. Follow me." Leading them out into the storage area, McCauliff points to a long line of trucks, Jeeps and other vehicles. "See all that equipment over there? Well none of em runs worth a shit, and you guys gotta fix em all before ya ship out."

"Well, do you know what's wrong with any of them?" asks George.

"No. But inside each one of em is a work sheet. All ya gotta do is read it. It'll tell ya everything." With that, he leaves mumbling, "Someday, I'm gonna get outta this goddamn repair center and find me a good fuckin job."

The well-equipped machine shop is large enough to house two or three vehicles at one time. Frankie suggests,

"Why don't we go an have a look at some of them there big uns and see if we kin get em in here? Cain't be that goddamn hard to fix."

And so they do just that. McCauliff is right about the work sheet. The first truck they look at has a long list of problems. Bad brakes, damaged doors, and bent axles are just a few of the problems noted. Hank climbs into the large cab.

"Let's see if this green hunk of shit will start. Stand back."

The truck's engine fires up amid a suffocating cloud of blueish-white exhaust smoke. He jams the transmission into gear, and the behemoth lurches forward into the repair stall. The four new friends then descend upon the ailing truck and begin to disassemble and correct the variety of defects listed on the work sheet.

It takes most of their first day to put the repaired truck back into service, but during this day, each man begins to see what the others are capable of doing. They work together well and, when all the tools in the repair center are found, they discover they have the collective talent to fix almost anything. After several days, the process settles into a basic twelve-hour operation. Mario finds it

223

ironic to be working in a civilian's job while most of the world is at war.

The strenuous schedule of 6:00 AM to 6:00 PM becomes a daily routine for the men in the repair center. When they think all the repairs are at last complete, another half a dozen vehicles arrive from some other base. The brutal weeks drag into a month, then two months, allowing the men little time for anything but work, food, and sleep since arriving at Fort Dix. Mario can't remember working so hard in his life, but he frequently reminds himself that someone else will have to take one of these vehicles into harm's way, so he rarely complains.

Sergeant Thompson has noticed the outstanding work the four men are doing, and he occasionally gives them a few hours off to visit the post-exchange and replenish their supply of cigarettes and treats. It's been the longest time Mario has gone without a hard drink that he can remember.

He writes to Giuseppi and tells him where he is, but he is unable to say anything more for security reasons. All letters are screened by the M.P.'s for any mention of the work or Operation Torch. It's now late October, and the men are starting to get restless and short-tempered.

One night, following the evening meal, Sergeant Thompson calls the squad together for an announcement. Tension is high over rumors of the invasion about to begin, and his men are all anxiously waiting to know if the rumors are true.

"Relax guys; you've earned a little break. I've got some important news to give you. The invasion of North Africa is finally ready to go."

"Oh baby, I knowed this was it," shouts Frankie.

"Settle down, Erskin. There's a lot more to talk about," warns the sergeant.

Hank gives Frankie a slight slap on the back of the head with his flat cap as Sergeant Thompson continues, "We're going to be shipping out in a little over a week, and that means we have to be prepared to leave on a moment's notice. For you guys in the repair center, that means you must load all your equipment into a shipping container and get it ready to go. You radio guys will have to do the same thing. Everyone else will help out wherever we need help. I don't think I have to lead anyone around by the hand. I expect full cooperation."

Mario feels the hair on his neck stand up and his skin tingle after he hears that the invasion will soon get started. Sergeant Thompson makes one final announcement.

"One more thing, Gentlemen. I'm giving the entire unit a few days leave as soon as we have everything ready to go, so the sooner you get packed, the sooner you can head into Trenton." The squad explodes in a loud cheer at the good news, but the sergeant warns, "Don't leave town. Confine yourselves to the immediate area surrounding the camp. If you miss your assignment, you'll be treated as a deserter. That's a lot of trouble to be in during a war. Understand?"

"Hey, Sarge. Can ya tell me if there are any good looking women in Trenton?" shouts a voice from the back. Sergeant Thompson smiles and says,

"Even if there are, you sure as hell won't find any." Again, the squad laughs wildly at the sergeant's taunting, and they begin to make plans for their only leave since arriving at Fort Dix.

For many men processing through Dix, Trenton will be the last taste of America they'll see. Realizing their lives will be at serious risk, the men's moods reflect a strange mixture of either somber prayers or wild celebrations in the local clubs. The more religious men plan to attend services held in the local churches. Others plan to find hard drinks, pretty gals, or both.

When they have the repair center equipment packed up and ready to move, Mario and his new friends obtain Sergeant Thompson's permission to leave the camp. After showers and a fresh shave, they return to the main barracks and begin to dress. Frankie hops around on one leg trying to pull up a fresh pair of trousers when George looks over at him.

"Damn, Frankie. Why the hell don't ya just sit down and do that? Ya look like a goddamn chicken with its head cut off."

"Don't you be a worryin about me. When we git inta town, this lil' chicken may end up bein a damn rooster."

George and Frankie go to great lengths to harass each other in a friendly sort of way. They share a similar background and seem to enjoy the chance to tease one another. Mario and Hank choose to ignore their bickering, having heard it for seven days a week, but Hank's patience begins to wear thin. He grumbles,

"Are we gonna get outta here sometime soon? We got a fuckin bus to catch to get inta town."

"Why are you in such a big hurry, Hank?" asks George.

"I wanna find a good meal and a loud bar, hopefully one with a lot of pretty girls in it. That's why I'm in a hurry."

"Hank's got the best idea. Lets get going before Sarge changes his mind," adds Mario. With their evening plans decided, they start out of the barracks when Mario suddenly stops and says,

"Wait a minute. I forgot something. I'll catch up with ya's in a second." Rushing back to his footlocker, he rummages around one of the small pockets on the outside of his duffle bag until he finds the little velvet bag containing Donnie's dice. Staring at the bag for a second, he smiles and stuffs it into his shirt pocket on his way out of the barracks, thinking some old habits are hard to break.

The others have already climbed onto one of the old buses that carried them from the train station. Frankie leans out of an open window and shouts,

"Will ya come on, Mario. This goddamn bus driver's been ready ta leave since we got on this piece of shit. Whattin the blue Jesus ya been doing?"

227

"I forgot somethin, that's all. Will ya relax for Christ sake?"

The bus driver starts the engine and heads for the main gate. The guards jump aboard and check everyone's pass, which allows the driver to leave. It's nearly 6:00 PM when they arrive in Trenton. Mario remembers seeing some Italian restaurants somewhere along this route when he arrived at Dix. The driver jams on the brakes, causing some of the men to crash forward into the seats before them.

"Where the fuck did you learn to drive? In armor training?" someone shouts.

Oblivious to the complaint, the driver looks up into the mirror over his head. He stares at his passengers and says,

"This bus'll be here every four hours ta pick you guys up. Otherwise, you're gonna have ta take a cab or walk."

The driver's warning is not taken seriously by the busload of soldiers anxious for a good time. They stream past him with hardly a comment. Mario and his buddies stand single file and slowly shuffle toward the door. When Frankie reaches the driver, he turns to him and says,

"If ya think we're going back to the base before sun up, yur crazy. I'll see ya in the morning."

After the bus chugs away, the four men begin to scout the area. It's only 6:30, and the area is fairly quiet. Wandering through the neighborhood, they stroll past a few small pastry shops, a butcher market, and a drugstore. The street reminds Mario of home. He wonders what his father and brothers are doing tonight. He misses them already. Further up the street, Mario spots a small, illuminated sign hanging from an old brick building. It reads *La Cucina Mia.* A good Italian meal is too tempting to pass up, and Mario says,

"I got a great idea. Let's get some Italian food at that joint ahead of us. Whatta ya say?"

"I ain't never had Italian food before. Is it any good?" inquires Frankie.

Frankie barely finishes his comment before Hank starts to razz him,

"Shit, now there's a big fuckin surprise. No Italian food in Tylerville, Arkansas. How'd ya ever survive?" Mario and George almost collapse in a fit of laughter over Hank's joke, causing Frankie to reply,

"Hey, that ain't my goddamn fault. I just wanna know what I'm a gonna be eatin, that's all."

"Just be quiet and follow us. This man knows what's good," replies Hank while slapping Mario's back. Mario realizes Hank has eaten Italian food before, coming from Chicago and all, but he assures Frankie and George,

"Trust me. Once you try it, you'll love it forever." They enter the little restaurant and sit down at a large round table near the window.

La Cucina Mia is very small, and the tables are tightly packed inside the old brick-walled dining room. A few ceiling fans stir the familiar aroma of simmering garlic and olive oil, sending it drifting throughout the room. Mario's sure he's made a good choice. While waiting for their order to be taken, he hears someone in the kitchen speaking Italian. A waiter charges through the swinging doors from the kitchen and rushes up to the table. Curious to know if it's the waiter he heard a few moments earlier, Mario decides to greet him in Italian.

"Buona sera il mio amico. Come siete stasera?"

"Ah, you speak Italian. That's good. Where are you from?" replies the waiter.

"I'm from Detroit. But my family's from Sicily."

"What's your name?"

"Mario, Mario Carlucci. It's nice to meet you."

Hank, George and Frankie sit in wide-eyed amazement while listening to Mario and the waiter go on in Italian. Until that moment, they had no idea Mario could speak another language. Hank is the first to quiz him about his hidden skill.

"You son-of-a- bitch, how come you didn't tell anybody you can speak Italian like that?" Mario begins to chuckle and says,

"I don't know. I guess I never thought I'd need to use it. I learned from my old man. He speaks it all the time, so I just picked it up by listening. Hell, if I didn't, I'da starved to death. So, you guys trust me to order dinner?"

No one objects to Mario's suggestion, and he places the dinner order with the waiter. A few minutes later, the waiter delivers two large bottles of Chianti to the table and pours the first of many glasses they will consume during dinner. He quickly returns with a mountainous bowl of spaghetti and meatballs and a loaf of hot, fresh-baked bread. When all the food is on the table, he tells them,

"You eata now and enjoy you dinner. Ifa you need something, just calla me in the back." The four friends drink both bottles of the delicious wine and eat the entire bowl of spaghetti. Mario orders a plate of cannolies, which make the perfect ending to their last meal in America. He looks at Frankie.

"So, ya had enough to eat, Frankie?"

"I ain't never had no food like that in Tylerville. Them little cannolies…damn, they sure is some good eatin." While they settle the bill, Mario asks the waiter,

"Can you tell me if there's someplace around here we can have a little fun tonight?"

"I thinka you boys will lika the Pelican Club. It'sa only three blocks uppa the street from here. Lots of soldiers like to go there."

After thanking him for the excellent meal and the suggestion to try the Pelican Club, they charge out of the little spaghetti house in search of one last night on the town.

The Pelican Club is a classic, turn of the century saloon. A wooden bar, well polished from having thousands of elbows rest on it, extends the entire length of one wall. The bartender is busy filling mugs of beer and sliding them along the slick bar top to waiting customers. In a darkened corner behind the bar sits an old Victrola radio. The amber glow from its oval-shaped lens resembles the color of an early autumn moon, and the distinctive sounds of Count Basie's band blare out of its linen-covered speaker. The old wooden floor is scarred with hundreds of small, black, wounds from years of discarded cigarette butts. Peanut shells, shaky wooden tables, and an assortment of stools and chairs are scattered all around the venerable old pub. The smoke-filled tavern reminds Mario of several such joints he's frequented in Detroit.

Unlike the restaurant, the Pelican Club is crowded. Mario starts to feel right at home.

"Whatta ya guys drinkin? I'm buyin the first round." After they tell him what they want to drink, Mario muscles his way up to the bar and shouts out to the bartender,

"Gimme two beers and two Crown Royals and water."

"Sorry pal, what's this place look like? The Ritz? We got no Crown Royal," says the bartender with a sneer.

"Then gimme any whiskey ya got."

With drinks in hand, the four friends begin to explore the club. They discover several additional rooms, all crammed with soldiers and civilians, including women. Hank finds an empty table and shouts,

"Let's sit here for a few minutes and see what's goin on." Mario and George each grab a chair and drag it over to the table. Then they notice Frankie has disappeared.

"Where the fuck did Frankie go? Anybody see?" asks George.

"There he is, over there. Talkin to some broad. Ain't that something. The dumb shit might just be a rooster," exclaims Hank. It isn't long before Frankie brings her over and introduces her.

"These here are the guys I told ya about. That there is Mario; this guy is George, and he's Hank. Guys, meet Katherine. She works in the local shipyard." Frankie scrambles off to buy her a drink and, while he's gone, Katherine asks,

"So, you boys all shippin out with Frankie?"

"Yeah, looks like we'll be goin in the next day or so," answers George.

"Where are you all from?" Frankie returns with her drink just as they begin to answer her question. She ignores them, however, and after taking a long sip from the gin and tonic, says,

"Thanks, Frankie. Let's go in the other room and listen to the radio. I love Benny Goodman, and he's playing tonight."

Frankie flashes a sly smile at his buddies and follows her off into the crowd, while Mario, Hank and George wonder what he could have said to win her attention. Mario begins to hear other familiar sounds coming from one of the back rooms. The wild shouting and cursing can only mean one thing; someone has a game going. He picks up his drink and tells Hank and George,

"Come on with me. This could be interesting." There, they find a small crowd of soldiers standing around a table watching a poker game being played. It's obvious there are more players than seats. Mario asks one of the men waiting,

Mono V. D'Angelo

"Is this the only game goin on here?"

"Think so. They let the guys have one game and nobody cares too much, but it takes all fuckin night to get a seat."

Mario runs his hand over his shirt pocket containing Donnie's dice, and he has an idea. He hasn't played craps since the bad night at Felston's club, and he can feel his excitement beginning to mount over the chance to get a crap game going. He positions himself near the center of the waiting crowd and calmly asks,

"Anyone wanna shoot some craps for a while?" Within minutes, several men say they want to play.

"You got some dice, soldier?" Mario reaches into his shirt pocket, and pulls out the little velvet bag.

"Right here, Buddy. Let's go find a place to roll em."

Hank and George are not sure what to make of Mario's little stunt, and they nervously pull him aside, wanting an explanation. George asks,

"What the hell are ya doin, Mario? We don't know nothin about playin craps."

Mario grins at them and says,

"Ya trusted me ta order your dinner, didn't ya? Well, you do what I tell ya ta do, and we'll have a lot of fun and make some money ta boot."

Six men follow Mario into a small room behind the bar area. They are eager to wager money that many of them believe they will

234

never get to spend. Mario pulls open the dice bag and rolls the ivory cubes into the palm of his hand.

"Who wants to shoot first?" In his usual style, he bets lightly until he sees who's betting and how they play. After a few passes, it's obvious that not many of the soldiers understand the game as well as he does. After warning Hank and George not to bet right away, he quietly tells them, "Watch my bets and follow me. These guys are beggin for a lesson."

Mario starts laying bets against the shooter, always one of his favorite strategies. It begins to pay off among the inexperienced players, and he and his friends start winning big. The excitement attracts more attention, and the game gets bigger and louder. The tiny room suddenly fills with betters, and soon there are almost fifteen men shouting, drinking, and having a wild time. The game continues until the bar closes. When Mario, George and Hank count their money, they discover they have won over nine hundred dollars between them. After leaving the Pelican Club, they sit on a small public bench, where Hank says to Mario,

"I've seen a few crap games in the past, but I ain't never seen anyone play like that before. It's like you was two rolls ahead of everybody. Where the hell did you learn to play like that?"

"My old man taught me how to gamble when I was young, and I used to play some in Detroit and Toledo, but it ain't always this easy." George checks his watch and says,

"We got time to catch the last bus back to the base. Where do ya think Frankie is? Should we wait for em?" Hank looks up and down the deserted street and sees Frankie standing in front of the Pelican Club, as if lost.

"Frankie, over here. Get your ass movin. We wanna catch the last bus," shouts Hank. After Frankie finally shows up, they wave fistfuls of money in front of his face. Hank says, "Man, I hope you got fucked, cause if you didn't, you missed a great time. Look at all this money Mario won us." Frankie looks at the pockets full of cash and is astonished to find out how much they actually have. He asks,

"Holy cow...Where in the blue Jesus did y'all get so much damn money?"

"Mario's got some dice, and he knows how to use em," says George.

The four friends stagger to the bus stop and jump aboard the last bus of the night back to camp. The fun-filled evening provides a fitting memory of their last night in America, for by this time tomorrow, the journey that will bring them face to face with the grim reality of a world at war will begin.

CHAPTER 11

The next several days spent preparing for overseas duty are as frantic as any yet experienced by the men. Sergeant Thompson storms through the barracks immediately after reveille, shouting out orders,

"Let's get moving. There's a lot to get done in a few days. Get dressed and stand down for orders in fifteen minutes."

Mario, Frankie, Hank, and George force themselves out of their bunks. They receive no sympathy for their lack of sleep because of the late night they enjoyed. After quick showers and shaves, they join the rest of the squad assembled in the barracks and await Sergeant Thompson's instructions.

"Here's the way things are going to happen today and tomorrow. After morning chow, I want you guys to head over to the supply office, pick up the clothes you'll be wearing and bring them

237

back here. After that, report to the arsenal and you'll receive your side arms, rifles, and a gas mask. You're going to get trained on how to use the masks in the gas chamber this afternoon. You're gonna love that," says the Sergeant.

The squad stirs about nervously after hearing about the practice run in the gas chamber.

"What kind of gas is in the chamber, Sarge?" asks a concerned soldier.

"This is tear gas, but intelligence reports say the Jerry's are using nerve gas that can kill you. I wouldn't miss the training if I was you." The squad recognizes the seriousness of the Sergeant's advice, and they listen in somber silence as he continues his talk.

"We're on a twenty-four hour operation from here on out. You catch some sleep and chow when you have time. After the gas chamber, you will have new photo I.D's made, your dog tags will be reissued if they are not correct, and you'll get time for a short phone call from a carefully monitored pay phone. When everyone finishes processing, we'll hop on a convoy of trucks that'll take us to the train station for the ride to our ship in New York. That's it, men. You're dismissed."

Mario feels shocked. The fatigue he is suffering adds more misery to an already gruesome day. He is grateful the repair center equipment is safely stored and ready for shipment. The only bright spot in the sergeant's orders is the chance to call home.

After picking up the new clothing and stacking it on top of their bunks, Mario and the repair crew march to the arsenal and then to the gas chamber for their training session. While they stand in a long line to enter the chamber, choking and teary-eyed trainees tumble from the exit with their masks half on. Another soldier in sergeant's stripes stalks along the line with a mask in his hand, shouting,

"That's what'll happen to ya if don't pay attention to me. You gotta know how to put on this mask under any conditions. The chamber is dark, and you don't put on your mask until you're inside. Watch me carefully."

The sergeant then demonstrates the proper method of using the mask by pulling his onto his face and adjusting the straps to properly secure it. He screams out further orders with the mask still on,

"Ya see, it's very easy. Just don't panic. Hold your breath and close your eyes until you get it on and you'll manage just fine."

With that, he opens the chamber door and Mario and the crew hesitantly enter. Once the door slams shut, Mario wastes no time securing his mask as the instructor demonstrated. Hank, George and Frankie also get theirs on without incident. Numerous others, however, struggle and panic, and there is more coughing and crying. Mario helps a man standing next to him by positioning the man's mask correctly on his face and holding it there while he tightens the straps. Although the poor man can't speak, Mario can see the thanks in his eyes as the soldier stares at him through the mask's goggles.

Following their experience in the gas chamber, the men in the unit return to the barracks and begin to pack their gear. Sergeant Thompson moves through the squad, offering suggestions that make the job a little simpler.

"Here, soldier. Pack the lightweight stuff on the bottom. You won't be needing it until we get to Africa. You guys might as well get used to wearing your side arms, too. From now on, that's standard operating procedure."

Mario likes Sergeant Thompson. He's firm but often takes the time to make sure each of his guys gets some help if he needs it. Mario feels confident in following his orders and considers himself fortunate to be assigned to his squad. The Sergeant continues to check with every man, makes sure the gear is packed correctly, and then says,

"Ok, men. Get this packing finished right away and get over to the security hut for your I.D. checks. After that, return here for final equipment inspection. Later, you will report to the medical building for one last check up."

The unending preparations blur the difference between day and night. Exhaustion begins to slow more than a few of the men. As some finish their physicals, they return to the barracks and fall onto their bunks fully clothed, even wearing their side arms.

When the entire squad has returned to the barracks, Sergeant Thompson gives the men further instructions.

"You guys look like you're holding up pretty good. I know this is tough. I'm getting very tired myself. But we're almost ready to go. One last thing you can do is call someone before we get on the trucks later tonight. There's a pay phone in the PX with an M.P. standing next to it. You'll get a couple of minutes to call whoever you want, but don't say anything about where you're going or he'll take the phone."

Mario is anxious to talk to his father and brothers. It's 6:30 in the morning, and he expects everyone will just be getting up. The men march over to the PX, where a line forms in front of the phone. Under the watchful eye of the M.P., the men tell the operator the number to call and wait impatiently for the call to go through. Tearful conversations with families, wives and girlfriends are easily overheard. The short call usually ends with an emotional promise to be careful. The line moves quickly, and Mario finally gets his turn. He gives the operator his father's telephone number and waits for the call to go through. When it rings several times and no one answers, he softly mumbles into the mouthpiece,

"Come on...come on. Someone pick up." The phone stops ringing and he hears the handset being jostled. Then Giuseppi answers,

"Hallo?"

"Pa, it's me. I'm calling from Fort Dix. Can you hear me ok?"

"Mario? Oh my God. Whatta suprisa. How are you? Isa everthing okay?"

"Yeah, Pa. I'm fine, but I only have a few minutes to talk. I'm shippin out later tonight, and I wanna tell ya goodbye and that I'll write to ya when I can."

"Shipping out? Whe...where arra you going, Mario?" asks the old man in a nervous voice.

"I can't tell ya, Pa. Is John or Joe home?"

"No, Mario. John, he'sa inna the plant anna Joe isa picking up some fresha fish froma the Eastern Market."

"Tell em I said ta stay outta trouble and good luck when they get married. I gotta go, Pa."

"I'ma gonna tella them, Mario, for sure, I'ma gonna tella them. Mario? You remember, you promisa me you gonna come home. Pleasa, be very careful. Okay?"

"Pa, don't worry. I can't tell ya everything right now, but I'm gonna be fine. I promise. Bye Pa, I gotta hang up now."

"*Ciao, Mario, boun viaggio,*" whispers Guiseppi.

Mario wipes his eyes after hanging up the phone. He finds Frankie waiting for him and, on the way back to the barracks, Frankie says,

"That sayin goodbye is a hard thing ta do, ain't it? My baby sister, she was a cryin so bad, I could hardly hear er."

"Sure is, Frankie. Are you all right?" asks Mario.

"I ain't no better then you, I figure," he replies with a weak smile.

The convoy of equipment and trucks extends the entire length of the small road in front of the barracks. Each man hauls his heavy bag out, stores it on one of the tent-covered personnel carriers, and then climbs aboard for the ride to the train station. Mario, Frankie, Hank and George are able to find enough space on one of the rigs to sit together on the narrow bench seat, each holding their gear between their legs. Each truck carries about ten men, and the trek to the train station is devoid of the usual jokes and wisecracks. Only Hank complains,

"This goddamn bag is so heavy, I gonna rupture myself carryin the fuckin thing. I knew I packed too much after-shave lotion and cigarettes."

The convoy rumbles off the base, and Mario watches his home for the last several months disappear for good. The caravan of military vehicles slowly snakes through Trenton and pulls up to another chaotic scene at the train station. Sergeant Thompson begins shouting out instructions to the squad,

"Grab your bags and line up for roll call once again."

Mario drags his bag from the truck and patiently listens to the sergeant call out each man's name.

"Anderson."

"Present Sergeant."

"Boykins."

"Present Sergeant"

Sergeant always does everything in alphabetical order. While waiting for his name to be called, Mario listens with mingled thoughts as *I'll Be With You in Apple Blossom Time*, blares out of the public address system.

"Carlucci," shouts the sergeant.

"Present Sergeant," answers Mario.

With all the men present and accounted for, they board the train for the trip to New York harbor. Fatigue and emotional stress take their toll, and most men use the opportunity to catch up on some much needed rest. Mario leans his head back against the seat and closes his eyes. The hours pass like minutes, and the train arrives in the New York station. After another roll call by the Sergeant, he announces,

"We have to walk from here to the docks. Let's keep together. This place will be swarming with troops, and we have to check in before we board the ship. If anyone gets lost, your ship is the Anacon. Find it and get on any way you can. Otherwise you're AWOL."

The half-mile hike to the docks is a constant parade of soldiers and equipment. Mario's heavy bag and physical exhaustion make it the longest half-mile he's ever hiked, and his arms and shoulders quickly give out. Like everyone else in the squad, he resorts to dragging his duffel bag along the ground for the last few hundred yards. Once in the dock pavilion, the men are allowed to sit and rest until the next round of torture is scheduled to begin. The wait is short, perhaps no more than an hour, and Sergeant Thompson rousts the unit up,

"There's another checkpoint we have to pass through to get aboard the ship. When you hear your last name called out, answer with your first name and middle initial."

The squad follows the sergeant to an expansive staging area, where Mario is able to see the ship for the first time. The Anacon is a huge ship with many decks. It might have been a passenger liner at one time and is capable of carrying thousands of men to North Africa. Never having been on an ocean liner before, Mario is curious as well as anxious over his first ocean voyage. The line moves swiftly, and his random daydreaming is abruptly cut short by the sound of his name being called.

"Carlucci? Is there a Carlucci here?" one of the checkers shouts out.

"Carlucci. Right here," answers Mario, his mounting nervousness countering the sergeant's instructions.

After checking his I.D. and dog tags, the inspector hands Mario a large, enamel button to wear. The button color and number designate the vicinity of his quarters and when he'll be admitted to the mess hall. The squad is housed on the same deck. After each man receives his button, he's permitted to board the Anacon.

Mario and Frankie follow right behind Hank and George. They are directed through corridors and up staircases until they arrive at their assigned cabin. Frankie stops for a second to look out onto the dock from the elevated deck and says,

"Where in blue Jesus are they gonna cram all them men? I ain't never seen this many people in one place in my whole life."

"Shit, even Chicago ain't this fuckin crowded," adds Hank.

Their stateroom is located well inside the third deck of the ship. All of its peace-time fittings have been replaced with floor to ceiling bunks that will accommodate ten men. The squad is housed in two adjoining staterooms. After inspecting the tightly packed space, Mario says,

"This place makes the barracks look like a goddamn mansion. It's gonna be real interesting after ten days in this shit hole." Sergeant Thompson arrives a short time later and says,

"I've been informed the ship doesn't depart for at least another six hours. From now on, there's not much more to do. You guys might want to get some rest for a while."

Everyone is tired after the long hike from the train station, and most guys don't even undress. They just drop their bags, weapons and belts in a pile in the middle of the stateroom and crawl into their bunks for some sleep.

The pace of the last forty-eight hours has pushed the squad to the edge of physical exhaustion. Mario sleeps for several hours, but the steady throbbing of the ship's giant engines awakens him. Crawling from his bunk, he shakes the others from their sleep and says,

"I think we're pulling out. Let's get out on deck and have one last look."

Then Mario and his buddies, along with most of the men aboard the ship, rush to the rails as the massive ship is about to be pulled from the dock by several tugboats. The third deck affords them a good look at the throngs of people on the pier, waving goodbye to relatives and friends aboard the Anacon. Dockworkers cast off the ship's lines and raise the gangplank. The tugboats begin maneuvering the great vessel away from the pier and out into the harbor. Vibrations aboard the ship increase, as the Anacon begins to make its way out of the harbor under her own power. Men line the rails in silence to watch the great skyline of New York pass before them. The ship's speed increases, and soon the Statue of Liberty is visible on the starboard side. Mario rushes over to catch a glimpse of the famous landmark. He feels a chill run through him as the majestic figure glides past. The Anacon moves swiftly through the harbor and makes her way onto the open Atlantic. George, Hank, and Frankie join Mario along the rail, as the cold November wind rapidly chills the air. As the temperature drops, the four men stay on deck and watch the coastline slowly vanish into the horizon.

Even a massive vessel such as the Anacon can be tossed around like a box of matches in a strong, Atlantic gale. During the first day at sea, Mario battles seasickness and lethargy and consumes little more than water or tea. He's not alone in his misery. Many soldiers spend long hours hanging onto the cold rail of the ship just waiting to vomit. The weather eventually calms, and the motion of the ship is far less noticeable. Mario, Frankie, Hank, and George find themselves frequently lost among the maze of corridors, decks and stairways of the ocean-going behemoth. When appetites return to normal, long, slow lines are routine in the mess halls. The mess halls become the center of any information. During one such long wait, Hank overhears several men talk of crap games. During the evening meal, he tells Mario and the others,

"There's supposed to be a big crap game on the deck below us, Mario. Let's go find out if it's there. Hell, we got nothin to do for the next eight days anyway." Mario's eager to do anything to end the boredom and a crap game's a perfect solution. He asks Hank,

"Where did ya hear that?"

"A coupla guys in front of me said they just left there."

"Let's go. Unless you guys wanna get back in the chow line for seconds."

Every corridor aboard the ship seems to come with its own M.P, and he takes great delight in reprimanding any G.I. caught wandering around the ship without a life preserver in his possession. During the search for the crap game, Frankie notices a pile of life jackets stacked up like chord wood outside a storage room. He says,

"Only reason them jackets is piled up like that is cause there's too dang many men inside that room. I figure we just found that fuckin crap game."

Frankie is right. When they enter the storage room, they find several games going on at the same time. Mario and Hank join one. Frankie and George play another. The play is loud and rowdy, reminding Mario of the games he played in the back room of the auto plant. He bets conservatively, winning and losing in like amounts, but it is not the money that matters here. He will spend many hours shooting craps with Donnie's dice all over the ship in order to take his mind off its destination.

Rumors that the Anacon will be entering the Mediterranean circulate throughout the mess hall. Following breakfast, most men scramble up to the promenade deck in hopes of sighting the first signs of land in seven days. The weather has improved significantly. Blue skies and warmer temperatures lure most men from the twenty-four hour a day crap games.

"Look. Over there. I'll bet it's the Rock of Gibralter," shouts a soldier pointing to a small spit of land on the horizon. Mario strains to find whatever the man is pointing to, but he can see only a small cloud-like shadow off in the distance. Within a few hours, however, the ship passes through the Straights of Gibraltar and into the Mediterranean. Hank and George are standing next to Mario when Hank says,

"Ain't that a sight, huh? Never saw water look that blue before, not even Lake Michigan."

Steaming under full power, the Anacon nears its destination of Casablanca. Sergeant Thompson calls a squad meeting in the adjoining staterooms to let everyone know what is about to happen. Mario and the rest of the unit squeeze into tight quarters as the sergeant explains.

"Reports are coming in that the first wave of Operation Torch has landed in several places along the coast, including Casablanca. I've been told that's where we're heading. The harbor there is intact and big enough to dock this ship."

"Was there much fightin goin on, Sarge?" shouts one of the soldiers.

"It was pretty light. Just a few French troops there raisin a little hell, according to radio messages from shore."

"So whatta we gonna do when we git there?" asks Frankie.

"Once the ship is secure, we have to see that all our equipment is unloaded onto waiting trucks and then get it all moved to a base near the airstrip. We'll be coming into port in about ten hours. I expect everyone to get his personal belongings packed up and ready to go."

Approaching the coast of North Africa, the Anacon begins to slow down and weave a cautious path through the hundreds of war vessels, which comprise Operation Torch. Aircraft carriers, battleships and landing craft are now readily visible to Mario and the squad. The size of the armada is formidable. He is awestruck by the collection of so much military power. While observing the massive fleet from the rail, he tells Frankie,

"Jesus Christ, look at that will ya. I'll bet you never saw anything like *that* in Arkansas."

"Jerry's gonna git his ass pounded real good now," replies Frankie while looking at all the warships.

Soon, the engines aboard the Anacon shut down, as Navy tugs come along side and take her into the harbor at Casablanca. Beyond the harbor, Mario can see many buildings made of white mortar extending up into the distant hills. Heavily decorated towers dot the unique landscape, creating a remarkable panorama from the deck of the ship. It is the most beautiful city he has ever seen. The tugs slowly guide the giant ship into its berth, and dozens of men ashore secure her lines to the dock. Looking out in the direction of the desert, he sees plumes of smoke near the horizon. Combined with the muffled sounds of distant artillery, they provide Mario with his first experience of the war's hostility. Activity aboard the ship increases as M.P.'s begin to direct the thousands of men and tons of equipment ashore.

Sergeant Thompson has already gone ashore and is waiting for the entire squad to disembark. Mario straps on his forty-five caliber side arm and hauls his duffel bag ashore. After the Sergeant does roll call once again, he says,

"The engineering guys are unloading the heavy equipment and will get it over to the base camp. In the meantime, I want you guys to load your gear onto those trucks parked at the end of this small road. From there, we have a two-mile march over to the camp being set up

251

for A Company. There's a lot of nasty shit going on around here. The locals don't like us, and there have been a couple of Stuka dive-bombers flying a few strafing missions already, so stay alert."

Even under a brilliant sun, the cool desert air surprises Mario. He's thankful the temperature hovers somewhere in the sixties as the soldiers plod along to their quarters. Within minutes, clouds of dust from passing vehicles cover everyone with a fine layer of the gritty substance. George begins to cough and says,

"Hell, we been walkin in this sand for less than an hour, and the stuff is all over everything. Look at that old ambulance over there. It's almost buried under the shit." Mario stares at a couple of bedraggled and exhausted soldiers driving by in a Jeep armed with dual machine guns. He asks Sergeant Thompson,

"Hey Sarge, who are those guys? They ain't wearin G.I. fatigues."

"They are part of the Long Range Desert Patrol. Worst job in the British Army. Those Tommies have to take a lot of crap."

Once the squad arrives at the camp, the Sergeant directs everyone to a group of tents assigned to the company. He groups the men together in one large tent to be used as the repair center and warns them of the many hazards they face.

"There's a lot of things that can get you killed here, so pay attention. The C.O. says if anyone dares to show a light at night, the Brits will shoot it out if the Germans don't do it first. Even though we're here to help the Tommies, they don't really like us," informs the Sergeant.

"Why the fuck not?" shouts Hank. Sergeant Thompson laughs a bit and says,

"They think we're all over-paid, for one thing. They get one-third the money we do, so they're pissed about that. They watch too many movies because they think we're all either movie stars, mobsters, or rich playboys. Just watch yourself when you run into them. That's all I'm saying." Sergeant Thompson's comments draw a round of laughter from the squad, but the serious business of war is never far from his mind. He begins giving orders to the squad.

"Let's get to work. Rankin and Porter, report to the radio shack at the end of the airstrip. There are a couple of fly-boys there who'll put you to work. Erskin, Forrester, Carlucci, and Pinkerton. Begin to set up your equipment in this tent. I hear there are a lot of beat up ambulances that need your help. The rest of you field support guys, come with me. I'll get you introduced to the British troops you'll be working with."

After moving their duffel bags into the small, six-man tent they will live in, Mario, Frank, Hank, and George spend the next twenty-four hours setting up the repair center equipment. They sleep and eat only when they can go no further without doing so. The teamwork they developed in Fort Dix begins to pay tremendous dividends as each man's individual skills are taken advantage of. Mario and Frankie can make practically anything, and George and

253

Hank are experts in diagnosing problems. Bedford lorries, Dodge trucks and a lot of mid-1930's French Foreign Legion ambulances require the most work, often forcing the crew to cannibalize old, discarded German equipment in order to make the needed repairs. The smell of dead and wounded soldiers inside the old ambulances brings the reality of the grim, brutal war to Mario and the crew. After pulling another Bedford into the repair tent, George goes about his usual inspection, when suddenly, he screams,

"Oh, shit. Oh my God...there's a severed leg in this goddamn thing. Some poor son-of-a-bitch lost his leg."

"Looks like one of them fuckin Bouncin Bettys that Jerry has planted all over the goddamn place. I hear they kin cut a man clean in two if they pop up high enough," adds Frankie.

Blood and body parts become a normal pattern whenever the crew works on an ambulance. Mario realizes, now more than ever, what the recruiter meant when he told him he was lucky. The daily reminder of a dying man relying on an ambulance or a truck to save his life is a thought not easily put aside. During daylight hours, there is no place to hide in the desert, but on a moonless night, infiltrators are reported in many areas near the camp. Because of the dangers at night, the work goes on every day until darkness forces everyone under the cover of full blackout tents. For the next several months, Mario and the crew will work harder than they ever did at Fort Dix.

The cool, November desert has given way to temperatures consistently above one hundred degrees. The nauseating odor of blood and decaying flesh coming from the ambulances attracts hordes of flies and insects to the repair tent. The intense heat forces everyone to wear clothing that will protect him from illness and sunburn. Mario wears long-sleeved shirts and full length pants to protect himself from insect bites and disease, but constant exposure and perspiration result in a mild case of desert sores. With water in such short supply, the crew members give up shaving regularly and bathe once or twice a week by giving themselves sponge baths from their helmets. To Mario and the repair crew, however, the most heinous condition of the desert is the sandstorm, or as the Arabs call it, *khamasseen*. With winds that can gust to sixty miles per hour, the *khamasseen* reduces the visibility to zero. Tents offer little protection, and the men often find shelter in trucks or some of the few hard buildings in camp. The fine desert grit covers everyone and everything, causing even more mechanical failures. The invading sand forces troops to wear facemasks and long-sleeved, uncomfortable clothing. Lung ailments and untreatable rashes become commonplace among the desert troops.

As the front line battles move eastward toward Tunisia and Tripoli, the increased distance to the front slows down the pace in the repair center and gives everyone time to get some long, overdue rest. Mario uses the time to write home and finally tell his family where he is. Pulling a pen and paper from his bag, he writes his first letter home since arriving in Africa.

Dear Pa, John, and Joe,

I want you to know that I am safe and I miss you all a lot. I have been in Casablanca for the last four months. The desert is a terrible place to live. It's always too hot or too cold. The food is awful, and there is never enough water. I ain't took a real bath since I got here. Fort Dix is like living in heaven compared to this camp. The British do most of the land fighting, and we help them with equipment and some troops. We got to come over on a big ocean liner, and I saw the Rock of Gibraltar and the Mediterranean Sea. The invasion fleet was the biggest thing I ever saw. I work in a repair center fixing damaged ambulances and other equipment, so I don't go near the front lines. It's a good job and I'm lucky I got trained as machinist. Rumors are we will be moving out again soon, heading for Egypt, but I don't know for sure. How are you all doing? Did John or Joe get married yet? I sure do miss your cooking, Pa. I can't wait to come home and have some of your sausage again. You can write me at the address here in this letter, so be sure to tell me all about the weddings. Good bye for now,

Mario

He addresses the envelope, places the short letter inside, licks the flap and seals it. Dropping it into a small, wooden mailbox near the airstrip control center, he tries to imagine his family's reaction to reading it several months from now and discovering he is not in a combat zone.

Sergeant Thompson surprises the repair crew with an unexpected visit. He sits on the fender of a battle-scarred Jeep and tells the men,

"We have been told by the brass that the Italians have given up and Rommel is getting squeezed out of Africa. The C.O. wants us to move the repair center closer to the front lines so, in the morning, start packing up the equipment. We have to move out by 0900 on Friday."

"Got any idea where we're goin, Sarge?" asks Mario.

"Not sure. Maybe near Tripoli. I think the British Eighth is moving in that direction," replies Sergeant Thompson.

"What in blue Jesus is in Tripoli?" quizzes Frankie.

"I don't know, Frankie. I've never been there. But I hear it's a pretty big city. Maybe we can get some time off and find out for ourselves," answers the Sergeant.

The mere hint of time off causes Frankie to scream out in a wretched pagan howl,

"Oh, thank ya Lord...I know this misery I'm in cain't go on much longer."

Mario smiles as he shakes his head and says,

"Let's get to work, Frankie. The Lord ain't gonna load up this equipment, you are."

Company A relocates to a base on the outskirts of Tripoli. After the repair center is put into operation, Mario and the crew begin to sort through a fleet of Jeeps and troop carriers damaged during earlier battles. With most of North Africa under control of British and American forces, the immediate need to put the vehicles back into service diminishes, and the brutal pace in the center relaxes. In the next few weeks, most of the critical work is completed. On a particularly quiet evening, Sergeant Thompson calls the squad together in the mess tent to offer up some good news.

"Hey Sarge, we don't have ta move again, do we?" shouts Hank.

"No. Not yet, anyway. But I do have some good news. As of a few days ago, North Africa is under total control of the Allies, and the Germans have either surrendered or pulled out," replies the Sergeant.

"So, can we go home now?" jokes someone from the back of the squad.

Sergeant Thompson smiles over the snide comment and says,

"No, we're not going home yet. But I've been given permission to grant all of you a little time off. I hear we're getting a couple of large water trucks in here soon, so you'll be able to take a real shower. If you want to get into Tripoli, you should be able to hop onto a truck making the trip to the port in town. Looks like things are going to be quiet for a while, so I'd take advantage of the time if I were you."

The excited squad files out of the mess tent, and the men return to their sleep tents to plan their leave. Mario, Hank, George and Frankie make their way back to their tent, when Hank says,

"I got a better idea for gettin to Tripoli. Follow me." He leads the crew to a tarp-covered vehicle hidden away behind the repair center. He rips off the heavy canvas sheet, revealing a hardtop Jeep. With a boyish smirk on his face, he says,

"This thing's been sittin here for a few weeks. I think the first Louie who brought it here got shipped off to Cairo or some goddamn place. Sure is a waste of a nice Jeep not to take it to Tripoli or somethin, don't ya think?"

"You goddamn thief...this is fuckin perfect. I ain't too excited about a two hour ride in the back of cargo truck ta get to Tripoli," squeals Frankie.

"Is this the kind of work ya did in Chicago?" asks Mario with a sarcastic chuckle.

"Sometimes," replies Hank with even a bigger grin.

After enjoying long overdue showers the next morning, the men put on fresh fatigues, pack small bags of spare clothing and sneak the Jeep away to Tripoli.

The road to Tripoli is littered with the burned-out remains of British trucks left twisted and tangled by recently fought battles. Nearing the city, beggars risk their lives, stepping before the fast moving Jeep in search of food scraps or anything of value that can be sold on the streets. On the edge of the city, Hank slows the Jeep down and pulls alongside a non-Arabic-looking warrior dressed in the tattered remains of a Legionnaire's uniform. He stops and asks,

"Do you speak English? Can ya tell us where we can find some place to stay?"

"You go to El Mina. Near the port. You find many old hotels there," replies the weary-looking soldier.

"Thanks buddy. Can we give ya a ride?"

The man simply raises his hand and waves it from side to side. Hank speeds away and finds his way into the ancient city of Tripoli. It is mid-morning and the city is alive with people. The war has done little damage to the historic beauty of this place, and Mario studies the spectacular buildings he assumes are the mosques he's heard of. Groups of children run after the Jeep, screaming out the only English they know,

"Candy, G.I?…candy, please."

Each man searches his bag for some small treat to give to the children, only to watch them fight bitterly to grab whatever is being offered. Arabic women stare at the passing men through the narrow openings in their head wraps. They say nothing and quickly turn away whenever the men try to make eye contact. Hank continues to weave his way along the crowded street when George asks,

"Hank, none of us know where we're going, but you keep driving. How do you intend to find this El Mina place?"

"Well, I ain't seen another road big enough to turn onto, so I figure sooner or later we gotta run into the ocean," he replies.

"Jesus Christ, Hank. That's the dumbest damn thing I ever heard," shouts Frankie.

"Unless you just learned how ta talk Arabic, I don't think you got any better ideas," replies Hank.

"Hank is right. We got no choice except to keep going in the direction of the ocean. Let em alone, Frankie," exclaims George.

After passing through the city, the men find themselves in the open desert again. The road leads to the ocean, which is now visible on the horizon. More buildings can be seen at the end of the road, suggesting another city district is nearby. Suddenly, Hank slams on the brakes and jams the gearshift into reverse. Backing up slowly, he stops once more and points to a crude, hand-painted sign along side the road. It's in English and it reads El Mina, followed by an arrow pointing to the distant city.

"See, I told you guys this would work out," gloats Hank.

"You're the luckiest goddamn son-of-a-bitch I ever seen," laments Frankie.

Mario and George laugh so hard they can barely breathe, while Hank shifts the Jeep into forward gear and roars off for the city ahead.

El Mina is the main port of Tripoli. Upon arriving, the four Americans see it is swarming with British troops, who do little more than sneer at them as they pass. Mario leans forward so he can be heard over the rumble of the engine and says,

"Sarge tells me these guys get one set of fatigues and about twenty bucks a month for bein over here. No wonder they're so damn grumpy."

"Yeah, and look at the uniforms the poor bastards gotta wear. Shit, half of em's fallin apart," notes Hank.

After a short ride through the port city, Hank pulls the Jeep over in front of a large building with several floors. The upper levels are a series of dark, wooden doors and curtain-draped windows that face the street. The lower level houses a small room full of dining tables and a large registration counter.

"If that ain't a hotel, I'll buy you guys dinner," says Hank.

"Let's go find out," suggests George.

The old hotel doesn't even have a sign or a name that the men can readily see. They are fascinated by the ancient but well-kept appearance of the hotel. Furnishings are simple, but elegant, with high-backed wicker chairs decorated with rich colored cushions, scattered throughout the main floor. As Mario approaches the registration desk, a short, balding man with a heavy mustache appears from behind a curtain of beads.

"You speak English?" asks Mario. The man nods his head up and down, saying,

"I learn from Tommies. You want room?" Reacting to the man's poor English, Mario holds up his right hand, displaying four fingers and says,

"We want four rooms. Do you have four rooms?"

"Yes. Yes...Many rooms here. You want bath with room?" inquires the clerk.

"We'll take whatever you have. Anything is good," replies Mario.

The men sign the guest register, and the clerk hands a room key to each of them. Following almost a year of living in barracks with dozens of other men, Mario looks forward to sleeping in a private room with his own bath. He tells the others,

"No offense guys, but if any of you bother me later tonight, I'm gonna throw yer ass off the balcony." The guys all laugh over Mario's half-hearted joke, but each of them shares the same anticipation after the long months on the desert. The day vanishes and, after nightfall, there is very little activity on the streets. After a short hike around the hotel area, they see more British troops, than Arabic residents, on the streets. More disappointing is the total absence of hard liquor in this area. George remembers something he's read in school and says,

"I don't think drinkin is allow in some of these Arab countries. They got some very different ways."

"I'm gonna get some sleep. I don't give a shit if I get a drink or not," states Hank. After an unsuccessful search for anything to do or drink, the men return to the hotel and each enjoys the luxury of a private room for the night. Mario unlocks the door to his room and falls onto the four-poster bed while still fully dressed. The quiet night puts him into a deep, refreshing sleep for the first time since he left Dctroit.

In the hour before dawn, Mario is awakened by the calls to prayer.

"Aliaaaahu Akbar! Aliaaaahu Akbar!" shout holy men from the mosque towers. One by one, they take up the chant from the many mosques until it sounds as if they are singing in the round to compliment and echo each other. Mario steps onto the balcony of his room to investigate the human sirens, only to have them stop as quickly as they have begun. At dawn, the call to prayer is no longer the predominant voice of the city. Slowly, life stirs. Pedestrians crowd the narrow roadway, where street urchins and beggars prowl the early morning chaos in search of a morning meal. Returning to his room, Mario fills the tub with water and treats himself to a leisurely bath. A heavy knock on the door interrupts the peaceful interlude, followed by Frankie's shouts,

"Mario. Git on out here. We're goin for some breakfast. Someone's a bakin somethin that smells real good."

Mario steps out of the tub, wraps a towel around himself, and opens the door. The great, boyish grin on Frankie's face is evidence enough that he's been awake for some time now. Mario stares at him menacingly and says,

"Didn't you hear me say I'd throw the first guy to bother me off the fuckin balcony this morning?"

"Aw, hell, I know that's you's just bullshitin around. Come on, let's go get some chow and see what's cookin around this place." Mario finds it hard to be angry with Frankie and returns to the room to finish bathing and shave. With his back turned to Frankie, he says,

"At least let me get dressed, will ya?" Mario joins the others in the lower level dining area, where they have already found something to eat. George holds up a large, oval-shaped doughnut and says,

"These are called *ka'ak*. Ya tear em open and sprinkle some thyme into the hollow insides and eat em. They're pretty good. Besides, I don't think they got anything else."

"So whadda we gonna do?" inquires Hank.

"Let's go sight seein. If we roam around down by the docks, maybe we can find someplace to eat," suggests George. They agree with George's suggestion and set out to explore the El Mina district on foot.

Roaming the ancient city during the day, they are unprepared for the restrictive Arab culture. Women, dressed in traditional *Jelibiahs*, intentionally cross to the opposite side of the street to avoid any close contact with the four Americans. Even through the small slit over their veil-covered faces, their spiteful stares catch Mario's attention. The war has done little to prevent small, street vendors from selling everything from elephant ivory sculptures to exotic jewelry. Anxious to trade for some American money, eager vendors thrust rare jungle parrots and wild, screeching monkeys into their faces, screaming,

"You buy, G.I. I make good deal. Yes?" While brushing them aside, Mario is amazed by the sight of beggars and black-market profiteers trying to eke out a living on the same road. The aimless journey leads them to an area near the ocean. Hank notices tables under a tent and says,

"Let's go see if we can get some food there. Seems like a lotta British guys around. Maybe we can get something besides baked bread." They squeeze together around a small table and are soon greeted by a young Arab man speaking limited English.

"Hallo, Hallo. You boys want to eat, yes?" he asks.

"Yeah. You got something besides baked bread?" responds Frankie sarcastically.

"Fresh lamb and rice. Very good. Very good. G.I.'s will like. I bring?"

Mario nods his head in agreement, as do the others, and the young man scampers away. He returns with servings of freshly-brewed Arabic coffee. The coffee is strong, pungent, and certainly better than any coffee the four friends have had in camp. While the men wait for their meals to arrive, two British soldiers stop and stare at them for a moment. One of them calls out,

"Any a you blokes interested in some war souvenirs?" George and Frankie look at each other for a moment, wondering if they are serious. Frankie suddenly blurts out,

"Maybe. Whadda ya got?" The Tommies approach the table, and one pulls a German Luger from beneath his shirt. He says with some pride,

"I shot the previous owner of this little beauty myself. Twenty-five American and its yours, gov."

"Naw. I don't want a gun. Ya got anything else?" replies Frankie.

The other soldier pulls open the flap on the small bag he carries and retrieves a neatly-folded German flag. It's bright red with the dreaded swastika insignia emblazoned in the center. Frankie's eyes light up.

"I'll give ya ten bucks, American. Deal?" Half a month's wages for the captured German trophy is too tempting an offer for the poorly paid Brit. He quickly hands the flag to Frankie. Holding it by each corner, Frankie waves it in front of the others, as he examines it more closely. Meanwhile, Mario has a thought and asks,

"You know anyone selling any liquor?"

"We have some gin and a few bottles of cognac, if you're willing to pay," replies one of them.

"We got some money, don't worry about that. Where's the booze?"

"There's an old warehouse located on the edge of the desert. If you follow this road to the end, you'll see it off to the left of a big olive grove. Just knock on the door and someone will let you in," replies one of the Tommies.

"We'll be there later. Thanks," comments Mario.

The young waiter returns with the meals as the Brits are leaving. Their first taste of Arabic food is delicious compared to the camp food they've been eating, and the four friends gorge themselves on second helpings followed by more coffee and dessert. During the meal, they cheerfully make plans to find the warehouse and purchase a few bottles of gin.

After returning to the hotel to pick up the Jeep, they drive out of town and carefully follow the twisting road out of El Mina. Night descends onto the unlit trail, and soon only the penetrating beams of the Jeep's headlights provide any visibility. George leans forward, as if spotting something, and says,

"There. On the left. Don't that look like some kind of grove or orchard or something?" Hank slows the Jeep, as the four men strain to find the warehouse the British soldier spoke of.

"I don't see no goddamn warehouse anywhere. I think we're on a wild goose chase," whines Hank.

"What's that? Up on the right? I'll bet that's it," says Mario.

"That's gotta be it. I can see a Union Jack flyin on the pole in front of the place," adds Frankie. Hank stops the Jeep in front of the building and turns off the engine. With the Jeep's lights still on, they can see a rugged-looking, tin-covered building. There are few windows, and no light is visible from any of them. Discarded crates and barrels are stacked haphazardly around its perimeter.

"Now what?" Hank asks as he clicks off the Jeep's lights.

"Aw, goddamn Hank, get the fuck outta the way. Whatta ya scared or something?" says Frankie.

Often demonstrating more fearlessness than intelligence, Frankie tramps along a slim, sand-covered path leading to the old building. He pounds his knuckles on the small service door and then smiles back at the Jeep, waiting for someone to answer.

"Someday that dumb shit's gonna git his ass beat doin stupid things like this," moans Hank. After a few more knocks, the door flies open and two British soldiers greet him. They stare at him in disbelief before one of them finally asks,

"What the hell do you want here, Yank?"

"We met a coupla your buddies today, and they said you might have some liquor y'all are willin to sell," replies Frankie.

"Oh, at's right. One of our boys said something about a few Yanks stopping in. You alone?"

"No, I got some friends sittin in the Jeep. I'll get em," says Frankie.

He signals to the others to come ahead and, after they join him, he says,

"This is the place all right. These guys are sayin they got some liquor they can sell us."

Mario tries to peek inside the dark building, but he sees nothing. Instincts from his days in the blind pigs back home kick in, and he cautiously looks around the outside of the building for signs of trouble. Nothing is out of the ordinary but the fact that this door appears to be the only way in or out bothers him.

"Follow me. Watch yourself in here. We got rats bigger than most bloody cats," comments one of the Tommies. The place resembles an indoor junkyard. Piles of old tires, stacks of weathered tent canvas, and an assortment of old engine parts are scattered throughout the foul-smelling building. They follow the British soldiers through the maze of junk and into a combined office and barracks facility. Mario takes a quick mental count and sees at least seven more British troopers. He doesn't like being outnumbered. One of the Brits says,

"All we ave ere is some gin we found in a German supply camp. Not nearly as good as Bombay Sapphire, but it's better than nothing, right?."

"We'll take what ever ya got. Don't worry about that," replies Mario.

The soldier steps into another room and returns a few moments later, cradling four bottles of crystal clear gin in his arms.

"Ere you are, boys. At'll be three dollars apiece." They gladly pay the money, but Mario is still suspicious and wants to sample the liquor before they leave the warehouse. He asks the Brit,

"It's a long ride back to town. Do ya mind if we have a few drinks before we leave?"

"Sure, Yank. If you must. Follow me." He leads them into another room furnished with battered tables and chairs. Mario twists off the cap to his bottle, hoists it up, and says,

"Here goes nothing." The others do the same. They raise the bottles in a cheerful toast and all take long swigs of the gin.

"Damn, that shit's not bad," remarks Hank.

"It ain't Crown Royal, but I'll take it," Mario chuckles.

They sit around for a half hour or more, sipping on the bottles and feeling the gin work its magic. Mario gets up to find a latrine and take a piss. He passes by another room in which a card game is in progress. His courage fortified by the cheap gin, he stops and asks,

"Any open seats for new players?"

"Sorry, mate. Game's closed for now," one of the men abruptly answers.

The Brit's short answer irritates Mario and, when he returns to his friends, he takes another long drink from his gin bottle. He quietly says,

"They got two open seats at a card game, and these pricks won't let me in. That's really starting to piss me off." With his eyes glazed and face flush from the booze, Frankie looks at Mario and breaks out in a mischievous grin. Clutching his bottle in one hand, he leans across the table and whispers to Mario,

"I...I gotta plan. We kin, uh...start a crap game. You know, like you did in Trenton. I betcha they'll be here in a fuckin minute." Now smiling from ear to ear, Mario's just drunk enough to go along with Frankie's suggestion. Reaching into his shirt pocket, he pulls out Donnie's dice and says,

"For a goddamn hillbilly from Arkansas, you can come up with some good ideas once in a while. Besides, I think those thieves overcharged us for the gin anyway. Let's see if we can get some of our dough back."

They drag a table and chairs out of a corner of the room, making as much noise as possible. With room to play, Mario makes the first pass. The rolling dice are easily heard as they crash into the metal sides of the warehouse. Frankie, Hank and George play along by shouting out phony epitaphs on each pass. The plan works to perfection, and soon several British soldiers are standing behind them and watching. One asks,

"You mind if we jump in, mate?"

"Sure, we got plenty of room. Step right in and have a turn," encourages Mario.

The game builds rapidly and, in less than an hour, there are as many as six or seven Brits playing at one time. The action becomes hectic, and Mario finds his game working to perfection. Most of the Tommies keep playing and losing for several more hours, but eventually, tempers begin to grow short. A larger crowd of British soldiers suddenly surrounds the game, and Mario's instincts warn him of impending trouble. With a large pile of money now being wagered, he knows it's too late to walk away. Hank throws the dice and wins his roll with a seven. A large, brutish-looking Brit suddenly steps into the middle of the game and grabs the dice. Wearing a pistol and large knife on his belt, he's prepared for any trouble. In a loud, threatening voice, says,

"Let's have a look at these dice, mate. You boys seem to be doing too bloody well to be just lucky." The man inspects them closely, even biting down on them with the few good teeth left in his mouth, but he can find nothing to suggest they are rigged. Mario can see the only way out is to leave whatever they've won on the floor and try and get out of there in one piece. Mario tells the man with the dice,

"Look, you can see the dice are clean. We're not lookin' for trouble. Just give em back and we'll just leave." The gravely voiced Brit tosses the dice back at Mario and says,

"At's a good way ta go, Yank. You boys ad better get the fuck out of here while you can still walk. And you bloody well better leave the money here."

Mario stuffs the dice back into his shirt pocket, and some British soldiers hastily escort the four to the door, where they angrily toss them out of the warehouse.

"Those fuckin' bastards, I can't believe they did that," whines Frankie.

"Sarge said the Brits don't like us; now I can see why. The pricks even kept our gin," growls Mario.

"I'll get even with those British pricks if it's the last thing I do," threatens Frankie.

"You're lucky ya didn't get yer ass kicked, Frankie. Let's just get outta here while we can," adds Hank. While finding their way back to the Jeep in the dark, they pass the wooden flagpole where the Brits' Union Jack still flies. Frankie rushes to the Jeep, and says,

"Someone git this damn thing started and turn the lights on for a second. I'm gonna fix this place up real good." He reaches under the seat of the Jeep and pulls out the German flag he purchased earlier in the day. The others quickly catch on to what he's about to do, and George says,

"Oh shit, he's gonna get us killed. If someone sees him doing that, they'll start shooting without asking any questions first." George's concern is wasted on Mario and Hank who, by now, are laughing so hard they can barely speak. The sight of Frankie lowering the Union Jack from the flagpole and hoisting up the German swastika is devilishly ingenious. Frankie climbs back into the Jeep, and they speed away from the warehouse and onto the desert road leading back to El Mina. Frankie can't stop laughing. He shouts,

"That outta piss of those British pricks, don't ya think?" The four friends can't stop laughing on the ride back to the hotel. Frankie adds,

"It's worth every dime I paid for that goddamn flag to do that. I wish I could see their faces when the sun comes up."

They arrive back at the hotel just after the daily call to prayers, and the city begins to come to life after the long night. After picking up their belongings, Mario and Hank find the hotel proprietor and pay the bill, while Frankie and George load up the Jeep. Frankie is sitting behind the wheel and, after everyone is in, he begins to drive out of town. Hank notices he's heading in the wrong direction and says,

"Frankie, this is ain't the way back to camp. You're goin back to the warehouse for Christ's sake."

"I know. I wantta see if they found the Nazi flag yet. Besides, they don't know it's us in this Jeep," he responds. George rolls his head back in disgust and says,

"You really want to get us killed, don't you?"

"Aw, just relax. I know what I'm doin." The route to the warehouse is busy with both U.S. and British personnel carriers. An armed squad of Tommies suddenly blocks the road. They cautiously approach the Jeep with weapons drawn, and one of them shouts,

"Let's see I.D., now." After checking the identification of the four G.I.'s, one of the troopers says,

"You're going to have to take a run out into the desert, Yank. We think some Germans may be holed up in a warehouse just ahead. Can't understand how they could be hiding this long, but we got a small brigade around em, now."

Frankie keeps a safe distance from the warehouse, but drawing nearer, they see several tanks poised with their guns pointed. Dozens of troops surround the perimeter with weapons ready. Frankie and the others start laughing once again.

"Jesus Christ, ain't this the damndest thing ya ever saw? They got the place surrounded. Those fuckin Brits are going to be so pissed off," adds Frankie.

"Let's get the hell outta here before someone recognizes us," warns George.

They return to the camp and go about their business during the next few days. Sergeant Thompson strolls into the repair center one afternoon and asks,

"Did you guys see any of the excitement in Tripoli while you were there?"

"You mean the Nazis in the warehouse?" answers Hank.

"We didn't see nothing, but it sure sounds like one helluva bad day for the Brits," adds George.

"So you guys never saw anything, huh?"

Mario and his friends keep the details of the warehouse incident to themselves, but the rumor that several G.I.'s were involved floats around for weeks. Camp activity has come to a near standstill now that the Allies control all of North Africa. For Mario and the repair center crew, boredom becomes the greatest aggravation, next to the desert conditions they must endure. Waiting for the next job, waiting for the next battle to begin, waiting for the war to end. The repair center is moved eastward several more times, but there is little to be done. For Mario, the downtime is an opportunity to visit a few of the exotic landmarks in this ancient part of the world. With unrestricted access to trucks and Jeeps, Mario and his friends are able to see such famous sites as Cairo, the Suez Canal, and the Pyramids of Giza. At times, it is difficult to remember there is a war going on.

One evening, Sergeant Thompson calls the company together to make an announcement. By now, everyone knows that these company gatherings usually mean something big is about to happen. This time is no different.

"Gentlemen, we've had things pretty easy lately, but that's about to change. You may have heard rumors that we're going to be reassigned, and now they're fact. We are joining Operation Husky and will be supporting the Fifth Army. Allied forces are preparing to invade Sicily and then the Italian mainland. The Germans are on their own because Italy has declared war on them. It's going to be a vicious battle for the infantry boys, so we'll be busy keeping them supplied with dependable gear. You know what to do. Get everything ready to go. We'll be moving out soon."

Mario has never expected to see much more than the African desert, and the thought of going to Sicily both excites and disturbs him. He is certain Giuseppi would be thrilled to know he will be visiting his homeland. He also knows that the news of the war invading that small island is certain to disturb his father. There is nothing to do except prepare to go to Italy.

CHAPTER 12

"Assunta, Assunta. Prego aspett un minuto. I want to talk to you," shouts Theresa Minelli. Assunta stops and waits for her to cross the street and join her.

"Theresa, how are you. I see you, too, cannot leave Napoli," responds Assunta with deep concern. The two old friends share an emotional hug with one another, and then Theresa asks,

"Have you heard the rumors? It is said that Mussolini has been overthrown and that the Army has surrendered in Tunis several months ago. Do you think it's true?"

"Yes, I do. I have seen many tired young men coming into the city. They look very weary, as if they have been on a long journey. I am told the Allies have invaded Sicily. Did you hear anything like that?" Theresa's eyes widen and her mouth drops open at the news. She places her hands upon her cheeks and says,

"Oh my God, no. Do you understand what that means? The invasion has started, and we are sure to be caught between the Nazis and the Allies. Assunta, what can we do? I'm so frightened."

"We can only pray, Theresa. Please be careful." The two women hug and try to comfort each other, as the reality of the war that will soon be fought on their very doorsteps sinks in.

Mussolini's army, once the greatest military power in Europe, rapidly disintegrates into a combination of partisan guerrilla loyalists and weary, homesick men, wanting nothing more than to put war and combat behind them. Small numbers of exhausted soldiers pass through Napoli on the way to their homes and families. Theresa has heard important news regarding one such soldier:

"Assunta, there's been a young man asking about you near the fishing beach. Has he been able to find you?"

"But no. What did he say? Maybe he has news of Giancarlo."

"I am not sure, Assunta. I did not speak to him, but others say he asks for you by name."

"What does he look like? Can you tell me, Theresa? I must try to find him. I'm certain he must have news of Giancarlo if he knows my name," pleads Assunta.

"I know that he does not wear an army uniform. He dresses like a farmer and wears a soldier's cap. One without any markings on it."

Not having heard from Giancarlo for over a year, Assunta repeatedly hopes and prays that he is still alive. During her daily outings in search of food, she keeps a watchful eye for any young man remotely matching the description given to her by Theresa. She often asks any young man she encounters if he knows her son, but she finds no one who is able to help her. After several long days of searching for the man, she gives up her unsuccessful quest, believing he is no longer in Napoli.

After an early morning rain shower, Assunta washes clothes in a small tub of the fresh water outside her apartment. She does not see a young man approach and only notices he is standing there when he asks,

"Pardonne mia, signora. Siete Assunta Cappodanno?"

Ever wary of strangers, Assunta immediately stops what she is doing and looks up at the boy standing before her. He is young, perhaps no more than twenty-three years old, but his unshaven face and dark, sunken eyes make him look older. He's dressed in a tattered vineyard coat and worn-out military boots. His cap is a soldier's cap, but it has no insignias on it. It is the same cap Theresa Minellli described, the one worn by the man asking for her. Assunta's heart pounds as much from fear as from the excitement of knowing this is the young man who's been asking for her by name. Cautiously, she answers,

"Yes. I am Signora Cappodanno. How do you know my name?"

"Signora Cappodanno! I'm so happy to find you at last. I have looked for days and this morning Signora Minelli...she stopped and asked me if I have been the one searching for you. I said yes, and she told me how to find you. I have news...from your son, Giancarlo." The mere sound of Giancarlo's name causes Assunta to quiver in anticipation. Hesitantly, she asks,

"You...you know Giancarlo? Is he...a...alive?" She stops breathing momentarily, clasping her hands over her mouth and awaiting the young man's answer,

"Yes, Signora. He is alive."

The incredible news overwhelms Assunta, causing her to tremble so she must sit on the lower step of the staircase to keep from collapsing. She weeps openly from the joy of knowing her son survives. Wiping the tears from her face, she stands once more and embraces the young man.

"Oh my God. Th...thank you...I'm so thrilled to know he is alive. You are a saint for traveling all this way to tell me this. Please, you must come in and rest. I have little food, but you are welcome to eat whatever there is. What is your name?"

"I am Tullio Cianetti. I'm on my way to Rome to find my family."

"Please, come.   Come with me, Tullio."   Leading him up the staircase, she thinks of many questions she wishes to ask him about Giancarlo. After inviting him into the apartment, she says,

"You must be very tired. Here, sit at the table and rest while I find you something to eat."

"Thank you Signora. You are most kind."   Returning to the table, she places a small plate before Tullio,

"I apologize for such a small meal, but food is difficult to find every day. This is some fresh fish and bread from my meal last night. You eat...Please."   Assunta watches Tullio eat the meager meal in slow, deliberate bites. It is obvious he has not eaten regularly and is enjoying every mouthful of this rare meal.   She cannot wait any longer, however, and while he continues to eat, she anxiously asks,

"Tullio, what can you tell me about my son?   Where is he? How did you meet him?"   The young man wipes his mouth with his hand, then rubs his hand on his coat before he answers.

"Giancarlo is a prisoner of war. He's being held at Ponte Olivio, in Sicily. There is an American airbase there. After the defeat in Africa, any Italian pilot who surrenders his plane to the Allies can live and work at the base until the war is over. The Americans treat him with the respect of an officer, and he is safe and healthy."

"He does not fly missions anymore?   God must be watching over him."

"Giancarlo has learned to speak very good English, and he interrogates other prisoners held at the base. He translates

282

information for the Americans. I was captured in North Africa and sent to Ponte Olivio. When Giancarlo spoke to me, he asked if I would be returning home when the base released the few prisoners held there. I told him I would, and he wrote your name on a piece of paper. He made me memorize it and then asked me to try to find you and tell you where he is. He is very sad over being held in Sicily and misses everyone dearly."

Antonella and Lucia are sleeping when the voice of a man in their apartment awakens them. Frightened by the presence of a stranger in their home, they nervously peer into the sitting room and see the bedraggled young man sitting with Assunta.

"Mama, who is this man. What is he doing here?" asks Antonella with concern.

"Antonella and Lucia, come here right away. I have wonderful news to share with you." The two girls join their mother and are introduced to Tullio,

"These are my daughters, Lucia and Antonella. Signor Cianetti has seen Giancarlo and informs us that...he's alive...and well. Our prayers have been answered, my children."

Antonella and Lucia cannot believe what they have just heard. Lucia excitedly claps her hands together and asks,

"Mama, are you sure? Dear God, please let it be true."

"Signor Cianetti met Giancarlo in Sicily. He is a prisoner at an American air base there." Overcome with joy by the long awaited

news of Giancarlo's whereabouts, tears fill Antonella's eyes. She holds Tullio's hand and says,

"We...we are so grateful to you for doing this. Thank you so very much, Signor Cianetti."

"I am happy to bring you such good news. It is very rare these days. Giancarlo made sure I was not mistreated before I was released, and I promised him I would to do this." Near total exhaustion, the young man rubs his eyes as a yawn overcomes him. Assunta says,

"You must be very tired. You can rest here safely for as long as you wish. My daughters will prepare my cot for you to sleep on."

"Thank you, Signora Cappodanno. You are very considerate." Antonella and Lucia prepare the small cot for the soldier to lie upon, and he quickly falls asleep for a much-needed rest.

Tullio sleeps soundly for several hours, awaking in the early afternoon. Sitting upright on the edge of the small cot, he looks around the room, and is slightly disoriented.

"You must have been very tired, Signor Cianetti. You slept for many hours," says Antonella.

"Yes, I have not slept so peacefully since leaving Sicily. I try to travel at night and rest during the day to avoid the Nazis, but it is difficult." Assunta and Lucia return to the apartment and join the conversation.

"Where will you go, Signor?" asks Lucia.

"I have a wife and baby in Rome. I must go there to find them. I'm worried because I have not received any letters from them for a long time."

"Tullio, you must be very careful. There have been many reports of torture and killings by the Nazis in Rome. It is terrible," warns Assunta.

"Thank you for worrying about me, Signora, but I, too, have heard the brutal stories and will avoid the Germans the best I can. But I must go." The sullen expression on his face foretells grim news. *"You must know that Napoli is in great danger. The Allies will be invading the mainland at any time, and the Germans will destroy everything to keep it from falling into their hands. Soon, there will be air raids and battles on your very streets. I have seen the Nazis preparing for this invasion, and many people will die. You must find some place safe to hide,"* warns Tullio.

Antonella, Lucia, and Assunta sit in silence after listening to the young soldier speak. But his warning comes as no surprise to the three women, for all of Napoli has expected such horror to visit their beautiful city. Tullio's personal experiences only confirm the rumors of the Italian surrender and the Allied invasion of Salerno.

"Mama, what will we do? Signor Cianetti cannot be mistaken," asks Lucia.

"I do not know what we will do, Lucia, but we must find somewhere to be safe before the invasion begins."

"It is almost nightfall, and I must leave, Signora. Thank you and your family for all your kindness. May God be with you in the days ahead."

"And with you too, Signor Cianetti. We will pray for you and your family," promises Antonella. Assunta hands him a small object wrapped in a faded towel.

"There is some bread to take with you on your journey. I wish I could offer you more, but I have nothing else to give." Tullio embraces each of the women before leaving and quickly vanishes into the night.

Accurate information regarding the war is rare in Napoli. With little else to go by, Antonella and her family take Tullio Cianetti's grave warnings seriously. In the days following his visit, Assunta begins to store water and what little food she has in any containers she can find, stacking them neatly on the table in their apartment. In the evening, Antonella asks,

"Are we to leave the apartment, Mama? What have you seen?"

"I have never seen so many ships in the harbor unloading troops and weapons. Everything Signor Cianetti told us is true. When the invasion begins, I'm afraid bombs will rain down on Napoli," answers Assunta.

"Mama, what will we do? We cannot stay here, can we?" Assunta stands before her two daughters and places her hands on their cheeks, saying,

"No, Antonella, we cannot. I have already stored candles and blankets in a small wine cellar under this building. It is well hidden, and I think we will be safe there. Help me carry this water and food there now, and I will show you how to get in."

Their arms loaded with their precious provisions, Antonella and Lucia follow their mother down the staircase and into a narrow alley behind the apartment. Located behind an abandoned produce cart is a badly-weathered wooden door. Assunta pulls it open, and after lighting a candle, proceeds down a narrow set of earthen steps to the bottom of a dark, foreboding passageway. The smell of human waste is overpowering. Piles of rusted barrel hoops and wine-stained boards litter the floor. Antonella stares at the tiny dungeon and asks,

"Mama, this place is so horrible. Is there nowhere else that we can go?"

"I know this is awful, but we'll be safe from the bombs here. I've placed our blankets and candles in a basket hidden in this corner. You and Lucia must know where it is in case you have to come here without me."

With the food and water carefully hidden away, the three women return to the apartment to await the inevitable. Antonella and Lucia find themselves constantly drawn to the window, searching both the street below and the skies above for the first signs of the fierce battle about to be fought before their eyes.

The sun has just dropped below the horizon on a warm September evening when sirens from within the Nazi compounds begin to wail. The three women rush to the window and see the night sky filled with racing beams of white lights coming from the German camps.

"I cannot see anything. Can you Lucia?" asks Antonella.

"No. Do you think the bombers are coming?"

"Wait. Listen...can you hear that? It's like the sound of far away thunder coming from over the ocean." Neighbors begin yelling and shouting to their families from the street below her window,

"Planes are coming! It's the bombers."

The muted drone of warplanes somewhere off the coast can now be clearly heard over the screams of terror and the shrieks of Nazi sirens. By now, all of Bagnoli has heard the same sounds, and many of the residents close to the harbor have begun running from the area in panic. Crowds of terror-stricken citizens run for the safety of the inland neighborhoods, leaving everything except whatever clothes they can carry. Assunta grabs Antonella and Lucia by the arms and says,

"It is the bombers. It can be nothing else. We must go to the cellar right now."

While running down the stairs, they hear a tremendous explosion rock the night, followed by a blinding white-orange flash that illuminates the black sky over the harbor. Lucia cries out in terror,

"Pl...please...we must hurry, before we are all killed."

With hands locked together, they dash through the alley and into the safety of the wine cellar. The first Allied bomb dropped on the terrified civilian population of Napoli is rapidly followed by dozens of more thunderous eruptions. Assunta lights a candle before closing the wine cellar door. She sees Antonella and Lucia trembling and crying. While terrified herself, she wraps her arms around them and says,

"We're safe here, my children. Let's all sit in the corner under that heavy beam until the bombs stop."

With only a single candle to illuminate the blackness, they huddle under the stout wooden beam as the very ground on which they sit begins to shudder all around them. Lucia removes the rosary from around her neck and begins to whisper in prayer,

"Our Father who art in heaven, hallowed be thy name..."

Antonella closes her eyes and covers her ears with her hands, but she cannot block out the report of anti-aircraft batteries, the wail of sirens, or the deafening sounds of exploding bombs. The thunderous blasts dislodge years of dust and debris from the overhead rafters, filling the air with a suffocating haze. To keep from breathing the foul air, Antonella covers her face with the hem of her dress, draping the coarse fabric tightly against her cheeks and forehead. She welcomes the total darkness, using it to try to escape from the living hell her family now endures. Then, without warning, she feels a sharp, scratching sensation, similar to the prick from one of her sewing needles, from something crawling across her exposed thigh. Looking down, she screams,

"A rat...On no, Mama, it's a rat...go...go away. Mama, help, please, Mama." Completely overcome by panic, she begins kicking violently at the beady-eyed rodent, while backing away on the palms of her hands. Jumping to her feet, she runs from one side of the cellar to the other.

"I...I can't st...stand this...I wish a bomb would just come and kill us all." She stands trembling in shock while watching her mother strike the rat with a heavy brick. Assunta takes her terrified daughter into her arms and holds her very tight.

"There, Antonella. It's dead. It will be all right now. You will see. It's going to be over soon."

The sounds of exploding bombs, anti aircraft-fire, and screams of fear and death fill the long night, as wave after wave of bombers delivers its deadly cargo on the harbor area. Antonella and her family cluster together until the morning light brings a temporary end to the destruction. After several hours of silence, they emerge from the sanctuary of the tiny wine cellar to see what remains of their beloved Napoli.

Assunta leads Antonella and Lucia by the hand out into the alleyway. The sky, once blue and pristine, is now filled with clouds of rancid smoke. The streets are choked with terrified residents from the harbor area, trying to return to whatever remains of their homes. Assunta's apartment building is spared serious damage, as is most of the surrounding neighborhood. The lack of sleep and constant state of terror exhaust Antonella.

"Mama. Do you think it is safe to sleep in my bed? I am so very tired."

"Yes. You and Lucia rest while we are able. I will stay awake to watch for the planes once again."

"Do...do you think they will come again, Mama?" asks Lucia.

"I think they will come until the Germans leave, Lucia."

Lucia begins to cry again at her mother's dire prediction. Assunta cradles her terrified daughters in her arms and leads them into their bedroom.

"Come. Try to sleep. You will feel better if you rest."

Antonella and Lucia huddle together on the bed they share and are soon asleep. Examining the apartment more closely as her daughters rest, Assunta finds cracked walls and several broken panes of glass in the windows, but very little serious damage. Standing before the window, she realizes how lucky her family is. She stares at the plumes of black smoke coming from the ruins of the harbor district.

Assunta sits in front of the window for hours, keeping a constant vigil for signs of another air raid. She, too, is exhausted and struggles to fight off the need to close her eyes and sleep. They have no food, and there is only a small amount of water left, and she knows they must leave the apartment before dark to search for supplies. Returning to the bedroom, she gently shakes Antonella and Lucia.

"Antonella? Lucia? You have to wake up. We must try to find some food before it gets dark. Come. We only have a few hours. Hurry."

"Yes, Mama. We will be ready in a few minutes," replies Antonella.

The three women leave the apartment and venture closer to the harbor area in search of something to eat. They do not travel far before encountering their first view of the devastation. The landscape resembles nothing they remember. Antonella stares at the hideous scenes of death and destruction.

"Oh dear God. Th...there is nothing left. Look Mama, all the trattorias and markets...they are gone."

"We must keep going, my children. Perhaps we can find fish near the beach. Hurry, we have little time." Moving closer to the ocean, they see that the damage is much more severe. Lucia covers her mouth with her hands and gasps,

"There...fl...floating in the water. I see dead soldiers...There are so many sunken ships...even the ocean is on fire." Antonella's favorite beach as a young girl is littered with oil and burning wreckage. Artillery bunkers built there by the Nazis, prime targets of the Allied raids, have been destroyed, and more dead or wounded German soldiers are everywhere.

But the Nazis are not the only casualties of the Allied bombs.

"Signora, signora. Can you please help me? My baby is buried under this rubble. I can hear him crying. Please, please help me," a desperate woman cries out to Assunta. The three women cannot ignore such pleas for help and rush over to the horrified stranger. Antonella asks,

"Where is your baby, Signora? Do you know?"

"He is under the wooden ceiling boards. Here...you can hear him screaming." Antonella climbs atop the pile of splintered timber and shouts,

"Here, Lucia. I will hand the boards to you. There are not too many. Hurry." Tearing away one board at a time, she slowly clears out an area near the sound of the crying child. Standing alongside the child's mother, they wrestle the heavier beams away from the collapsed building. The child's voice seems only inches away when the baby's mother shrieks in terror,

"Paulo. It's my Paulo."

Looking down, Antonella sees the body of a man impaled by the shredded, spear-like end of a fallen beam. Under him, she can see the baby's legs flailing wildly. The baby's mother crawls down to the bloody, lifeless body of her husband, screaming,

"He's dead...he's dead. They murdered my husband...oh God, we did nothing. Why? Why?"

Concerned for the baby, Antonella and Lucia try to ignore the gruesome discovery and help the distraught woman pull her child from beneath its dead father. The baby is bathed in blood but appears to have no major injuries. The terrified woman tries to wipe the child clean with her sweater. Dazed and disoriented by shock, she begins to wander off.

"I...I must f...find a doctor...Paulo must be helped." Assunta calls out,

"Signora, wait. There is nowhere to go. The city is destroyed." The woman pays little attention to Assunta and soon vanishes in the crowded streets. Antonella turns away from the destroyed building and feels dizzy and faint. She falls to her knees and whispers,

"I...I'm going to be sick."

She vomits violently after rescuing the baby from its dead father. The graphic violence of the first bombing raid on the once beautiful city totally overwhelms her senses, and she falls into a state of shock. Returning to the apartment, the three women are badly shaken by the brutality of the war they have just witnessed up close. In a matter of a few hours, the beautiful city in which they grew up has become a massive pile of rubble, stained with the blood of both its captors and its citizens. When Antonella walks into the apartment, she looks at her mother and says,

"Has the world gone mad, Mama?" Assunta hugs her daughters in an attempt to comfort them, but she cannot admit to Antonella that she is correct.

The bombing attacks become a nightly routine for several weeks. The shrill of the sirens, followed by the report of rapid-fire anti-aircraft guns, serves as the signal to return to the tiny wine cellar and pray the apartment will be spared once again. The air raids destroy the black market along with the city, making food and water even more difficult to find. Going without food for days at a time is commonplace, and starvation is a reality for many. Only a few wells remain safe to drink from, making daily trips to fill water containers more perilous as air raids now occur during daylight hours. Italian Partisans, remnants of Mussolini's defeated army, battle the Germans throughout Napoli. Gunfire is a daily occurrence, as the Germans concentrate on defending themselves long enough to move northward toward Rome. They plant hidden bombs and landmines throughout the city and destroy anything of value to the Allies. All of Napoli expects a fierce battle to be fought between the Allies and the fleeing Germans, and its residents seek out ways to keep from being caught in the crossfire. For Antonella and her family, there is nowhere to hide. They can only pray that they will be spared when the fighting begins.

Exhausted, both physically and mentally, the three women share the duties of watching and listening for signs of the impending invasion. As Assunta sleeps, Antonella and Lucia monitor the activity on the street below. Lucia asks,

"Antonella? Why do you think our neighborhood has not been destroyed by the bombs? Do you think it is a miracle?"

"I am not sure, Lucia. But, I think God has spared us for a reason."

"Do you think the fighting will end when the Allies come?"

"I pray every night that it will. It must. We cannot survive like this for very long. Mama has lost so much weight. Have you noticed? She looks so tired. I am so worried about her."

"We must let her rest as much as possible. That's the best way we can help her."

The bombing raids lessen considerably in the ensuing weeks, with only an occasional daylight attack taking place in the south near Salerno. An uneasy quiet falls over Napoli as rumors on the street have the Allies very close to their city. Sitting at the bottom of the apartment stairway, Antonella hears the increased popping of gunfire coming from the harbor. The telltale report of machine guns, the crisp crack of hand grenades and the powerful detonation of fifty-millimeter tank guns all grow steadily louder. She notices Theresa Minelli dashing past the apartment.

"Signora Minelli, Signora Minelli. It is Antonella Cappodanno. Have you any news? Why is there so much shooting in the south?" Theresa Minelli hurries over to Antonella. Her expression is a mix of fear and excitement. Hugging Antonella, she anxiously explains,

"You've not heard? The English and Americans have taken Salerno and are moving into Napoli this very moment. The invasion has started. You must stay off the streets. Tell Assunta, please. I

must go. God bless you, my child." Antonella rushes up the stairway and into the apartment, shouting,

"Mama. Lucia. I just talked with Signora Minelli. She says the Allies have invaded Salerno and are moving into Napoli. I can hear the guns and the fighting in the south. What shall we do, Mama? Will we hide in the wine cellar once more?"

"Yes. It is the safest place. Hurry and gather some blankets and clothing."

The sound of fighting grows louder by the hour, and soon the first wave of fleeing Germans passes through the neighborhood. The three women return to the dark, hidden space that has become so familiar to them.

"Quickly, my children. I must close the door." Antonella's paranoia over the rats in the cellar drives her to the edge of panic.

"Mama, pl...please light a candle. Hurry. I am so afraid of the dark in here." Terrorized by the impending battle and her fear of the rat infested cellar, Antonella nervously runs her hands through her hair and paces about the secluded bunker watching out for any further signs of rodents.

"Antonella, please sit with me. I'll make sure no rats touch you again," pleads Lucia.

Distraught and crying, Antonella finally collapses next to Lucia, who takes her into her arms and rocks her gently to sleep.

They hear more Germans moving past the apartment in trucks and tanks.

"Unterhaltbewegen. Die Verbündeten sind hier in einem Stoff von Stunden," shouts a Nazis only a few yards from the cellar.

"*Shhhh...*" whispers Assunta, holding her finger to her lips. A burst of machine gun fire, followed by increased shouting by the Nazis, bring the fighting to the street directly in front of the apartment. The shooting rages on for hours, but the windowless cellar provides no clue to what is really taking place. After an extended period of calm, Assunta says,

"*I must find out what has happened. I want to look on the street and see if the Germans have gone. Wait here quietly.*"

"*Mama, wait. Don't go. It's not safe yet,*" pleads Lucia.

"*I am in no danger as long as the shooting has stopped. I will only look on the street and return.*"

Assunta gently eases open the door of the wine cellar and looks for any soldiers in the alleyway. Seeing none, she proceeds to a corner of the apartment and checks the deserted street for the presence of Nazi troops. At the farthest end of the street, a German tank sits with its guns pointed in the direction of the harbor. Ground troops cluster behind it and begin to exchange gunfire with approaching Allied forces. She runs back to the cellar and tells her daughters,

"*It's the Allies. They are fighting with Germans on our very street. We must stay hidden.*"

Of all the frightening events Antonella and her family have endured, being so close to actual combat is the most terrifying since the encounter with the Cossack. The pinging sounds of ricocheting

298

bullets and shrapnel bombard the buildings all around. The three frightened women sit in the corner furthest from the door and hold each other's trembling hands. They wait for any sign that the Germans have been forced out of the neighborhood. Once again, they hear shooting only a few feet from their hiding place, but this time a different voice shouts out orders.

"Watch yourself moving through these buildings. These Jerry bastards are leavin booby traps all over the goddamn place."

"Mama, they speak English. They're Americans. Oh God, at last. The Allies are here," whispers Antonella.

"Yes, it sounds like Americans, but we cannot go out there yet. It is still too dangerous. We will wait until the shooting stops."

The Germans and the Allies remain locked in a brutal struggle to control the area for many more hours, often exchanging fire only a few feet from the battered door of the winecellar. Slowly, the gunfire subsides, and the only voices they hear in the area are those speaking English. After the fiercest battles gradually move to the north, Antonella and her family cautiously proceed to the war-torn street once again. Destroyed tanks and trucks are everywhere. Antonella, Lucia and Assunta move through carnage, as frantic American medics shout,

"Stand back. Stand back. Ya gotta get out of the way. We got some wounded men here who need a lot of help."

The sight of several German soldiers lying dead inside a small alcove only a few buildings from the apartment stuns Antonella.

Their bullet-riddled bodies lie in contorted positions, surrounded by pools of their own blood.

"I've never imagined it to be so bloody and ruthless," she confesses. Casualties are everywhere, and the British and American forces continue to pour into the destroyed city to tend to their dead and wounded. Assunta has seen enough and says,

"The Nazis are gone now. We will welcome the Allies after they take care of their wounded. Let's return to the apartment."

The months of bombings and weeks of street warfare have left the city and harbor in total ruins. There is no power or water, and food shortages plague everyone. But even now, from amid the ruins of the most horrible experience her family has ever known, Antonella's long-absent optimism begins to rekindle itself. Believing the worst is over, she is thankful her family survives. Knowing Giancarlo is alive and that he will return home someday buoys her spirits and lifts her heart. With thousands of Allied troops pouring into the city to Napoli, the local citizens line the streets to celebrate their arrival. Antonella, Lucia, and Assunta join in the jubilation, joyfully laboring to find English words to express their gratitude.

"Grazie, l'Americanos. Tanka you, G.I.s," shout Antonella and Lucia. The awkward-sounding words cause them to laugh out loud for the first time since their nightmare began so many months ago.

The task of rebuilding the shattered city begins immediately. The Allies, joined by local Partisans, begin to restore essential services to Napoli. They rebuild power stations; using generators from damaged ships in the harbor, they soon repair water supply aqueducts and clear major roads, allowing trucks and some buses to operate once more. They clear the decimated harbor, and soon dozens of supply ships begin delivering urgently needed food and medical supplies. In spite of the improvements, providing food and shelter to the many homeless citizens remains difficult. The black market re-emerges as an even greater force in the war-ravaged economy, and prostitution flourishes as desperate women do whatever they must to simply survive. The most terrifying German legacy left behind, however, are the land mines and explosive booby traps planted throughout the city. Allied troops spend much of their time finding and removing these deadly hazards, but the extremely dangerous work moves slowly and at a great cost.

"Mama, maybe Giancarlo has written letters to us now that the Nazis are gone. What do you think?" asks Antonella.

"I am sure he would write if he could. You know your brother is very concerned about you and Lucia."

"And you too, Mama." Assunta smiles at Antonella's touching comment and says,

"Perhaps, if you check at the post office, you can see if any letters have arrived with our names on them."

"Antonella, why don't you and I go there this afternoon?" suggests Lucia. Antonella is anxious to leave the boredom of the apartment for any reason.

"Yes, that's an excellent idea, Lucia."

The outing to the post office reveals that the areas of the city away from the harbor have escaped serious damage during the air raids. The women even discover that several small markets selling fruits and vegetables have reopened.

"Oh look, Lucia. Fresh tomatoes. How I would love to have caprese again. Do you remember when we would steal Papa's caprese at the trattorias?" Antonella comments wistfully.

"Yes, of course I do, Antonella. But you know we have no money for such luxuries. We must go." But Antonella is in no hurry. She explores the market as if it is the first time she's shopped.

"Antonella, please. We must leave before it gets too late. You know how Mama worries when we are not home before dark." After much prodding, they are on their way again. A short time later, Antonella asks,

"Lucia, are you sure you know where the post office is located? We have been walking for a long time."

"I'm very sure it is only a few more blocks. We will be..."

Lucia's comment is interrupted by the sound of a horrendous explosion heard a short distance before them. They instinctively jump into a nearby doorway and stand frozen in terror.

"Lucia, what could that be? Do...do you think the...the bombing has started once again?"

"I don't know. Let's wait here until the soldiers arrive."

They soon hear blaring ambulance sirens, and armed troops rush past them in the direction of the explosion. Slowly regaining her courage, Antonella says,

"Come, Lucia. With all the Americans there, it should be safe to go see what has happened." Mindfully following the soldiers at a safe distance, they round the next corner but are abruptly stopped by hordes of screaming medics and military police.

"Get going...now. This area is dangerous. There could be more booby traps around here," shouts one of the men as he turns and directs his attention back to the disaster.

Unable to understand what the man has said, Antonella and Lucia stare at the dozens of dead and wounded victims of the massive Nazi booby trap who lie directly in front of them. Injured soldiers and civilians cry out for help, as medics arrive to care for those still alive. The force of the violent explosion has dismembered many of the dead. The gruesome scene sickens the two sisters. Lucia grabs Antonella and says,

"Antonella...oh dear God. That building? It...it is the post office...the one we are looking for...I think I'm going to be sick. We must go." They hold hands and begin running away from the bloody disaster until their lungs burn from gasping for air. Stopping to catch her breath, Lucia looks at her sister and says,

"Antonella, if...if you had not stopped to look at the tomatoes...in that little market, we...we would have been in that post

office." Antonella begins trembling and crying at the thought of nearly dying. Lucia holds her in her arms and says,

"We are not hurt, Antonella. A guardian angel watches over our family." Antonella holds her sister tightly and whispers,

"It's Papa, Lucia. It's Papa who protects us." Returning to the apartment, they tell their mother nothing of the brutal scene they have just witnessed. To keep her from being needlessly upset, all they say is that the post office was not open for business.

In the months following the Allied invasion, Napoli slowly returns to normal. Greatly influenced by the free-spending Americans, cafes and tratorrias open to serve their craving for good food. The local fishermen, once again, sell the daily catch on the wharfs near the ocean, and farmers bring their produce to the weekly open-air markets scattered about the city. Babies are being born once again, and Assunta finds her midwife skills in great demand, enabling her to provide food and other essentials for the family. While she works, Antonella and Lucia make the daily trips to the market to do the shopping. On their way, they meet Theresa Minelli.

"Boun Giorno, Signora Minelli," exclaims Lucia. While the women exchange friendly hugs, Theresa says,

"How beautiful you two girls look. It's very nice to see you. How is your mother?"

"She is well. She keeps busy delivering babies again, you know," answers Antonella with a giggle.

"Ah, that's a good sign," admits Theresa, laughing. *"Have you heard from Giancarlo? Do you know how he is?"*

"Only that he is in Sicily. That is what the young soldier told us several months ago," answers Antonella.

"I'm sure you are happy to know he is well. He will be home soon; you shall see."

"We are hopeful, Signora Minelli. We miss him very much," replies Lucia. Reaching into a large tote bag she is carrying, Theresa pulls out a torn dress, holds it up in front of Antonella, and asks,

"Antonella, can you repair this dress for me? I will pay you whatever you want. New clothes are impossible to find, you know." Examining the garment, Antonella excitedly answers,

"Yes, of course I will repair it for you, but you don't need to pay me. We already owe you so much for your kind generosity."

"Oh nonsense, my child. I know of your incredible talent. I am grateful that you are willing to do this for me." The thought of sewing once again excites Antonella. She takes the dress.

"I will return it in two days. Is that soon enough, Signora?"

"Yes, of course, my dear. I must go now. Please kiss your mother for me and tell her I said hello, will you?" she asks as she hurries away.

"We promise we will, Signora Minelli. Thank you once again," answers Antonella.

The request to make a simple repair re-ignites her dormant creativity. She grabs Lucia by the hand and begins running and shouting,

"We must hurry back to the apartment, Lucia. I have to sew again." Repairing Theresa Minelli's torn dress is a far simpler task than creating one of her beautiful gowns, but the opportunity to sew and work once again renews her spirit. Returning to the apartment, she asks her sister,

"Lucia, will you help me find my sewing machine? It is buried beneath the small dresser in the bedroom."

They spend the next several hours pulling it from storage and examining it to make sure it still operates. After unpacking it from its case, Antonella spins the big flywheel on the end to test its operation. The machine spins freely and purrs with a familiar tone, indicating it is in good working order. Standing in the middle of the apartment with her hands on her hips, Antonella slowly studies the room to find the best possible location to set it up.

"There, Lucia...by the window. The light is good and I can watch people on the street while I work." Lucia helps her position the sewing machine where her sister wants it.

"I promised Mama I would prepare our dinner tonight, so you will have to finish this by yourself,"

Antonella sits before the machine for the first time in two years and is eager to explore her talents once again. For now, however, she is satisfied to make the minor repairs for Signora

Minelli. The pumping motion of its foot-operated pedal powers the fine, old machine. Testing its performance, Antonella finds it, too, still works smoothly and effortlessly. She has no fabric and very little thread, but she begins to mend Theresa's dress by cleverly removing fabric from hidden areas, using them to fashion an almost invisible repair. Finishing the work in a matter of hours, she hungers for more to do and searches through her sister's and mother's clothing for anything needing repair. The window near the street not only provides the best light to work, but it also creates many opportunities for Antonella to attract new customers.

"Signorita, do you take repair work? I have many shirts to be fixed," asks a stranger passing on the street below.

"Yes, of course. You may bring them by any time," she cheerfully responds.

New clothing of any kind is rare in Napoli, and soon many customers seek out Antonella's talent to make repairs. She attracts enough work to keep herself busy for several days a week, trading her services for food and sewing supplies. She loves the wonderful feeling of working with her hands and exploring her creativity again, even if it is only to make simple repairs on worn-out garments. As the images of the death and destruction caused by the war slowly recede, her beautiful voice again sings arias from *La Traviata*, her favorite opera while she works. For Antonella, the opportunity to sew again suggests the end of the terrible war that has stolen much of her life and destroyed her city. She prays she will never have to stop sewing again.

The need for Assunta's services as a midwife increases significantly, as many Italian soldiers return to Napoli. She delivers several babies a week, often traveling to distant areas of Napoli on the few city buses that have been put back into service. Assunta makes the long journey to Pomigliano D'Arco, a small city on the western outskirts of Napoli, to help with yet another birth. While eating her lunch in a nearby park, she visits a small market in hopes of finding some fresh fruit to bring home.

"Can I help you Signora?" inquires the proprietor.

"I had hoped to find some pears or peaches to take home, but I see you do not have any."

"I have more in the back if you want some. I do not put them all out at one time or the Americans from the base will take them all. My customers get very angry with me then."

"That is very kind of you. I will take two or three pears and peaches if you have them." The storeowner vanishes into the back of his tiny market and returns with the fruit.

"These are very nice. I know they are delicious. I ate one for my lunch. I usually save them for one of the Americans at the base. He works in the post office there and speaks Italian. He is a very nice man."

"A post office? There is a post office near here?" inquires Assunta with growing interest.

"Yes, Signora, it is near the base, only a few blocks from here."

"Thank you for the wonderful fruit. My children will enjoy it very much."

She scours the area for almost an hour and finally locates a small, tin-sided hut near the entrance to the Allied camp. She hesitantly enters the building, when an American soldier asks,

"Can I help you, Senora?" Unable to understand him, Assunta replies,

"I'm sorry. I don't speak English. Can you speak Italian?" They stare at each other in a moment of awkward silence when another man enters the room.

"I'll take care of this, Andy," he tells the soldier. Then turning to Assunta, he says,

"My name is Private Carravelli, Signora. This is a military post office, not a civilian one. What is it you want here?"

"You speak Italian. The owner of the fruit market near here said one of the Americans speaks Italian." Reaching into her handbag, she pulls out a letter written to Giancarlo. She has carried it with her since the young soldier told her where her son was a prisoner. She hands the letter to Private Carravelli.

"My son is an Italian pilot who surrendered his plane and is at the Ponte Olivio airfield in Sicily. I have not heard from him for many months. Is it possible to send him that letter?"

The private stares at the letter for a moment and lifts his eyes to look as Assunta. He sees desperation in her expression and cannot turn away from it.

"Your son's name is Giancarlo Cappodanno? Are your certain he is at Ponte Olivio?"

"I learned he is there from a soldier who spoke to him. That is all I know," she says with renewed hope in her voice. He steps from behind the desk and moves closer to her. In a lowered voice, he says,

"It's against military policy to take civilian mail, but I know where this base is and I send mailbags there all the time. I'll try and get this letter to him. If you come back in a week, I can tell you if he has received it." Private Carravelli's generosity brings Assunta to tears. Taking his hand into hers, she says,

"You...you are a very kind man for doing this, Signor Carravelli. I...I don't know how to properly thank you." Wanting desperately to show her gratitude, she takes a large pear from her handbag and offers it to him.

"Please take this. The owner of the market told me you enjoy his fruit. I want you to have it. It's the only way I know how to repay your kindness." The private smiles and graciously takes the pear from her.

"This is not necessary, Signora, but I will enjoy it very much. Thank you." She shakes his hand once again and begins her lengthy trip home, hoping for a miracle.

The following week passes slowly, but the time has come for Assunta to return to the post office and check on her letter. The arduous bus ride takes almost two hours to travel from Bagnoli to Pomigliano D'Arco. She constantly wrings her hands together to fight off the increasing anxiety and tension she is feeling. After stepping from the bus, she walks the short three blocks to the post office. Entering, she sees Private Carravelli is not there. She immediately asks the attending soldier,

"Private Carravelli, per favor." He steps into the next room and, a few moments later, the private steps out. A wide smile on his face encourages Assunta.

"Boun giorno, Signora Cappodanno. I have some very good news for you. Your son has received your letter." Assunta feels a tremendous sense of relief and happiness over the joyous news. Tears well up in her eyes once again, as the private continues,

"I have a letter from him." Assunta trembles with emotion as she holds the letter from Giancarlo in her hand. With tears streaming down her cheeks, she hugs the private.

"Thank you signor, thank you. This is wonderful." He guides her to a bench in a quiet corner of the office.

"You can sit here and read the letter if you want. No one will bother you."

311

"Thank you, again." Her excitement makes it difficult for her to open the letter.

"Please let me help, Signora." He takes the letter from her, carefully slits open the edge with his pocketknife and hands it back to her. *"I'll be in the other room if you need me, Signora."*

Her heart pounds with anticipation as she prepares to read Giancarlo's first letter in over a year.

> *Mother dearest,*
> *I am so happy to hear from you. When your letter came telling me you are all alive, I cried with relief. I have lived in terror for the last twelve months not knowing if you and my sisters survived the German occupation, air raids, and battles in Napoli. It must have been horrible for you. I wanted so desperately to come home, but as a prisoner of war, I could not leave. Please forgive me for not being there during such terrible times. I will forever feel like I deserted all of you. I hate this war, and I am thankful it is almost over. I have had to do some terrible things during this awful time, and I will never forget them. I know I was responsible for killing innocent people. That is such a terrible truth to carry with me for the rest of my life. I hope I will never have to hurt anyone again. The Allies have treated me well, and I have been given a clean place in which to live. I miss you all very much. I look forward to coming home soon. I have been told that, when the Allies hold all of Italy, they will release us and help us return to our families. I am not sure when that will be, so we must wait for a little while longer. I am sure this hell will end soon. Please tell Antonella and Lucia I love them and miss them deeply and I will be home at my first opportunity. You must all remain*

careful, for there are still many dangers all around. Please write again soon.

Your loving son,
Giancarlo

Sitting motionless, Assunta can only stare at Giancarlo's letter in disbelief. He is truly alive and will return home some day soon. She realizes the war is over for her entire family and they have all survived this barbaric invasion of their lives. Clutching the letter to her breast, she feels as if a great weight has been lifted from her shoulders. She can, again, think of the future and what might be. She dreams of someday having grandchildren, now that her children's lives have been returned to them. She slowly rises from the bench, hugs Private Carravelli, and returns home to share Giancarlo's letter with Antonella and Lucia. Her family has a future again, but her sorrow is not yet over.

CHAPTER 13

"Son of a bitch! I'm gettin tired of packin up all this goddamn gear over and over again," moans Frankie.

"Aw, shut up will ya? All ya been doin lately is cryin about every goddamn little thing that pisses ya off. Just keep packin those floor jacks and get em ready ta go," growls Hank.

"Look at it like this, Frankie. Maybe this time, we'll get out of this shit hole of a country," adds Mario.

The process of moving the repair center, a routine now dreaded by Mario and his crewmates, is well underway. Knowing they may finally be getting out of the desert has them overly anxious and edgy. In the midst of the moving preparations, Sergeant Thompson enters the board-sided tent housing the repair center. Looking at the progress being made by the four men, he smiles and says,

"Well, I don't know about you guys, but I've had enough of this desert sand, bugs, and heat sores."

"Come on Sarge, you know somethin, don't ya? Where we goin?" asks Mario pressing him for more information.

"Yeah, I'll go anyplace ya want me to right now. Jus git me outta this goddamn desert," shouts Frankie.

"The brass tells me Patton and Montgomery have kicked Jerry out of Sicily and are pushing him north to the mainland. Once the company is ready, we're going to a port city in Tunisia called Bizerta. A Navy transport is waiting there to take us to Palermo. I want to get going no later than tomorrow morning, so work all night if you have to," instructs the sergeant.

"I'll have this shit ready tonight. I cain't wait ta git goin," squeals Frankie.

"Don't get too excited, Frankie. There's a lot of work waiting for us there. The combat boys had a pretty tough time and broke a lot of equipment that has to get fixed right away," warns the Sergeant. He then looks at Mario.

"I've been told you speak pretty good Italian, Mario. Is that true?"

"Hell yeah, he does. Ya shoulda heard em orderin dinner for us that one time in Trenton," blurts out Frankie.

"For Christ sake, Frankie, will ya shut up for a second and let the man answer the question?" gripes Hank. Frankie shoots Hank an indignant scowl, as Mario says,

"I do speak some Italian, Sarge. I learned it from my old man. He's from Sicily. Why do you wanna know?"

"When we get there, I want you to help me talk to the locals. We'll be needing information, and you're going to help to translate."

"Sure, Sarge. I'll be glad to help. Anything to get away from these guys for a while."

"So, do you have family in Sicily?"

"Yeah, in a small city called Catania, I think. My old man used to talk about em when the war broke out in Europe."

"Be nice if you could find them, wouldn't it?"

"Yeah, I'd like that. My old man would get really excited about it, but I don't have any idea where they are."

"Well, who knows? Maybe you'll get lucky and run into one of them by accident. Meantime, you guys get ready to go. I'll be back in a few hours to assign trucks for loading up the gear."

The well-rehearsed drill goes smoothly, and Company A is heading for the coast before sunrise. When they arrive in Bizerta, the scene is reminiscent of the previous boarding in New York, except the ship is much less luxurious. Hundreds of vehicles are staged on the docks for loading into the cavernous storage hold of the transport. More waiting, more shouting of instructions by M.P.'s and more boredom, this becomes the pattern for the day as debarkation is a painfully long ordeal. The company's equipment is, at last, loaded aboard the ship. Following an agonizing afternoon in the intense heat, the men are allowed to board the ship. Soon, tugs begin to guide the vessel from the harbor, and the ship's engines begin powering up. As the Mediterranean distances them from the shore, Mario and his buddies stand on deck and gratefully watch the North African desert slowly disappear below the horizon.

The rugged, mountainous outline of Sicily is clearly visible on the horizon the next morning. Standing alone on deck, Mario is struck by the incredible beauty of snow-capped mountains surrounded by the deep, blue waters of the ocean. He's never truly experienced a family connection to this place, but seeing it this morning gives him an unexpected chill and strange sense of homecoming. Mesmerized by the moment and in awe at the thought of soon standing on his father's homeland, his trance-like behavior blocks out everything around him for a short time.

"So that's where your family is from, huh?" asks George, after joining him on deck.

Surprised by George's presence, Mario is a little embarrassed at being caught daydreaming. He quickly collects his thoughts.

"Oh, it's you George. Yeah, I never thought I'd ever get a chance to see it, but there it is. This war is full of surprises, ain't it?"

"Sure is. I never thought I'd get out of Iowa, let alone travel halfway around the world. This is really something, Mario."

The pulsing vibration of the ship's powerful engines fade rapidly as the transport is intercepted by Navy tugs. After the tugs guide it into the dock, Mario gets his first look at Palermo. Signs of heavy fighting are everywhere. Sunken landing craft litter the beach, and many buildings in the immediate area are heavily damaged. Abandoned German tanks and artillery sit alongside destroyed machine-gun bunkers up and down the beach. Large bomb craters are visible on the main roads leading into the harbor. The evidence left behind is proof enough for Mario that the fighting was severe. He's again reminded of how fortunate he is not to be in the combat zones.

"Once everyone is off the ship, find someplace along the dock and wait there for the trucks to be unloaded. Stay together," shouts Sergeant Thompson, as he moves through the company. The deckhands lower the gangplank, and men begin filing from the ship. Company A congregates on a small roadway just off the harbor wall. Mario's attention is immediately directed to several elderly men nearby, who are engaged in a heated argument.

"Siete pazzesco," shouts one man.

"I am not crazy. You don't know what you talk about. It's the Americans who will win this war, not the British," argues the other.

For Mario, listening to the men scream at one another in Italian reminds him of the many arguments he's heard at his father's card games. He continues to stare at them when one of them notices he is watching.

"Look. You yell so loud, the Americans there, they can hear you," says one of the Sicilians to the other. Mario cannot resist the temptation to jump into the discussion.

"Your friend is right, Signor. The Americans are going to win this war." The two Sicilians stop arguing and look at Mario with sudden interest.

"Where do you learn to speak Italian, Signor?" one of them asks.

"My father is Sicilian, and I learned to speak from him." Listening to Mario's conversation, Frankie, George, and Hank are dying to know what's being said. Hank asks,

"Mario, what the hell do they want? Do you know what they're saying?"

"It's ok. They just wanna know how I learned to speak Italian, that's all."

"What is your name, Signor?" asks one of the Sicilians.

"Mario Carlucci. Do you know any Carluccis?" The two men consider the question for a moment, then one of them says,

"There are Carluccis on the other side of the island, near Mt. Etna, but I know of none in Palermo." Mario is disappointed but not surprised by their answer. He knows the odds of finding any family by chance are very remote, but he feels compelled to try.

"Signor Carlucci, please excuse us for not introducing ourselves. I am Luigi Messe, and this is Ugo Graziani."

"I'm happy to meet you," replies Mario, as he shakes their hands.

"Where do you live in America?" asks Luigi.

319

"In Detroit. Do you know where that is?" answers Mario. Ugo's face lights up with a wide grin, and he answers in very limited English,

"Ah, Detroit. I knowa Detriot. I spenda sixa yeahr ina Pittsburgh. You knowa Pittsburgh, Mario?"

"You speak good English, Ugo. I know Pittsburgh."

"Mario, when you have time, you come to the little trattoria at the end of the harbor road. I have some wine the Germans did not find, and we will drink and talk again. Yes?" asks Luigi.

"Yes, of course. I'd like that very much." Frankie, George and Hank continue to listen with growing curiosity. Frankie is again impressed with Mario's Italian and asks,

"Come on, Mario. We ain't been here no more then twenty minutes, and you already makin friends with them Sicilians. What in blue Jesus did ya say to em?"

"I just introduced myself, that's all. They sure are friendly enough, too. They invited me to have some wine with them in a little trattoria down the road. This ain't North Africa, that's for goddamn sure."

Speaking to the Sicilians in their own language is one of the most pleasant moments of the war for Mario. They seem eager to please, and Mario looks forward to spending more time talking to them. Sergeant Thompson arrives after the company has fully assembled and provides instructions on what will happen next.

"Let's pay attention here. Our new bivouac area is located right next to the airstrip at the edge of town. It's in an almond grove of all places, and I'm told it's a short ride from here. When the trucks come ashore, we'll set up operations there. The C.O. says we're going to be moving east, toward Messina, when we finish all the work here. After that, it's on to the mainland to mop up after the invasion."

The company breaks into its regular work groups. Mario and the repair crew await the trucks containing their equipment when Sergeant Thompson calls out to him,

"Mario, I need your help. Can I see you for a minute?"

"Sure, Sarge. What's the trouble?"

"No trouble really, but you're not going to be working in the repair center for a while. The C.O. says we have to find some of our own chow. I guess there's fresh produce available from the farmers in the hills-you know, stuff like tomatoes, radishes, and even lettuce. Since you speak the lingo, I want you to find out where we can buy some. Grab a Jeep or a truck and start nosin around as soon as we get to the airstrip."

"You got it, Sarge. I'll get right on it. I already met a coupla old guys a little while ago. I'll bet they can help me find some provisions."

After the trucks roll from the cargo bay of the transport ship, the men load their duffel bags and climb aboard for the short trip to the new camp area. Rolling into the airstrip, the company finds several rows of barracks tents and a large, hard-roofed pavilion containing damaged trucks and personnel carriers. The repair center is operational within a matter of hours, and the company settles down to the business of cleaning up the combat-damaged gear.

The next day, Mario hunts through the collection of badly damaged trucks and Jeeps, looking for something that will run. Finding a Jeep with several flat tires, he climbs into the driver's seat and pushes the ignition switch. The engine cranks over repeatedly but shows no signs of starting. Mario pumps the gas peddle several more times and tries again, this time finding himself shrouded in a cloud of blue exhaust fumes as the battered machine rumbles to life. Satisfied that the Jeep runs, he replaces the flat tires with good ones, cannibalized from another vehicle, and drives it back to the bivouac area. Spotting Sergeant Thompson in front of his tent, Mario brings the Jeep to a sliding stop. He jumps out.

"I found this old bucket of bolts in the back of the pavilion and got it to run, so I'm goin into Palermo to find some chow, like ya asked."

"That's good, Mario. These guys will give you a month's pay if you bring back some fresh food. Whatever you find, have it delivered to the mess tent, and we'll pay em cash. And be careful. Some areas haven't been cleared for landmines yet, so stay on the main roads."

Mario returns to Palermo. Inching along the rubble-filled street near the harbor, he studies each building carefully as he passes. He snakes the Jeep around abandoned trucks and carts in search of the two Sicilian men he met the day before. Nearing the end of the street, he sees an old building with an ochre-colored façade and dark green shutters. There are three small tables located in front of it, and two men are sitting at one of them. Mario recognizes Ugo and Luigi lounging in the warm late-morning sun. They have been watching the Jeep make its way along the road for some time, and when they see Mario, Luigi shouts,

"Bouno giorno, Signor Carlucci. Benvenuto." Raising his arm and waving, Mario says,

"Ciao, Luigi e Ugo. Come sta?" Mario parks the Jeep, joins the two men at the table, and shakes their hands.

"Mario, the Sicilian from America," exclaims Luigi with a roar of laughter.

"It is good to see you today, Mario. Will you drink some wine with us?" asks Ugo.

"Of course. I'm honored to drink some of your wine. I came from North Africa, and I haven't drunk any wine for over a year."

"That's not good. You must drink a little wine every day. It's good for the blood. Look at me, I'm seventy-seven years old, and I drink a glass every day," brags Ugo.

"Ugo, you old fool. You drink a bottle of wine every day, not a glass," adds Luigi in another fit of laughter.

"Are you going to bring our guest some wine or are you going to talk all day?"

"Yes, yes. Rosa will bring us a bottle. Rosa, Rosa, please come here, my dear." He leans over to Mario and winks.

"Rosa's my niece. She's a nice girl and is very curious about America. Maybe a handsome, young man like you can tell her what the U.S. is like." Luigi's subtle matchmaking hint does not go unnoticed by Mario, and he politely smiles but says nothing. Moments later, Rosa arrives at the table. Luigi flashes a broad grin.

"Rosa, this is Signor Carlucci. He is Sicilian and lives in Detroit. In America. We want a bottle of good Chianti to welcome Mario to Sicily." Rosa extends her hand to Mario.

"It's so nice to meet an American who speaks Italian, Signor Carlucci. I'll go find a bottle of excellent wine."

Rosa is a pretty girl in her late teens. She is wearing an old, summer dress and has a simple scarf tied around her head. She appears older than she really is. A white apron, stained with the wine and sauce of many meals, hides the frayed edges of her clothes. Her full, round figure and shapely legs remind Mario of how long it's been since he last slept with a woman. Returning with a gallon-sized jug of wine, Rosa sits at the table and begins to pour Mario several glasses of the homemade Chianti.

"Luigi, this is delicious. Do you make this yourself?" he asks.

"Yes. Here, drink some more," replies Luigi, pouring another tasty glassful for Mario.

Mario is deeply touched at the kindness shown to him by Luigi and Ugo. They treat him as if he is one of their own sons returning home. The strong wine quickly relaxes him and, for a short time, he is able to forget there is a war on. He spends the next several hours telling them of his family and his life in America. Rosa asks about the fashions, the music, and the movies. Her questions never end, and Mario is delighted to have the company of a friendly girl for a change. It is quickly mid-afternoon, and Mario remembers his mission. He asks Ugo and Luigi,

"I want to buy some fresh produce for the camp. Do you know where I can find some?"

"Ah, Mario that's simple. My cousin has a farm in the hills, and he brings me fresh vegetables every week. He even has half of a cow if you want it. Tell me what you need, and I will have him bring it to you," says Ugo.

"I'll buy anything he can deliver to the airbase, including the cow."

"I will see that he goes to the base tomorrow," says Ugo.

"You are very kind to help me like this. How can I repay you?"

"You can bring some of your friends here to eat dinner tonight. I'll make you a wonderful meal for very little money. Is that fair?" asks Luigi.

"That's fair, Luigi, that's very fair. I'll be back here tonight at about 8:30 with three of my friends."

"Oh, how exciting. We can have a party," exclaims Rosa with a flirtatious glance.

Preparing to return to the base, Mario thanks his new friends for their hospitality and climbs into the Jeep. He cannot recall being treated with more respect than this. Being Sicilian has never been very important to him, but he begins to understand why his father was always so proud of this place.

After returning to the camp, Mario tracks down Sergeant Thompson.

"Sarge, I got some good news. You remember the two old guys I met at the pier yesterday? One of em has a cousin with a farm, and he's gonna have em deliver some food tomorrow. Hell, he might even have some fresh beef."

"That's terrific, Mario. If the guy shows up with steaks, we're liable to give you that job permanently."

"Ugo and Luigi, those are their names, they invited me back for dinner later. Do ya mind if I go and take the other guys with me?"

"No, I don't mind. The guys have been working their asses off lately and can use a break. Just stay away from any German warehouses." Mario cracks a slight smile at the reference to the North African flag incident.

"You can bet on that, Sarge. We don't want anyone from our squad gettin into any trouble, now, do we?"

"No. We don't," replies the sergeant with a laugh. Mario rushes back to his barracks tent and finds Hank resting on his cot.

"Go get yourself cleaned up; we're going into Palermo."

"What the hell for? I just got done fixin some busted up ole truck, and I'm tired," replies Hank.

"Look, I got us invited to a small restaurant for some home-cooked chow and great wine. But if ya don't wanna go…"

"Whoa…I didn't say that," says Hank, scrambling from his cot.

"I'm goin to tell Frankie and George. We'll leave as soon as you guys are ready."

A few hours later, the four friends return to Palermo. Mario leads them into the trattoria, where Rosa greets him with a friendly hug.

"Buono sera, Mario."

"Hello, Rosa. How are you tonight?"

"I'm very glad you came back. Are these your friends?"

"Yes. This is Hank, George, and Frankie."

"Guys, this is Rosa. Her uncle Luigi is one of the owners here." She takes Mario by the arm and directs him to a table near the window overlooking the street. The inside of the trattoria is devoid of frills. There is nothing more than bare, wooden walls, a floor of carefully fit granite stones, and a small number of tables and chairs that appear to have been recently painted white.

"You sit at this table. It's the best view of the harbor. Ugo and Uncle Luigi are in the kitchen cooking. I'll go tell them you are here and then bring you some wine," says Rosa with a charming smile. She slides her hand lightly across Mario's shoulders as she

leaves. Her friendly behavior does not go unnoticed, and Hank is the first to razz Mario.

"I'd say she kinda likes you, Mario. What the hell did you tell her?"

"Nothin, really. I just talked with her and her uncle earlier today. We drank some wine, and had a real good time, that's all."

"It's lookin like your good times ain't over yet, buddy," says Frankie with a grin.

Ugo and Luigi come out of the kitchen and rush up to the table to greet Mario. After being introduced to Mario's friends, Luigi says,

"In a few minutes, I'll have some wonderful spaghetti with shrimp sauce for you to eat. You enjoy some wine until it's ready."

Soon, Rosa is placing large platters of pasta and shrimp in front of each man, followed by fresh baked bread and much more wine. She continues to flirt with Mario during every trip to the table and, after the dinner is finished, she sits next to him and asks,

"Mario, would you like to join me for a walk through Palermo? There are many beautiful things to see here, and I would enjoy showing them to you."

"Yes, I'd like that, Rosa. Thank you for offering." His smirk foretells his intent, but before he is able to say anything to his friends, Hank pulls Mario closer to him and says,

"I ain't sure what you two just said to each other, but I'm bettin you ain't comin back to the base tonight, are ya?"

"I've been asked to go do some sightseeing, that's all."

"At night?" squeals Frankie.

"You guys take the Jeep back. I'll walk back to base later. And pay the bill." Before the men are able to tease him any further, he takes Rosa's hand and slips out of the door.

The cool evening air is a welcome change from the stifling desert heat, and Mario is enjoying the best day he's had since leaving Fort Dix. He blindly follows Rosa along the harbor road to its end, then up a small footpath leading to the ocean.

"Where are we going, Rosa?"

"I want to show you the beautiful view of the Mediterranean from the bluff at the end of the harbor. It is not far."

The footpath ends at the top of the hill, and from there Mario catches a breathtaking sight of the harbor under the endless tapestry of a star-filled sky. Rosa steps in front of Mario and, without warning, wraps her arms around his neck and kisses him several times. Mario is easily aroused by Rosa's seductive boldness after the many months of forced celibacy. He wraps his arms around her and pulls her tightly against his chest. The softness of her breasts and the warmth of her skin are intoxicating to him. She suddenly stops kissing him.

"I have a small room near the trattoria, Mario. Do you want to stay with me tonight?"

"Yes. I'd like that very much, Rosa."

Taking his hand in hers, she leads him to a small shop on the harbor road near the trattoria. They descend a set of wobbly steps leading to a darkened doorway. While standing there, she retrieves a key attached to a small chain suspended between her breasts. After pulling the chain over her head, she unlocks the door. Pushing it open in front of her, she motions for Mario to enter, but he hesitates. In that split second, he reconsiders what he is about to do. Puzzled by his reluctance, Rosa asks,

"What's the matter, Mario? I thought you wanted to sleep with me tonight."

"I do, Rosa...very much. I think you're pretty. But it's your uncle. He's been kind to me, and I feel I'd dishonor him if I do this. Maybe it's best if I go."

"Mario, my uncle will not know what we do. I have lived here alone for many months since I moved to the city. He never comes here."

Although confused by his own behavior, Mario chooses to ignore the moral dilemma he faces and gives in to his physical desires.

"Are you sure he won't come here?"

"I'm sure. He always goes to sleep early when he works in the trattoria."

Mario steps into the tiny dwelling and Rosa follows, closing the door behind her. She moves through the dark room easily, knowing exactly where every piece of furniture is located, and lights a small oil lamp that sits on a dining table. The glow of the lamp reveals a small bed, a worn settee, and a blackened fireplace with an oak mantel. Several photographs, mounted in tarnished bronze frames, perch there. They are all that adorn the barren room.

"It is not very big, but I don't need much," remarks Rosa. She stands before Mario and begins to kiss him again. Mario takes her into his arms and embraces her as he did earlier. His response to her touch is immediate, and they become more passionate. Rosa backs away.

"I will come back in a moment, Mario."

She goes into the bathroom, and Mario looks about the apartment. The photographs on the mantel show a much younger Rosa with a woman he assumes is her mother. She returns dressed in a nightgown. Taking Mario's hand, she leads him to the edge of the bed, but his attention remains fixed on the pictures.

"Is that you and your mother in those pictures?"

"Yes, they are the only photographs I have of her anymore."

"Where is she?" Rosa's passion is quickly replaced by a look of pain. In a barely audible voice, she says,

"She...she was killed by a German land mine. It happened at the beginning of the invasion. I...I don't want to talk about that now, Mario." In that instant, he knows he cannot sleep with her. Gently holding her hands in his, he says,

"Rosa, I've never said no to a woman before, but this is different. I lost my mother when I was young, and I know how terrible it is. I'm so sorry for you, but I can't do this. Do you

331

understand?" He sees her eyes beginning to tear up. She wipes them with her hand and, without looking directly at him, says,

"Yes, I think I understand, Mario. But it's late. Why don't you stay here tonight, anyway? You can sleep on the settee if you like."

He accepts her offer and Rosa gives him a far less sensual kiss before climbing into her bed for the night. Lying on the settee, he cannot stop thinking about her loss and wonders if she tries to sweep away the pain by sleeping with strangers. It all seems so familiar to him. He's relieved about not sleeping with her. He can face Ugo and Luigi, knowing he's returned the respect they have shown him during his stay in Sicily. He feels an unexpected connection to them and this place and, for the first time in his life, understands his father's pride in being Sicilian.

The company's stay in Sicily is short. Only weeks after arriving in Palermo, Sergeant Thompson enters the repair tent early one morning and calls the squad together for another briefing. He begins to explain the next phase of the operation.

"Well, the good news is that the Allied invasion of the mainland has pushed the Krauts well north of Rome. Like I said when we got here, we'll be moving out and heading north."

The men react with a mixture of curious anticipation and typical annoyance at the orders to relocate. Frankie is pissed again and asks,

"Hey Sarge, where in blue Jesus we gonna end up this time?"

"Pomigliano D'Arco. I'm not exactly sure how to pronounce it, but the fly boys just call it Pomig. It's located ten miles inland from Naples. The combat boys already have secured the camp, and we'll be setting up a long-term operation there."

"Hey Sarge, ain't Naples a pretty big city?" asks one of the men.

"Yeah. It's almost as big as Rome. But I hear there's not much left of it. The air raids wiped out most of the ocean front near the main harbor."

"So when do we get moving?" asks Mario.

"We'll be heading for Messina in three days to catch a small transport for the mainland. There's still some broken gear out there to repair before we pack up the camp again. And you're now our official translator, Mario. I want you to stick close to me until we get to Pomig."

"No problem, Sarge. Maybe I better make one last trip into town for supplies before we leave, huh?"

"Might be a good idea, but no overnight stays this time." The men burst into laughter at Sarge's subtle humor. Mario forces a slight smile. He wonders what the others would think if they knew the truth about what really happened the night he never returned to camp.

Working around the clock for the next three days, the squad finishes up the repairs needing attention before packing up. With most of the work complete, Mario returns to Palermo one last time.

Finding Ugo and Luigi seated in their familiar places in front of the trattoria, he sits with them.

"I've come to say goodbye, my friends. Our company is shipping out for Naples tomorrow, and I won't be back here again."

"We knew you were not going to stay here for very long. We are sorry to see you go, but this means you are closer to going home again, yes?"

"I think you are right, Ugo, but I won't be going home for a long time yet."

"You be careful in Napoli, Mario. The Nazis, they plant bombs all over the city."

"Thank you for telling me, Luigi. I'll be careful. I want to say goodbye to Rosa. Is she here?"

"No, Mario. She has gone to work at the farm for a few days. She will be disappointed she was not here to tell you goodbye herself."

"Please tell her goodbye for me. Will you do that Luigi? I must be going."

"Of course. You have a safe journey, Mario."

"Grazie, amico mio," answers Mario.

The following morning, the convoy of loaded trucks leaves Palermo and follows the northern coast road to Messina. The loading zone there is another scene of chaos and frustration, much like Bizerta was. Frequent delays and hours of arguing severely test Sergeant Thompson's will, as he sorts through the confusion to locate a staging area for the company. Mario and the repair crew can do nothing but sit in the back of the truck and wait for instructions.

"I don't know how Sarge puts up with all the shit he's gotta deal with. I'd be punchin someone's face in about now," states Hank.

"I don't ever want Sarge's job," adds Frankie.

"Don't worry, Frankie. That's one problem you don't have ta worry about," replies Hank with a laugh.

Sergeant Thompson finally returns to the convoy. His fists are clenched, his lips are tightly pursed, and his face is flushed.

"I'll never figure out how some of those goddamn Navy boys ever got past the enlistment exam. They have no fucking idea how to get us aboard a ship. Christ, I had to go all the way aboard ship and talk to the deck officer to get a loading area assigned. This is such bullshit."

Taking a few minutes to calm down, he directs the company to the staging area and they begin loading the trucks and equipment aboard the small transport ship for the short trip to the mainland. Mario is on his way to Naples and a date with destiny.

After several more hours of frustrating delays, Company A at last climbs aboard the vessel. Standing on the deck, Mario watches shore men release the dock lines and looks at this wonderful island for the final time. As the ship slowly eases away from the dock, a powerful sense of belonging has him feeling strangely melancholy about leaving. Now, more than ever, he wishes he could have located any members of his family and let his father know they are safe.

The passage across the Straits of Messina is uneventful, and it's not long before the ship is entering the harbor at Reggio de Calabria, a port on the tip of the boot-shaped mainland referred to as the toe. Unloading the ship is no faster than loading it, and as in the past, the company regroups on the wharf to wait for their equipment. The men cluster in smaller groups, using their duffel bags to sit on. Lighting up cigarettes, they discuss their destination and ask Sergeant Thompson about the next assignment.

"Sergeant, do ya know how far Naples is from here?" asks one soldier.

"I'm not sure. Maybe a hundred and fifty miles. But I don't know if the road is any good after all the fighting. I hear Jerry blew up almost every bridge going north, so it could be a long ride if the engineers are still rebuilding them."

Eventually, the trucks and equipment are ready, and the small convoy begins its journey northward. Because of the heavy damage to the main roads, the disjointed route from Reggio to Naples takes the convoy through many small, southern cities in Italy. Sitting in the lead personnel carrier with Sergeant Thompson, Mario enjoys his many opportunities to use his Italian.

"Potete dirmi se questa è la strada a Catanzano?" He never tires of watching their eyes brighten and their smiles grow wider when he speaks to them.

"You speak Italian, signor?" responds an old woman with delight.

336

"Yes, I do. Can you help me with direction to Naples?"

"Of course, signor. This road will lead you to Catanzano. It is maybe three or four hours away. It continues into Salerno and then Naples." Concerned about land mines, he asks,

"Have there been any Nazis on this road?"

"No, they travel along the coast road, but not here."

"Grazie, signora," answers Mario, as the convoy moves on.

Traveling through the small southern cities like Catanzano and Cosenza, Mario is surprised to see they have escaped the heavy damage observed in Sicily. Vineyards and olive groves remain standing throughout the picturesque hillsides and, in some areas, it is difficult to see any signs of war. Beautiful, ancient cathedrals and quaint, mountainside farmhouses dot the landscape. As the convoy proceeds northward, Mario continues to greet the liberated Italians standing along the roadside, many of whom are cheering and waving small, American flags.

Arriving in Salerno, one of the main targets of the invasion, Mario sees the evidence of heavy fighting scattered throughout the city. As in Sicily, burned Nazi tanks and artillery are everywhere, and huge bomb craters pockmark the area. Sergeant Thompson spots an American flag flying atop an old school building, and he stops to check the condition of the road leading into Naples. After talking to an officer in charge, he returns to the personnel carrier and tells Mario,

"Looks like it's an easy ride to Pomig from here. The lieutenant inside says the main road leading to Naples is clear, and it should only take us another few hours to get there."

Entering Naples, Mario sees more of the massive damage caused by the Allied bombings and Nazi destruction tactics. The entire area surrounding the harbor has been leveled, and the tops of sunken ships are still visible in the harbor. The streets are clogged with civilians and soldiers alike, and in spite of the vast destruction, life seems to be returning to the largest city captured by the Allies. Cafes and small shops are open for business amid the shattered remains of the surrounding neighborhoods. Small children race up to the slow-moving trucks, shouting out in half English and half Italian,

"Welcome, *Americano*...you ava candy, *per favor?*" Reaching into his bag, Mario pulls out a few pieces of chewing gum and tosses them to the young beggars.

"This is all I have to offer you. I'm sorry."

"You speak Italian...how do you know to speak Italian?" one of the youths shouts out. Before he is able to answer their question, the convoy moves ahead and continues on to Pomigliano D'Arco.

Moving slowly through the crowded city, the convoy does not stop until it reaches the base. Pomig is home to both American and British troops. It is also a major air base used by B-17 bombers and their fighter escorts conducting raids on German positions to the north. Heavily armed guards greet the convoy and, following a brief inspection of company orders, they direct the convoy to a cluster of buildings near the main airstrip.

"Holy shit...Will ya look at that? Them's real fuckin barracks," hollers Frankie.

For the first time since leaving Fort Dix, the company will be housed in newly-constructed, wooden barracks. Although not as well equipped as the barracks back home, having a real roof over their heads and not sleeping on the ground are unexpected luxuries to Mario and the crew. Sergeant Thompson is the first to enter one of the barracks, and after a short inspection, he returns to the convoy.

"These are our barracks, men, and they're brand new. You guys should be real comfortable here. Start unloading your gear and find a bunk inside, while I go find the C.O. and get our orders. When I get back, I'll tell you what we're supposed to do here. Don't go wandering off, got it?" The company splits into different squads and begins moving in.

"Goddamn, real fuckin bunks. Now this is gonna be a nice change," exclaims Hank.

"Yeah, but there ain't no showers or a latrine in here," notes Frankie.

"You ain't never satisfied, are ya? This is the best fuckin place ya had to stay in since we left the States. If I was you, I'd quit bitchin," lambastes George.

"I ain't bitchin, goddamn it. I was just a saying...Cain't I even say somethin?" whines Frankie in return. Mario can only laugh at the never-ending needling going on between the two. He finds a bunk and lies down to catch a little rest.

A short time later, Sergeant Thompson returns and informs the squad,

"I've got our orders, and I want everyone to meet in this barracks at 1400 hours for a briefing." At precisely 1400 hours, the sergeant steps around men sitting on the floor and stands in the center of the barracks. Smiling and high-spirited, he jokes with several of the men before making his announcement,

"You guys like this place?" he asks sarcastically. When the men scream out their delight in unison, he laughs out loud.

"That's what I thought. Good thing, too. The C.O. says we're going to be staying here for a while, maybe even for the duration." An even louder cheer follows the good news as he fills in the details.

"With the Germans still dug in north of Rome, the Eighth Army needs a lot of supplies. Most of you guys will be helping to transport a lot of that equipment. I need to have the repair equipment operational today. Frankie, Hank, George and Mario will get that going right away. The radio gear needs to be set up in the communications building near the flight control building. There's a Sergeant O'Leary waiting for you there. If anyone doesn't have a job, come and see me."

"Hey, Sarge. One more thing…Where's the showers and latrines?" asks Frankie.

Annoyed by Frankie's childish persistence, Hank rolls his head back, and moans,

"Jesus Christ, Frankie. Whadda ya care where the latrines are, as long as they got em?"

"Why in blue Jesus do ya care about what I'm a saying?"

"Well, ya complain so damn much, ya can't see how good ya got it here. And another thing, I'm gettin sick and tired of hearin ya use that blue Jesus thing all the time. Knock it off will ya?" Most of the squad leaves the two men to finish the debate on their own. Tired of listening to them antagonize one another, Mario grabs Frankie by the arm.

"Come on, we got work to do, Frankie. You can finish this later." He leads Frankie out of the building.

A facility has already been erected to house the repair center equipment. It is a large and spacious structure with a solid foundation and a full roof. The equipment is quickly set up, and within a matter of hours, the four men are ready to go to work. Jeeps, half-tracks and more ambulances are parked all around the storage yard, and the familiar process of sorting through them begins. The schedule is a familiar one, with fifteen-hour days becoming routine. The four men have become a highly efficient crew by working together for the past year, and within a few weeks, they manage to put dozens of badly damaged vehicles back into service. After the first month in Pomig, the torrid pace begins to ease, and late one afternoon Sergeant

Thompson stops by. Admiring the valuable work being done by the four men, he says,

"I have to tell you guys what a good job you're doing here. The C.O. knows all about the hard work and long hours you've been putting in, and he personally told me to stop in here and give you some time off. Why don't you grab a truck and have a look around Naples?"

"Thanks, Sarge. A few days off will be great," says George. Sarge looks at Mario and says with a smile,

"I guess speaking the language makes you the tour guide, Mario. Can you keep these guys out of trouble for a few days?"

"Hell, if I'm in charge, we're all gonna be in deep shit."

"Well, do what you can, but just remember, I need all you guys back here, not in a brig somewhere."

Returning to the barracks after work, Frankie giggles and says,

"Damn, a coupla days off in a big ole city…with plenty of wine and women? We gonna have us a good ole time."

"Don't be so sure about the wine. Some of the Brits been comin by and tellin me what wine there is, ain't much good," warns Hank.

"When were you talkin to the Brits?" asks Mario.

"A coupla days ago. They were lookin for the radio building cause they heard there's a pretty good card game goin on there," replies Hank.

"A card game, huh?"

Hank catches on first and starts grinning, then George figures out what Mario is suggesting. Feeling like the neighborhood kid who's been left out of the baseball game, Frankie looks at the others and says,

"What?...Whattin the hell are you guys grinnin about?"

"Maybe there's a few Brits that might wanna play some craps. Whatta ya think, Frankie?"adds Mario.

"Oh shit...I get it. Yeah. That's a great fuckin idea. I still hate them pricks for screwin us outta our booze. I can still see that goddamn Nazi flag a hangin out in front of that ole shit hole they was livin in," screams Frankie, as he heads for the shower building.

After showering and changing into fresh fatigues, the four men locate the card game that the Brits talked about. The several tables inside the radio hut are ringed with both British and Americans. As usual, there are more players than seats. Mario pulls Donnie's dice from his pants pocket and eases himself into the crowd watching the action. Hank takes a position next to him and, a few minutes later, Mario gripes to the Tommie standing next to him,

"Hey, how long does it take to get a seat at one a those tables?"

"Not sure, Yank. I've been standing ere for a bloody hour now, and no one's movin," he complains. Right on cue, Hank joins in the conversation.

"Anyone got any dice? There's room in the back corner for a small crap game." Holding the tiny, purple bag in the air, Mario answers,

"Right here, buddy. Anyone else wanna shoot some craps?"

At first, the staged invitation attracts only a few players, but in less than an hour, more than a dozen men join in. Another run of good luck, combined with Mario's skillful play, realizes a quick profit for them all. After only a few hours, they leave with their winnings amid shouts of anger and threats of not giving anyone a chance to win his money back.

"We'll be back, don't worry. You'll get plenty of chances ta get even," says Mario.

"Let's get outta here before these guys won't let us," warns Hank with a grin. With their pockets full of other soldiers' money, they jump into the truck set aside earlier and head for Naples.

Pomigliano D'Arco is a small, colorless town. Only the presence of the military base has brought some prosperity and life to it. The war damage is minor compared to Naples, and a limited number of trattorias have re-opened, attracting both British and American troops stationed there. But the real jewel of the Allied victory is Naples, a sprawling collection of smaller communities surrounding the bays and islands of the central mainland. Exploring the city for the first time, Mario and his friends find several places to eat and stop to enjoy a good dinner at one of them. While sitting at one of the outdoor tables, Mario motions for a waiter. The portly little man hurries to the table and, in very limited English, asks.

"Hallo, Joe. You wanta soma dinner?"

"Si. Che cosa avete stasera?" responds Mario.

"You speak Italian, Signor?" asks the startled waiter.

"Yes. What are you serving here tonight?"

"We have only a simple pasta with clam sauce, but it is very delicious. You will like it. I promise, Signor."

"That's good. Do you have any wine?"

"I have some wine from the mountains. I will bring you and your friends a bottle."

"What did ya tell em? Are we gonna get somethin ta eat or was ya just practicin your Italian," jokes Frankie.

"Just relax Frankie. We have some pasta and wine comin in a few minutes."

As promised, the waiter returns with generous servings of delicious pasta and several bottles of wine. Although tasting more like mild vinegar, a few glasses of the home-brewed spirit make them forget its sour bite. And despite the poor-tasting wine, the food served in the trattoria is much better than any found on the base. After dinner, Mario suggests,

"Let's drive down to the ocean and have a look around. It can't all be bombed out."

Since arriving in the Mediterranean, Mario has been fascinated by the ocean. He finds both the smell of the sea air and the sounds of the crashing surf soothing. There are many little towns along the Mediterranean, each with its own special attraction. Being able to communicate with the local citizens allows him to travel freely throughout Naples, and he hopes to see many more of them before returning home.

With the Nazis retreating to Germany, the workload at Pomig begins to lighten considerably. He hasn't written to his family since leaving North Africa, so Mario takes advantage of the free time and writes home for the first time in many months.

Dear Pa, John, and Joe,

How is everything at home? I miss you guys. Things are going good for me at last. I got out of North Africa a few months ago and spent some time in Sicily, near Palermo. I didn't know Sicily was such a beautiful place. I really liked it there. I met some nice people who made me feel at home. They were surprised to find out I was Sicilian and could speak Italian. I asked about our relatives, Pa, but no one knew them. I wish I could have found them.

I'm stationed in a place called Pomigliano D'Arco. It's near Naples. Sarge says it looks like I'm going to stay here for a while, maybe until the war is over. All the fighting is over around here, so things are slowing down a lot. I even get some time off and have been into Naples a couple of times. The bombing wrecked most of the city near the main harbor, but the rest of it is still standing. The ocean is only a few miles from the middle of the city, and there are a lot of fishermen selling all kinds of fresh fish. Joe would love to have some of it for the store.

I'll write again soon, but you can send letters to me here for now.

Mario

With the war essentially over in Italy, there is much less to do in the repair center. Mario and the crew are usually able to finish their work in one or two days, leaving them a lot of free time. Mario has been working on a badly damaged Jeep for several weeks. He thought, at first, that it was beyond repair, but he's managed to put it into good working order. Mario assumes it's been overlooked and considered out of service, and he begins to use it for himself. The slow pace in the camp bores him, so he decides to get off the base with the Jeep and do a little exploring on his own. He locates Sergeant Thompson in his office, knocks on the open door, and says,

"Hey Sarge, I just got that old Jeep in the back running. I'm gonna take it for a little test ride and see how it runs. That okay with you?" Smiling, the Sergeant looks at Mario with a slight bit of suspicion, but he is willing to trust him.

"Sure, Mario. Just try and be back here before nightfall."

"Thanks Sarge. I will."

Under a warm, morning sun, Mario guides the roofless Jeep through the camp's gates and on to the main road leading to Naples. Driving around with no particular destination in mind, he passes through several smaller inland cities before arriving in Bagnoli. The ocean quickly lures him to seaside, and after parking the vehicle next to a long stretch of beach, he hops out to have a closer look. There are several fishing boats tied to an old pier, the owners hawking their fresh catch to the many customers bartering for a good price. The negotiations are loud and animated, and Mario finds the conversation amusing.

"Five lire for that fish is too much. Look how small it is. I give you three, but no more," shouts one woman.

"Signora, if you do not want to pay five lire, then you can go hungry. It's up to you," replies the disinterested fisherman.

Strolling along the beach, Mario delights in the combination of balmy weather and fresh, sea breeze. He sits on a large rock, removes his shoes and socks and holds them in his hands. His mind wanders as he continues walking along the surf line, allowing the rushing water to soak his pants to well past his knees. He thinks of home and how different this place is. His life in Detroit no longer seems real to him. It's easy to forget that a brutal war has brought him to this amazing part of the world. He wonders how beautiful Naples was before the war. The Mediterranean's cool, blue water feels refreshing on this hot afternoon, and he moves slowly through the surf, savoring the moment. He knows that, once he returns home, he is not likely to have this opportunity again.

The magnificent day continues into the early afternoon, and Mario is in no hurry to return to the base just yet. Hiking further down the beach, he discovers the local fish market in Bagnoli. The large, wooden deck is crowded with dozens of cleaning stations and display tables, all glistening with the oozing fluids from recently-butchered fish. Fresh swordfish, mackerel, and even squid are only a small portion of the daily catch. The distinctive smell of cleaned fish reminds Mario of his brother's store. He imagines how excited Joe would be to have such a wide variety of seafood to sell every day. Dressed in his standard work fatigues, it's obvious that he's an American G.I. Several teenaged boys, busy cleaning fish, stop and stare at him. They begin laughing.

"Look at the Americano. He doesn't have enough sense to roll up his pants when he walks in the ocean." Mario abruptly stops in front of their cleaning table and smiles innocently at them. Not wanting to reveal his ability to speak Italian immediately, he replies in English,

"Did you say something to me?" The boys begin laughing even harder. Thinking he'll go away, one of them says,

"Non parle, Inglais, Signor. Their cocky behavior is a perfect target for Mario's little ruse, and he continues to speak English.

"Oh, you don't speak English?" The boys shake their heads and raise their hands in front of them, indicating they don't understand. Mario decides it's time to spring his little surprise and switches to Italian.

"You boys should be careful what you say. You never know who will be listening. Maybe you want to apologize for making fun of my wet pants." His use of Italian results in the familiar reaction it has from the other Italians he's met.

"How do you know to speak Italian? Are you really an Americano?" one of them asks in astonishment. Mario, again, explains that his family is from Sicily, and that he's learned to speak Italian at home. After revealing his secret, the boys' behavior changes dramatically. They begin to bombard him with many more questions.

"What's America like?"

"Does everyone have big cars, like in the movies?"

Mario's fluent Italian draws the attention of others standing nearby, and he's soon the center of attention. He's offered glasses of wine and has a marvelous time talking with the small group of fishermen.

"Signor Carlucci, if you come back tomorrow, I will save some wine for you," says one of them with a loud laugh.

"It must be good wine, like you would serve to your priest," teases Mario in return. They laugh loudly at his humor and are anxious to know more about him.

Amid the fun at the market, the afternoon has become early evening, and Mario is starting to get hungry. Not having eaten since leaving the base, he asks one of the fishermen,

"Do you know of a café or trattoria nearby where I can get something to eat?"

"You go four or five blocks into the city; maybe you will find something there," advises one of the men.

Mario follows the vague directions and enters a part of Bagnoli that appears to have escaped serious war damage. Most buildings are intact, and a few shops are open for business, but his search for a café or trattoria is fruitless. Asking the occasional passerby for help, he receives a different answer from every person he speaks to but has little success. With the afternoon sun still high on the horizon, he decides to rely on his luck and continues his random search through Bagnoli.

Making his way down another street, he hears what sounds like someone singing. Straining to listen more carefully, he decides it's clearly a woman's voice singing opera from somewhere nearby. The voice is clear and bright and echoes through the buildings like a child's ball bouncing along the street. Thinking it might be originating from a café, he follows the elusive voice toward its origin. Looking up and down the adjoining streets, he sees nothing but more old homes and apartments. The woman's voice becomes louder, and he's certain it cannot be much further. He sees no signs of a café or trattoria, however. Puzzled, he stands with his hands on his hips and carefully looks around the immediate area. The powerful voice seems to be practically in front of him, but it's source still remains hidden from his sight. On the opposite side of the brick-lined street is an old, two-story apartment building with several windows facing the street. There, sitting before one of the second story windows, is the source of the angelic voice he's been following.

With many more customers coming to her, Antonella devotes a large portion of the day working before the well-lit window in her apartment. Hurrying to finish the hem on the dress she is repairing before the fading light forces her to stop, Antonella does not notice the American soldier staring up at her from the street below. When he crosses the street to get closer, she becomes aware of someone's presence, but thinking it is a neighbor, she pays little attention at first. After realizing the motionless figure is not moving away, Antonella casually glances down to see who it might be. Seeing an American soldier staring at her from just below her window frightens her. She instinctively sits back and hides behind the edge of the curtain to avoid his direct stare. Watching him for a moment, she sees that his shirt is open and his pants are wet to the knees. Soldiers are rarely seen in the neighborhood, and she is afraid this peculiar looking man may be a thief or a rapist. She jumps up, bolts the door and runs to the security of the back room in the tiny apartment.

With Assunta and Lucia away, Antonella sits on the edge of the bed with her hands clasped between her knees. She gradually becomes more angry than afraid. With the Nazis no longer a threat, being a prisoner in her own apartment infuriates Antonella. She decides to confront the crazy-looking man and insist that he leave. Making sure the door is locked and secure, she cautiously returns to the main room and peeks out onto the street. Seeing the soldier has not left, she grows angrier. With her hands on her hips, she paces wildly around the apartment. Her heart races and her pulse quickens, while she decides what to do next. Standing erect, she throws her head back to clear her hair from her face and steps to the window in full view of the soldier. Her threatening stare does little to discourage his unwanted attention. Using the few English words she knows, she says,

"You go froma here. *Pronto.*"

After waiting on the street for several minutes, Mario has all but given up any hope of meeting this girl with the siren's voice. But, when she stands before him in defiance, he can see her clearly for the first time. Having only a brief glimpse earlier, he is curious, but looking up at her now, he is pleasantly surprised by what he sees. She appears to be young and extremely beautiful. Her black, wavy hair is uncombed, and she is wearing no make up. Her dark, brown eyes are highlighted by a golden complexion, and she is wearing a simple, white cotton dress, left slightly unbuttoned at her breasts. With a shapely and athletic figure, her wild beauty mesmerizes Mario. He continues to stare from the street and makes up his mind not to leave until he knows more about her. Smiling at her poor English, he asks,

"Do you speak English?" She shakes her head from side to side, and Mario can see she neither speaks nor understands much English at all. With his interest in her skyrocketing, he speaks to her in Italian.

"Siete un cantante professionista?"

Her angry expression suddenly turns to one of puzzled interest. Leaning forward, she places her hands on the windowsill.

"You speak Italian. But you are American, yes?"

"Yes, but I come from an Italian family. You didn't answer my question. You have a beautiful voice, and I've been following it for several blocks. Are you a professional singer?" Feeling slightly embarrassed, she smiles.

"No, I do not sing for a living. I just enjoy it very much. I had no idea someone can hear me from so far away."

"What do you do, then?"

"Before the war, I designed and sewed gowns and dresses. I used to sell them all around Napoli. But now I repair clothes. No one needs pretty gowns any more."

Mario's fascination with her increases with each passing moment. Hoping to keep her from hiding from him again, he asks,

"I have some uniforms that need repair. Can you fix them for me?" Before answering him, Antonella holds up her hand with her forefinger extended and disappears from the window. Looking up at the vacant window, Mario is afraid she won't return. Then she suddenly reappears on the street, directly before him. She is even more beautiful up close, and he starts to feel nervous and anxious in her presence.

"I can fix anything, Signor. What do you need me to sew?"

"I have some shirts with missing buttons and rips in them and pants that are torn. I can bring them by tomorrow if that's good for you?"

"Tomorrow will be fine. I am always happy to get new business." Elated over having another opportunity to see her, he extends his hand out to her.

"My name is Mario Carlucci. What's yours?" Taking his hand into hers, she answers,

"I'm Antonella Cappodanno. It's nice to meet you, Signor Carlucci. What part of Italia are you from?"

"I'm Sicilian. My father is from Sicily, but he moved to America before I was born,"

Antonella giggles over his admission to being Sicilian. She teases him, saying,

"You know that Sicilians and Napolitans don't get along very well, don't you?"

"I hope that isn't a problem here. I do need my clothes fixed," says Mario. Antonella laughs out loud.

"I don't think it will, do you?" They both laugh again, and then Antonella says,

"Tell me, Signor Carlucci, how did your pant legs get so wet?" He looks down at his pants and snickers,

"I was walking along the beach earlier, and I got too close to the surf. There's no ocean where I live, so I like to spend as much time there as I can."

"That is too bad you have no ocean. I've loved the sea since I was a little girl." Remembering he must return to the Jeep parked along the seaside, he says,

"I must go and find my Jeep. I promised my sergeant I'd be back before dark. I'll come here tomorrow afternoon, if that's a good time."

"Yes, I will be here. I have more work I must finish. Maybe you can tell me what America is like?"

"I'd like that. I'll see you here tomorrow." Antonella shakes his hand once more and, with a gentle laugh, says,

"Ciao, Mario Carlucci de Sicily."

She turns and climbs the flight of stairs leading to the apartment, but before she is out of sight, Antonella looks back in his direction. Flipping her long hair out of her face, she smiles and waves one last time, vanishing as quickly as she appeared.

CHAPTER 14

Standing on the street beneath Antonella's apartment, Mario stuffs his hands into his pants pockets to help ward off a case of anxiety. Meeting beautiful women is nothing new to him, but he senses something different, something unexpected, going on here. Maybe it's this place, or the long war, but whatever the reason, he's certain he wants to see her again. It's getting late and he's still hungry, but he doesn't seem to notice. He doesn't really know where his Jeep is parked, or whether it's even still there. While heading off to look for the Jeep, he repeatedly looks back at the apartment, hoping to catch one more glimpse of this intriguing woman. Her natural beauty and apparent talent fascinate him, and he wonders if she is just being nice to him because he's about to become a customer, or whether she actually likes him.

While he wanders around Bagnoli, questions about this interesting woman come to him. How old is she? Does she live alone? Is she married or engaged? Lost in his thoughts for many minutes, he berates himself for not finding out more about her while he had the chance. Then, as if emerging from a dense fog, he's back on the ocean road, not far from his vehicle. Driving back to the base, he decides to improve his chances of seeing her more often.

Arriving back at Pomig, Mario parks the Jeep outside the barracks and immediately goes inside. Frankie is sitting on his bunk reading a letter, but when Mario walks by without saying anything, he asks,

"Wher'in the hell you been all day?" Without looking at him, Mario answers,

"I, uh, went into Naples for a few hours...ta look around. Wanted to see what the beaches look like around here." Heading straight for his footlocker, Mario flings it open and stares at its contents for a moment. Still feeling ignored, Frankie tries to get his attention by resorting to mock anger.

"Ah, the hell with ya then. If ya don't wanna talk, just say so, goddamn it." Oblivious to Frankie's whining, Mario begins rummaging though his footlocker, pulling out any old pants and shirts he can find and tossing them onto his bunk. With Frankie watching his bizarre behavior, Mario sits on the edge of his bunk, grabs a shirt, and begins tugging at the seams. After watching Mario tear small holes into larger ones, Frankie can't stand waiting for an explanation.

"You ain't drunk or something, are ya? What in blue Jesus are ya doin?" Recognizing how ridiculous he must look, Mario flops down on his bunk and stares at the ceiling in a fit of laughter. Propping himself up on his elbows, he looks over at Frankie.

"I…uh, met a woman in Naples today. It was the strangest thing. I heard her singing and I just kept following the sound of her voice until I found her."

"Ya didn't meet up with one a them there street girls, did ya?"

"No, it's nothing like that. I'm not sure how to describe her, except she's good looking and talented. I've never met someone like that before."

"So, why inna hell are ya rippin up all yer shirts for?" Frankie asks, still very confused.

"She used ta be a fashion designer, but now she repairs clothes for a living. I'm going back to see her tomorrow and bring her some work."

"Man, she better be more than pretty, cause if she cain't sew, you inna heap of trouble. I think I saw Hank's initials on somma of those shirts you just tore up." Mario examines the pile of clothing on his bunk, only to discover Frankie's right. He smiles.

"Let's go to the mess hall. I'm starving. Hank won't even know the difference."

Returning home from a shopping trip to the local outdoor market, Assunta and Lucia find Antonella standing in the main room of the apartment. To their amazement, they see the room is littered.

Mono V. D'Angelo

Dresses cover the table, the small settee, and they hang from any available clothes hook in the room. After pulling her favorite designs from the large suitcase she had packed them in before the war, Antonella studies them with great concentration. Holding a gown in her outstretched hand, she slowly twirls the hanger between her fingers, looking for any stains or damage. Confused by her daughter's behavior, Assunta asks,

"Antonella, why are all these dresses scattered everywhere like this?"

"I have a new customer who will bring me more work tomorrow, and I want something nice to wear."

"What woman in Napoli has money or material for a new dress?" asks Lucia.

Lucia and Assunta wait for an answer, but Antonella resumes her examination with renewed interest, hoping to avoid answering her sister's question. Becoming noticeably impatient over Antonella's stalling tactics, Assunta sternly asks,

"Antonella! Are you going to tell us who this customer is or not?" Antonella knows her sister and mother will not give up and walk away if she says nothing, so she reluctantly says,

"My...my new customer...is not, ah, a woman from Napoli."

"Well, where is she from? Is she rich?" asks Lucia.

"It's...it's a man. An American soldier. He has clothes that need repair," admits Antonella. Staring at her younger sister in confused disbelief, Lucia asks,

360

"An American soldier? Here in Bagnoli? How did you meet an American soldier? You speak no English. You...you must not do this, Antonella. The Americans and British, they think all young women in Napoli are prostitutes. They are only interested in one thing. We must lock the windows and doors before he returns."

"Lucia, please stop. There is nothing to fear right now. We always keep the door and windows locked," Assunta says, trying to calm Lucia down for a moment. She directs her attention to Antonella.

"Tell me, Antonella. How are you able to talk to this American?"

"Mama, he speaks Italian. His family is from Sicily. I was singing while finishing my work and he heard me. He is not like the other Americans; he is very polite."

"He can speak Italian?"

"Yes...He thought I was a professional singer. When I told him I repair clothing, he asked me if I could mend some of his uniforms, and I said yes."

"What does this American look like, that you need to wear a special dress to repair his uniforms?" Lucia asks. Antonella's sudden smirk reveals her answer before she speaks. With a playful laugh, she says,

"The poor man's pants were wet from walking in the ocean, and his uniform was very sloppy looking, but I think he's, maybe, a little handsome, as well as polite."

361

Mono V. D'Angelo

"Your sister and I will be here when this American soldier returns. If he is what you say he is, then he will not care if we are here to meet him when he arrives." Antonella smiles and resumes searching through her creations for the perfect dress to wear the next day.

After accumulating enough damaged shirts and pants to justify his return, Mario decides to bring Antonella a small gift, hoping to make a good impression on her. Searching through his belongings, he finds nothing appropriate. Even a trip to the PX the following morning fails to provide anything more than candy or cigarettes. He later corners Hank in the barracks.

"Hey Hank, if I wanted ta give a gift to a local…you know, something they would really like, what would it be?"

"OK…what the hell are ya up to now? This local wouldn't happen to be a woman would it?"

"Yeah. It just so happens to be a woman…someone I met yesterday in Bagnoli. She repairs clothing, and she's gonna fix some of my shirts and pants. I thought I could bring her a little something…you know…to make sure she does a good job."

"Come on Carlucci, quit bullshittin me here. You ain't goin all the way back ta Naples just ta get your clothes fixed. I'm bettin she ain't one of them ole ladies all dressed in black, right?" says Hank.

362

"Yeah, well...so what? Come on. Help me think a somethin ta bring." Hank quits his teasing and gives Mario's request some serious consideration for a few moments.

"I got just the thing. I'll be back in a little while," he says. He charges out of the barracks and disappears for over an hour. When he returns, he tosses a white linen bag with a drawstring top, onto Mario's bunk. Mario looks at Hank.

"What's in there?"

"Open it. You'll see." Pulling open the drawstring, Mario dumps the contents of the bag on his bunk. Confused by what falls out, he says,

"Hank, it's just coffee and sugar. Is this the gift ya told me about?" Hank stands in front of Mario, places his hand on his shoulder. Suddenly sounding like someone's father, he explains,

"Mario, listen to me carefully. There's a few things that are worth their weight in gold on the black market around this town. One is good booze. Do ya know what the other is? Of course ya don't. Well, it's coffee, my friend. And if ya throw in a little sugar...well, ya can git just about anything ya want on the streets."

"How the hell do you know all this?"

"One of the cooks in the mess hall told me. He's got a coupla street girls doin anything he wants em to, for half a that."

"If this stuff's so valuable, why's he givin it ta you, for Christ's sake?"

"I borrowed your dice one night…uh, hope ya don't mind, but the cook's inta me for a few bucks, so I just collected from him."

"I don't know, Hank. I was thinking about something a little more personal. Maybe…" Cutting him off in mid-sentence, Hank says,

"Trust me on this, buddy. If ya wanna make a good impression, this is gonna do it." Still not totally convinced, Mario places the coffee and sugar back into the linen bag and stuffs it into a laundry sack containing the clothing he's having mended.

Checking in at the repair center, he finds Sergeant Thompson talking to Frankie and George.

"Mornin, guys. Hey Sarge, we got anything important goin on today?" Mario asks.

"No, looks like it's going to be fairly quiet. Why do you want to know?"

"I just found someplace to get a few of my fatigues repaired, and I wanna drop em off later, that's all."

"Sure, that's OK with me, Mario. Let me know if they do a good job. I have some things of my own that need some work."

"Hey Mario, how's about I go along with ya?" says Frankie.

"Brush up on your Italian, Frankie, then I'll be happy to take ya with me."

"You two want to tell me what's going on here?" asks the sergeant.

"Come on Sarge, you know this guy. Some gal he met's gonna fix his stuff, or so he's a sayin."

"Frankie, I guess no matter how hard we try to smartin you up, a part of you is gonna always be a hillbilly," Mario says. Sergeant and George howl at Mario's response. Still laughing as he walks away, Sarge says,

"I think he's right Frankie. Just stay out of trouble, Mario." After showering and changing into a fresh uniform, Mario grabs the laundry bag and jumps into the Jeep for the trip back to Bagnoli.

As Mario drives through the maze of narrow, twisting streets, the many neighborhoods begin to look alike, and he quickly becomes lost. Not knowing the name of the street or the address of her apartment, he must rely on his memory to find her again. Returning to the familiar beach, he begins to retrace his steps that led him to Antonella's apartment originally. All he remembers are the old bricks in the roadway, and he keeps driving around until he locates such a street. The old buildings look familiar, and while slowly driving through the neighborhood, he recognizes Antonella's apartment windows. He parks the Jeep at the edge of the narrow road and shuts off the engine. Sitting there, he realizes he's become the center of attention for many people on the street today. Smiling casually, he greets several passersby who have stopped to stare at him.

"Come siete oggi?" The now familiar string of questions immediately follows their surprised smiles.

Mono V. D'Angelo

"You speak Italian, signor? Are you lost? What do you want here?" asks a kindly old man.

"No, I'm not lost. I have some clothes to be repaired by the woman who works here,"

"Ah...Antonella. I see. She's very talented and will do a good job for you." The brief conversation with the old man draws even more attention to Mario, and more of Antonella's neighbors begin to encircle the Jeep and ask questions. He smiles and talks with them for a few minutes.

"Please excuse me, but I must go." Grabbing his bag from the rear of the Jeep, Mario follows the broken walk to the stairway. He climbs to the top landing, stands in front of the door for a second and takes a deep breath before knocking. When the door swings open, Antonella greets him.

"Signor Carlucci? It's good to see you again. Please come in."

"Thank you. As you can see, I have a lot of clothes that need repair," he says, holding up the laundry bag. Once again, Mario finds himself fascinated by her beauty. She's wearing a dress made of Prussian blue silk. Its conservative style is simple and tasteful, with a high neckline and short sleeves. The clinging material follows every curve of her figure, and Mario sees the extent of her creative talent for the first time. She appears even more radiant and exciting than he recalls from their first meeting. He nervously looks for something to say.

366

"That's a very beautiful dress. Is it one of your own designs?" Before she can answer, Assunta and Lucia enter the main room. Their piercing stares and stoic expressions shout their displeasure at his presence. The two women say nothing, and the awkward seconds seem more like hours to him. Not expecting to see anyone else, Mario stands frozen in place while being closely scrutinized. Trying to defuse the tension-filled moment, he looks to Antonella and politely asks,

"Is this your family?"

"Yes. This is my sister, Lucia and my mother, Assunta," Mario smiles, extends his hand to Lucia, and in his best Italian, says,

"Hello, Lucia. My name is Mario Carlucci." He then turns to Assunta and does the same.

"Signora, thank you for allowing me come into your home. I'm very pleased to meet you."

Mario's dashing looks, charming smile and fluent Italian begin to disarm Assunta's initial reservations about him. Still cautious, she allows a slight smile.

"Your Italian is very good, Signor Carlucci. How did you learn to speak it so well in America?"

"Thank you, Signora. My family is Sicilian. Giuseppi, my father, speaks Italian all the time. If I didn't learn to use it, he wouldn't let me eat." Assunta's cool reception fades more rapidly, and even Lucia smiles at Mario's quip. Lucia asks,

"And your mother? Is she Sicilian, too?"

Mono V. D'Angelo

"Yes, she was. She and my father went to America many years ago. She died when I was young, so I didn't know her very well." Lucia's expression instantly changes, from one of suspicion to one of compassion.

"I'm sorry for you. We know how it feels to lose a parent. Our father died when Antonella and I were young." The shared experience of loss creates a small bond of trust between Mario and Lucia. She begins to relax but continues to ask more probing questions.

"American soldiers don't often come to this part of Bagnoli. What are you doing here?"

"Well, I was looking for a trattoria, and I got lost. When I heard Antonella's singing, I followed it here, hoping to find something to eat." Lucia and Assunta find Mario's explanation quite funny. He can see they are more comfortable with him as they start to question him about his life more than his intentions. Assunta invites him to sit down.

"How long have you been in Napoli?"

"For several months now. I was in North Africa for over a year, and then I got shipped to Sicily for a few months before coming here."

"Do you have family in Sicily?" asks Antonella.

"I do, but I couldn't find them. I wish I could. My father worries about them all the time."

"Where do you live in America?" asks Lucia.

368

"In Detroit. Do you know where that is?" The three women look at each other, hoping one of them might know, but they shake their heads simultaneously, indicating they do not.

"Do you have brothers and sisters?" asks Lucia.

"Yes, two brothers. John's the oldest and Joe's the youngest. I miss them a lot," Mario says proudly. The friendly conversation continues for a short time, with Mario answering many more questions about his life in America. No longer feeling like a trespasser, he enjoys seeing Antonella and meeting her family, but he realizes he should not overstay his welcome.

"I think I've taken up enough of your time for one afternoon. Here are the clothes I need repaired. There are three shirts and four pairs of pants in the bag."

"That's fine. I will be able to start on them right away."

"I almost forgot something," he says with a smile. Pulling open the laundry bag, he sticks his arm inside and fishes around for the linen bag containing the coffee and sugar. At the last second, his instincts tell him to hand the bag to Antonella's mother. Both surprised and slightly embarrassed by the unexpected gift, Assunta asks,

"What is this?"

"It's a small gift. I hope you like it."

"You did not need to bring us gifts, Signor Carlucci. But this is very kind. Thank you."

After walking to the dining table, she pulls open the drawstring on the small bag and carefully empties its contents. Realizing what it is, she covers her mouth with her hands and emits a subtle gasp.

"Oh my God...this is coffee and sugar. Signor Carlucci, where did you get this? Coffee is almost impossible to find these days."

"A friend on the base gave it to me."

"It's been so long since I last made espresso, I can't remember when it was. This is very generous, Signor Carlucci. You will not get into trouble taking this from the base, will you?"

"No Signora, I will not." Holding the bag of coffee in her hands, she places it under her nose to enjoy its almost forgotten aroma. Smiling contently, she says,

"This is very kind of you to do this. You don't even know us, yet you bring such a wonderful gift. I insist you join us for espresso when you return to pick up your clothes."

"Thank you. I'd like that. I'm sure your espresso will taste better than the coffee on the base." When everyone laughs, Mario sees that Assunta and Lucia are now treating him more like an Italian than an American. He's pleased that their first impressions have been good ones.

Antonella watches and listens with great interest. She is delighted her mother and sister have found Mario so charming and interesting. She makes eye contact with him and smiles approvingly at how he's won them over. She suggests to her mother,

"Mama, maybe Signor Carlucci can return the day after tomorrow. I will have his clothing repaired by then. I would love to hear more about America while we drink espresso. What do you think, Mama?"

"That would be nice. Can you return then, Signor Carlucci?"

"Yes...I think so. I would enjoy talking to you and seeing Antonella again."

"Well then, it's all settled. We'll meet here on Thursday. Maybe after espresso, I can show Signor Carlucci some of Bagnoli. Can we do that, Mama?" asks Antonella. Surprised by Antonella's bold request, Assunta is reluctant to answer her immediately. In spite of her warm feelings for Mario, she is not prepared to give her daughter permission to go out alone with him. Mario sees she is hesitant.

"Signora Cappodanno, if you allow it, I promise we will return whenever you say."

"We shall see," responds Assunta. Antonella is convinced her mother will allow them to go out and says no more about it. Mario looks at his watch and says to Lucia and Assunta,

"I must get back to the base. My sergeant gets worried about me if I'm gone too long. It's very nice to meet you both. I look forward to Thursday."

"I'll walk you out," says Antonella.   They descend the staircase together. She faces him and says,

"Thank you for bringing the gift. I think my mother and sister enjoyed meeting you."

"I enjoyed meeting them, too. I hope we can see each other again sometime soon."

"I'm sure my mother will allow me to go for a walk on Thursday. I'm looking forward to showing you our city." She extends her hand to shake his.

"Buono sera, Signor Carlucci."

"You can call me Mario, if you like," he says, taking her hand. She giggles and looks away from his face, feeling a little embarrassed.

"Good night, Mario."

"Good night, Antonella."

Standing at the bottom of the staircase, she waves to him as he climbs into his Jeep and drives away. His kindness and respect for her family are a pleasant surprise. If it were not for his uniform, he could easily be mistaken for a local. He is a charming and attractive curiosity, and she wants to know more about him. With only her brother and father to compare him with, she has little personal experience to help her judge how sincere he is, but she is willing to take a risk to find out. Having survived four brutal years of war, she is eager to lock those grim images away in some distant corner of her memory and reclaim her life. She wants to design her beautiful clothes again. She wants to know what it's like to be in love. With her passion for life reawakening, this handsome American soldier has stepped into her world at a time unlike any other, and she is determined not to allow romance to slip away from her.

Rolling up to the sentry at Pomig, Mario flashes his identification and roars off to his barracks. He slams on the brakes, stops the Jeep directly in front of the entrance and rushes inside looking for Hank. Not finding him anywhere, he shouts,

"Hey, anybody seen Hank? I gotta talk to em right away."

"I seen em headin out the door in his skivvies carryin a towel. Ya might wanna check the showers," someone answers.

Wearing nothing but a towel wrapped around his waist, Hank leans forward, wipes clear a spot on the steam-covered mirror and starts to shave. With the straight razor almost to his cheek, he spots Mario walking up behind him. Grabbing him in a bear hug, Mario looks at Hank's reflection in the mirror and says,

"How the hell did you get so goddamn smart?"

"Jesus Christ…whatta ya tryin to to? Cut my throat?" yells Hank, as his towel drops to the floor. Standing naked after wrenching himself free of Mario's grasp, Hank looks at him and asks,

"Ya mind tellin me what this is all about?"

"It's the coffee and sugar. You know…the stuff I brought to the girl who's fixin my clothes. Well, it was perfect. She lives with her mother and sister…and when I pulled it outta my bag, ya shoulda seen the looks on their faces. I got invited back for espresso and might even get to go out with her," explains Mario. Hank picks up his towel, wraps it around himself again and asks,

"What's goin on with this girl? You're actin a little strange, ain't ya?"

"You know? I'm not too sure. She's pretty and all, but there's something else about her...something different. She's real talented. Ya shoulda seen this dress she was wearin."

"Well, she sure has made an impression on you, that's for sure," replies Hank with a laugh.

"Yeah, I guess she has."

It's Thursday morning, and Mario finds Sergeant Thompson sitting at the desk in his barracks office.

"Hey Sarge, I'm gonna take off for a little while this afternoon. That OK with you?"

"Where are you going?"

"I'm going back to Bagnoli...to pick up my uniforms I got fixed."

"Should be alright. We don't have much going on today. So, you're going back to see that gal again?" Mario glances at the floor while gently rocking his head from side to side. He looks up at Sergeant Thompson with a grin.

"Can't a guy do somethin on his own around here without it becoming everybody else's business?"

"Take it easy, soldier. I was just asking," replies the sergeant with a chuckle. Mario responds to Sarge's good-natured ribbing with a hearty laugh.

"Oh hell, I know you're just messin around with me. But I am goin to see her again, so thanks for givin me the time off."

"It's a good thing I like you, Carlucci. Otherwise, you'd be walkin to Bagnoli."

"I know, Sarge. I owe ya one."

Finding his way back to Antonella's apartment is much easier this time, and Mario parks the Jeep. While sitting there, he hears one of the neighbors shouting,

"Buon giorno, Signor. I see you have returned once again."

"Yes, I've come to pick up some uniforms Antonella has repaired for me." He gets out and shakes the man's hand.

"Of course, I remember now. Have you met her sister, Lucia?

"Yes, and her mother. We met the last time I was here."

"Assunta is a wonderful woman. She is the reason her family survives today. Do you know any movie stars in America?"

"No Signor, there are no movie stars where I live," answers Mario, amused by the strange question. Not wanting to appear rude, Mario patiently answers several more amusing questions, but then says,

"You must excuse me, but I have to go. Maybe we can talk again another time."

"Oh, I'm sorry. I didn't want to make you late. Yes...let's talk again."

From the apartment window, Antonella watches the conversation between Mario and her neighbor. She finds his willingness to subject himself to an endless barrage of questions a gracious gesture. As he makes his way to the apartment, she tells her mother,

"Mama, Signor Carlucci is here. I'll let him in." Dressed in another of her original designs, she holds open the apartment door and waits for him to climb the stairs. She greets him.

"Buon giorno, Signor Carlucci. Excuse me, I mean Mario. It's nice to see you again. Please come in."

"Thank you. Your neighbors are very friendly, I was talking to one of them for several minutes."

"I know. I watched him asking you so many questions. You must get tired of answering them all the time."

"Sometimes I do. But I really enjoy meeting the people here. I never realized my Italian could be so useful." Seeing her mother enter the dining area from the small bedroom, Antonella says,

"Say hello to Mario, Mama."

"Mario? May I call you that?"

"Of course, Signora Cappodanno. I'd like that."

"Do you have time to stay for espresso? I will make some right away if you do."

"I've been looking forward to having some of your coffee ever since you asked me to come back."

"Mama, I can show Mario his repaired clothes while you make the coffee," Antonella says. Assunta agrees and scurries off to the kitchen while Antonella and Mario sit together at the dining table.

"Your mother seems very excited about making espresso, doesn't she?" Watching her mother preparing the coffee with such joy reminds Antonella of the days before the war. She tells Mario,

"Mama loved having friends over for dinner when my father was alive. This is the first time in many years she's done this. Your gift is very special to her. It's wonderful to see her so happy." Almost forgetting his clothes, Antonella jumps up, grabs the bag containing Mario's uniforms.

"Let me show you what I've done to your shirts and pants while we wait."

Watching her carefully as she pulls his shirts from the laundry bag, Mario continues to find Antonella beguiling. Holding up one of his shirts to show him the repair, she says,

"Look. You cannot even see where I've fixed it. It's like new." Trying to look interested, he takes the shirt and examines it closely.

"Thank you. It's perfect. Your neighbor told me you did very good work, and I can see he was right." Trying not to stare at her while they talk becomes increasingly awkward for him. He's thankful

377

when Assunta arrives at the table carrying a tray of tiny cups and a pot of the freshly brewed espresso.

"That smells very good, Signora. It's been a very long time since I've had espresso."

"Here, Mario. The first cup is for you. Don't forget to add plenty of sugar. Drink and enjoy." Mario takes several small sips while Assunta watches with great pleasure. Her beaming smile and bright eyes show the joy she derives from this simple, Italian tradition. He smiles and holds the cup in the air.

"Please sit and drink with us, Signora. Your coffee is delicious." Assunta joins him at the table, where he politely listens to her talk of her family's life before the war. Enjoying holidays with her children and lunches on the beach after Sunday mass with Pirrone are only a few of the things she misses dearly. Her expression saddens when she mentions her husband, and Mario sees the deep sense of loss. He's fond of Assunta and feels increasing sympathy for her as she reveals more of her difficult existence. Her ability to enjoy coffee with a total stranger, after surviving such terrible events, illustrates her desire to accept the past and look to the future. Astonished by her strong will, Mario gains greater respect for her. He's reminded of his own mother, thinking they would be about the same age, and wonders if she would have welcomed a stranger into her home as Assunta has.

During his conversation with Assunta, Mario is periodically distracted by Antonella's friendly smile. In each instant, he shifts nervously in his chair, trying not to appear too attentive. Aware of her daughter's interest in him, Assunta surprises them.

"Antonella, why don't you go into Bagnoli with Mario and show him some of the city? It is still a beautiful place to enjoy." Casting a hopeful glance toward Antonella, Mario looks for her reaction. Smiling, she feigns surprise.

"That's a wonderful suggestion, Mama. What do you think, Mario? Would you like to go for a walk?"

"Yes. I'd like to see more of Bagnoli without being lost most of the time. I'll be sure to get you back here safely. Why don't we go before it gets too late in the day?" Mario stands and tells Assunta,

"We'll come back in a few hours if you agree, Signora."

"Yes, that's fine. Please return before dark, that's all I ask." Following Antonella down the stairway, Mario can feel his heart beating a little faster, as he is about to spend several hours alone with her for the first time. His aloofness regarding women he's known in the past has been replaced by a new curiosity. He wants to know all there is about this beautiful woman, and his instincts suggest that she is eager to tell him.

Antonella's palms are moist and her breathing shallow. She's never felt so nervous. Being out with a man for the first time in many years is exciting, but being out with a handsome American soldier is something she could never have imagined, and she's unsure how to act. Remembering his fondness for the ocean, she suggests,

"Would you like to go to the beachfront? It's not far from here."

"Any place you want to go is fine."

"This time, we'll try to keep your pant legs dry," she teases. After he laughs at her little joke, she begins to feel more comfortable with him. She takes his hand and leads him down another small street.

"Let's go this way. There's a small market place only a few blocks away. It's fun to go and see what's for sale." While the streets of Bagnoli have not been cleared completely of the war debris, businesses are reemerging. Small markets selling fresh fish, vegetables and baked bread are flourishing. The air is heavy with a wonderful aroma of provolone cheeses and strings of fresh garlic cloves. Aggressive shop owners hawk their goods to passing customers, engaging them in the age-old tradition of bartering for a fair price. Antonella enjoys the confused reaction of the many residents as she escorts this American through the market place. She giggles and leans closer to Mario.

"They are so curious to know what you are doing here. Isn't this fun?"

Before he can answer, a loud voice shouts to her from across the street.

"Antonella? Antonella Cappodanno? Is that you, my dear?" Wearing a wide-brimmed straw hat and carrying a large shopping bag in each hand, Theresa Minnelli waddles through a maze of fruit carts

380

clustered in the middle of the street. She sets her bags on the ground and hugs her.

"I knew it was you, dear. No one else in Bagnoli wears such beautiful dresses."

"Hello, Signora Minelli. It's so nice to see you again. How have you been?" Theresa looks at a grinning Mario with some suspicion, and then blurts out,

"I'm fine, my dear. Do you know this American?"

"Yes, he's a new customer of mine. Theresa Minnelli, meet Signor Carlucci."

"Un piacere venirli a contatto, Signora Minelli," says Mario, shaking her hand.

"You speak Italian? He speaks Italian?" she says, first staring at Mario, then looking at Antonella in amazement.

"My family is Sicilian, Signora."

"I see. Your Italian is so flawless. It's nice to meet you, too, Signor Carlucci." Visibly confused by his presence, Theresa awkwardly asks,

"How...how do you know each other?"

"We met when Mario got lost in our neighborhood. We must go Theresa. I promised Mama that I would be home soon. I'll tell her you said hello." Grabbing Mario's hand once again, she hurries away before Theresa starts to ask any more embarrassing questions.

"I love her very much. She has done many wonderful things for our family, but she will talk for hours," admits Antonella, with a sheepish grin.

As they casually stroll through the streets of Bagnoli, Mario asks her,

"Your clothes...well...they look very expensive. I don't know very much about women's fashions, but yours are so different. How did you learn to be a designer?"

"I started when I was a little girl...first making costumes for my school's festivals and then making them for other students. I became very good at it and just taught myself. Before the war, I had over thirty women, many of them from wealthy families, who bought my dresses. But after the Nazis invaded Napoli, most of the people moved away to escape the bombs."

"Why didn't you move away?"

"After my father died, we had little money. Signora Minnelli, the woman we met earlier, owns the apartment we live in and charges us very little rent. We could not afford to go anywhere else." The pride in her business and great disappointment over its loss is unmistakable. Mario detects a sadness in her eyes as she talks of its demise. Attempting to cheer her up, he says,

"Now that the war is almost over, I'm sure your old customers will want to buy new things from you again. It will take a little time, that's all."

"I hope you are right, Mario. It would be wonderful to start my business and sell dresses again." Reaching the boulevard along the oceanfront, Antonella kicks off her shoes.

"Take your shoes off, Mario. Let's walk in the sand for a while."

The area has been heavily damaged during the air raids, and very little of it remains as Antonella once remembered. She stops, points to piles of rubble along the roadway.

"When Lucia and I were little, our father used to take us here after mass. He loved spending the afternoons along Via Pozzuoli. There...along the other side of the street...were many trattorias. We'd have lunch and spend the afternoon just watching the ships come and go. It was so beautiful here. I think I miss that more than anything else."

"I can see why you love the ocean so much. I've only been here for a few months, and I already think about what it will be like not to enjoy it every day. There are no oceans where I live."

"Do you see that beach? The one with the bunker? I used to swim there all the time. I'd swim out to the large ships...and Lucia...she would get so mad at me." Antonella abruptly stops. Looking at the far end of the beach, she becomes excited at something she sees there.

"Mario? Can you see that? It looks like outdoor umbrellas next to that small building. Let's go and see what it is. Maybe a trattoria has reopened." Grabbing Mario's hand, she starts running

through the sand and pulling him with her. Nearing the end of the beach, they discover the umbrellas do, in fact, belong to a newly-opened café on the beach.

Listening to Antonella speak so fondly of the days spent here as a young girl, Mario is thrilled at the incredible good fortune of finding such a place amid the war rubble. He pulls her to a stop.

"Do you want to stop and see if they have something to eat?"

"Can we, Mario? That...that would be so perfect."

"Let's go." She jumps up and down like a child about to open a birthday gift. Turning to face him, she wraps her arms around his shoulders and gives him a long hug. Her unexpected embrace catches him off guard at first, but then he gently places his hands around her waist and returns her affection. Her touch feels warm and inviting, her body, taut and firm. The delightful moment sends shivers through him. He looks into her eyes for several seconds, and she neither turns away from his stare nor tries to pull away. When she returns his smile, he's certain she finds the shared caress equally enjoyable. Then she tears away from him.

"I'll race you to the trattoria. See if you can catch me." She's off in a flash, running at breakneck speed along the beach, with Mario chasing right behind her. She arrives at the eatery only a few steps ahead of him, and they stop to put their shoes on. Laughing and trying to catch his breath, Mario says,

"You win...this time." The trattoria is a simple, wooden building facing the Mediterranean. It sits atop a newly constructed

platform with railings on three sides. A crude, hand-painted sign with the name *La Palicio* hangs from the timber arch over the entranceway. Its six tables are positioned randomly about the dining area, and each has a traditional umbrella with red, green, and white colored panels. Swaying gently in the fading sea breeze, they seem a strange sight on the nearly desolate beach. Mario can hear the sound of loose sand scratching loudly beneath her feet, as Antonella dashes to a table nearest the beach. When he joins her, she reaches out and touches his arm.

"Let's sit here, shall we? I love to watch the ocean while I eat. What shall we have?"

"You can order whatever they serve. I'll trust you to pick something good." Moments later, a young, teenaged boy approaches the table from the small adjoining building. Carrying a towel, he wipes the fine layer of dust from the tabletop.

"Welcome. Allow me to clean this for you. It would be a shame to get your clothes dirty. We've just opened and don't have many customers yet."

"Do you have a menu we can look at?" Antonella asks.

"No, signorena. I'm sorry, but we do not. But today, you can order some nice linguini and home-made bread. And we have some good wine...my uncle in Salerno makes it, and it's much better than the wine from the local vineyards."

"Would you like some wine?" Antonella asks Mario.

"Only if you'll drink some with me." Smiling, she tosses her head back, pulls her hair away from her face and says to the boy,

"Bring us some wine, then. And can you tell me if we can order some caprese or bruchetta?"

"I'll bring the wine and ask my father...he's the cook," says the boy, as he hurries away.

The young waiter has directed all his attention to Antonella, and it's easy for Mario to understand why. Sitting in the late afternoon sun, she looks more radiant than ever. Saying nothing for a few moments, Mario feels captivated by her natural beauty. As she gazes out at the ocean, lost in her own thoughts, he finds it difficult to keep from staring at her.

The young boy returns, balancing a wine bottle and two glasses on a tray. Placing it onto the table, he fills the glasses with the burgundy-colored liquid.

"I have good news, signorena. My father will prepare some caprese or bruschetta...since you are our only customers right now. Which would you like?" Before Antonella can answer, Mario tells him,

"Why don't you bring us an order of each? Is that enough to eat for now, Antonella?"

Thrilled at having her favorite foods, she leans over and gives him a hug.

"Yes...yes. Thank you. That will be wonderful."

While waiting for the food, they sip some wine and begin to talk of Mario's life in America.

"Tell me about where you live, Mario. Do you stay in an apartment?"

"No. I live with my father. He has a big home with two floors...much like a small apartment building. There's a big kitchen and dining room on the first floor and several large bedrooms on the second. Pa...he likes to grow his own peppers and tomatoes in the back yard garden."

"Your father has a big home and a garden? Is he rich?"

"No...he's not rich. Many people have homes like that in America." The warm sun and powerful Chianti lessen Antonella's inhibitions, and she becomes increasingly more relaxed with him.

"So, Mario. Do you have a girlfriend in America?" The question amuses and slightly embarrasses him. He stares into his wine glass for a second, then looks up and says,

"No, not really. I was going out with one girl before the war, but we stopped seeing each other before I enlisted in the Army. And what about you? Do you have a boy friend or fiancée?"

"Oh no! Mama would not allow me to see any boys until I grew older. But then, when I started my business, I had no time. After that...what with the war, well I don't know...the time just disappeared." Mario finds her explanation both tragic and fortunate. He's deeply sympathetic for the terrible adversity in her life, but as

his attraction to her increases, he's grateful to whatever destiny that has brought them together in the aftermath of the war.

Dining on fresh tomatoes, provolone cheese and bruschetta, Mario and Antonella enjoy the special afternoon together. They've learned a great deal about each other by sharing very private and personal feelings. Mario wants to know much more about her, but as the afternoon sun sinks to the edge of the horizon, he recalls his promise to Assunta. It's been an extraordinary day with an extraordinary woman. Although he'd like to spend more time with her tonight, he says,

"I think we should go. I don't want your mother to be upset with me for bringing you home late." Mario calls the waiter to the table and pays for the food, giving the boy a generous tip. The waiter says,

"Please come back again. My father, he's a very good chef, and he says he will make you caprese and bruchetta anytime you want. Soon, we will have a better menu as well."

Returning to her apartment, Antonella slides her hand around Mario's arm. She's never met any man to whom she's been so attracted, and the time spent with him today is the most romantic experience she's ever known. His Italian heritage, charming manner and handsome features are a combination she finds difficult to resist. As they stroll along the busy street, she says,

"I've had a wonderful time today, Mario. Thank you for stopping at the trattoria."

"You don't have to thank me. I enjoyed talking to you today. I hope we can do this again, sometime."

"I would like that. But is it difficult for you to leave the Army base?"

"No, not any more. There's not much to do these days, so my sergeant will let me come and go almost anytime I want."

"Your sergeant seems like a nice man."

"He is. I'm sure he'll let me off in a day or two. I'd enjoy seeing you then."

"I'd like that, too."

Returning to the apartment, they stop at the foot of the stairway to say good night. The awkward moment leaves her unsure of what to say or do. While staring into his eyes, she places her hands on his shoulders and gives him a light kiss on the cheek.

"Thank you again, Mario. I'll see you in a few days." After entering the apartment, Antonella rushes to the window and sees Mario sitting in his Jeep. When he looks up at her, she waves to him one last time. He waves back, starts the engine, and slowly drives away. Standing there until he vanishes from sight, Antonella can feel her emotions for this American soldier becoming stronger and more exciting. She can think of nothing but seeing him again.

Mono V. D'Angelo

CHAPTER 15

In the ensuing months, Mario and Antonella are together with increasing regularity. As the war migrates north into Germany, the activity at Pomigliano d'Arco shifts from supporting ground troops to keeping B-17's flying, reducing Company A's workload to basic equipment maintenance. Able to more easily leave the base, Mario visits Antonella several times a week, and they spend many carefree hours together. Acting as his personal guide, she shows Mario many beautiful and historic sites, which survived the war in Napoli. The ancient ruins of Serapeo, the Castel dell'Ovo and Mount Vesuvio fill Mario with an appreciation for the rich traditions and centuries of culture. Discovering this world with Antonella draws him closer to her. Their outings rapidly escalate from moments of curious interest to days of romantic interludes.

During one such outing, Antonella suggests,

"Mario, I've been told the ferry boat to Capri is running again. Can we go there today? It's the most beautiful place in Napoli. You must see it."

Mario finds it impossible to say no to her.

"Yes, Let's go. It sounds like fun. What's on Capri?"

"It's an old fishing village, with cafes and hotels all along the harbor. I'm sure we can have a delicious lunch there." The Isle de Capri is a small island about an hour from the main harbor of Napoli. Arriving at the battered city dock, they walk-hand-in hand, searching for the boat that will take them to Capri. They find nothing at the first dock, then try a second where, at the end of the adjoining pier, Antonella sees an old vessel.

"There it is...I'm sure that's the ferry." She runs toward the boat, dragging Mario along. Tied to the pier is an old boat, identified as the ferry by the simple name, CAPRI, painted on its bow. It has two decks, an enclosed lower deck and an open sun deck. Originally painted white with green trim, its metal hull is heavily rusted from the years of neglect during the war. The upper deck is lined with rows of weathered benches and several lifeboats. Looking at the rickety old craft, Mario asks Antonella,

"Are you sure this thing is safe?"

"Mario? How can you ask such a question? I've ridden these boats since I was a little girl." Her answer doesn't allay his concern, but it's soon too late, as a man standing on the deck announces,

"Andate a Capri, venite a bordo ora." The passengers line up, pay the small fee and board the ferry.

"Let's go up to the second deck. I love the view there," Antonella says. Climbing a short staircase, they find a place along the rail and await the ship's departure. Moments later, vibrations from the engine sputtering to life resonate throughout the old vessel. Amid billowing clouds of black smoke and sounds like those of a hammer clanking against an anvil, the ferry gently eases from the pier and onto the rolling swells of the open Mediterranean.

Standing on the upper deck, Antonella looks at the shattered remains of her once beautiful Napoli, and her playful mood becomes somber. She grips the railing more tightly, her knuckles appearing white and taut. Mario sees her reaction.

"Antonella, are you feeling ill? What's wrong?"

"It's so ugly now...Mario. Napoli was such a beautiful city before the war...but look...look at it now. Why did this have to happen?" she says in almost a whisper.

With no answer to her painful question, Mario simply takes her into his arms.

"It will be rebuilt again, you'll see. Someday this will all be forgotten."

She turns away from the view of her destroyed city and looks into his face. Alone on the deck, they hold each other tightly and share a tender kiss.

"Thank you...you always make me feel better when we're together. Since we've met, I've never been happier. Do you feel that way, too?"

"I've felt that way from the first time I heard you sing. I can't believe I've come halfway around the world to find you," he replies softly. They kiss again, this time their underlying passion for each other becoming more evident. She takes his hand into hers.

"I...I've never felt this...so close to a man, Mario. I...I'm not sure what it feels like...to be in love, but I think I love you." After brushing her windswept hair from her face, he daubs a tear from her cheek with his finger.

"I love you too, Antonella. You are all I ever think about anymore."

Although she had little doubt about Mario's feelings, she is elated by his admission of love for her. As the old ferry plows through the Mediterranean swells, they hold hands and say little else, each wondering what will become of their fragile commitment to each other.

Arriving at Capri, the boat glides into the tiny harbor and bounces into the well-worn pilings along the wharf. A crewman tosses heavy lines ashore to waiting dockhands and, after the vessel is secured, the loud engine is shut down and passengers are allowed to go ashore. Mario can see how anxious Antonella is to show him this beautiful place. He notices that, whenever she's excited over something, she pulls him by the hand, as if in a great hurry. Leading him from the ferry, she says,

"I love to come here. Capri never seems to change. It looks exactly the same as it did when I was a little girl. Are you hungry? Shall we find something to eat?"

"Yes, I am hungry. Let's stop someplace for lunch."

Largely ignored by the war, Capri's quaint harbor remains intact. With towering cliffs rising hundreds of feet straight up from the ocean, the picturesque village seems to crawl to the very top of the canyon walls. Small fishing boats, each painted with its own distinctive colors, sit in rows on the beach adjacent to the main waterfront district. An assortment of markets, cafes and pensiones lines the cobblestone street opposite the ocean. Strolling along the waterfront of this ancient island with Antonella by his side, Mario cannot remember being so at ease or comfortable with someone. Blindly following her through the center of town, Mario follows her up a small road leading away from the ocean. His curiosity piqued, he asks,

"Where are we going, Antonella?"

"I recall a small café near the top of the cliffs. We can have lunch there if it's still open for business. The view is...well, you'll see." The narrow, winding road twists and turns its way to the top of the highest bluff. Breathing heavily when reaching the top of the often-steep trail, Mario wishes he smoked less. Antonella encourages him onward.

"I don't think it's too far now, Mario. It should be around the next turn, just ahead."

The trail is shrouded by densely packed trees and brush, limiting the view to only the pathway before them, but Antonella surges ahead and stops before a small clearing.

"You see...isn't the view from here breathtaking?" she says. Through the void in the wild shrubs, he sees the deep, blue Mediterranean extending all the way out to the horizon. A strong breeze lifts thousands of whitecaps, adding an even greater contrast to the remarkable blue-green color of the sea. The mainland is visible, as is the small island of Ischia to the north. A cloudless sky drenches the harbor far below in brilliant sunlight, highlighting the rich texture of the earthen-colored hillside and harbor. He's reminded of Enzo's paintings at the Little Café. The natural beauty of this part of the world once again astounds him. Enzo's paintings pale in comparison to the view from this hilltop. He holds Antonella's hand while continuing to look at the spectacular vista.

"This is so amazing. It's hard for me to tell you how different this world is from mine." Antonella kisses him on the cheek.

"Come. We can enjoy the view from the trattoria. It's only a few steps from here."

The trattoria is nothing more than a small farmhouse. It's constructed of traditional white mortar with a clayed, tile roof. Vines and flowers hang from a large trellis covering a stone-floored garden. Several dining tables are located there, each offering an unobstructed view of the surrounding ocean. One of several women sitting at a table stands and greets them.

"Boun giorno. Do you wish to eat?"

"Yes...we're starving after the walk up the path to get here."
His Italian response confuses the woman. She stops for a moment, looks at him carefully.

"Why do you dress like an American? You are not Italian?"
Antonella has come to enjoy the reaction to Mario's language skills and says with a devilish laugh,

"He's a Sicilian...from America. Such a terrible combination, no?" Her joke amuses everyone. She leans against Mario's arm and in a playful, almost seductive voice, says,

"You don't mind if I tease you a little, do you Mario?"

"No, but let's order something from this poor woman before she gets too tired to wait on us."

"We only have cheese and hard salami for lunch, but I've just baked some fresh bread this morning. Will that be good enough for you?" They nod their heads in agreement, and the woman disappears into the farmhouse. Antonella gives Mario another gentle kiss and asks,

"Do you like Capri?"

"I think it's a very special place. I'm very happy to be here with you. We must come back again, sometime."

After their lunch arrives, they leisurely share the simple but delicious meal. Mario cannot recall having a more romantic attraction to any woman. While she eats and talks to him, he sometimes catches himself simply staring at her. He never seems to tire of her innocent charm and remarkable beauty.

Antonella does not want this day to end. Their admission of love for each other brings her more joy than she's ever dreamed possible. While sitting and enjoying this intimate and wonderful moment with him, she realizes she must reveal the one last part of her life she's kept a secret. Holding on to his hand more tightly, she says,

"Mario. I...I have something I must tell you. It's important you know this."

"What's wrong? You look so serious. I hope I didn't say something to upset you."

"No, no...you have done nothing. You are the most wonderful man I've ever known. But I never expected to fall in love with you, and...well, I didn't tell you everything...about my family."

"Antonella, you can tell me anything...whatever it is." She looks away from his eyes for a second, breathes deeply and says,

"I...I have a brother. His name is Giancarlo."

"Why did you think you couldn't tell me about him?"

"Let me try to explain. He's older than Lucia and I. He took care of the family when my father died...he became our father. But...he's an officer in the Italian Air Corps...a capitan. He's flown combat missions, Mario...missions against the Allies. I just didn't know what you would do or say and, when we first met, it didn't seem to matter. That's why I didn't tell you."

Mario sits quietly after hearing of Antonella's brother. She looks for a reaction, but he says nothing immediately. Then, a slight smile returns to his face.

"I'm not sure what to say, Antonella. But I'm glad you decided to tell me. Do you know where he is now?"

"A nice man at your base sent one of Mama's letters to him. He wrote back and, in his letter, he tells us he is being held in a camp in Sicily until the war is over. That's all we know,"

"Do you think he will be angry to know you have been seeing an American soldier?"

"I don't know. I haven't seen him for over two years...I don't know what he thinks about Americans. Tell me what you are thinking. Do you hate me for not telling you about him?"

"No, Antonella. I don't hate you. I could never hate you. This doesn't change how I feel. But I can see how important he is to your family. I have brothers...I know how you must worry, but the war is over for him. When he returns home, I hope he's ready to forget it. I know I am, and maybe that will help us get to know each other." Mario's uneasy acceptance of her brother is discomforting to Antonella. She's equally worried about Giancarlo's reaction when he returns to discover she's in love with an American soldier. She knows the day will come when the two men will have to confront each other, but for the moment, she gives him a lengthy hug, another tender kiss and says,

"Grazie, amore mia."

Finishing lunch, Antonella tells Mario,

"Let's take the path to the top of the island and see what else is here. I've never visited this part of Capri before." Mario agrees, and they begin exploring the surrounding hillside. Not far from the café, they discover an abandoned farmhouse. The old, stonewalled structure is set well off the path.

"Mario, let's go inside and look around. Maybe we can find a souvenir to take back with us." With child-like curiosity, she dashes off in front of him before he can respond. The old run-down structure suffers badly from neglect. Bright beams of sunlight penetrate the roof through its many holes, and all the windows are either broken or missing entirely. Remnants of previous occupants are scattered about the floor, like pieces to a puzzle. Broken dishes, blackened pans and tattered furniture are all that remain of its former tenants. Standing just inside a doorway, Antonella grabs Mario's hand once again.

"You go first, Mario, in case there are any rats. I can't stand rats." Cautiously stepping around the debris on the floor, he leads her into the house.

"What are we looking for?" he asks.

"I don't know...just keep looking until you see something interesting." Moving into another room, she hears something crawling beneath an old dresser. It tears from its hiding place and scrambles out of the room through a nearby window. Terrified, Antonella jumps behind Mario and screams,

"Oh God, it's not a rat is it Mario? Is it a rat?"

"No, it's just a cat, Antonella. It's alright." He turns to face her and wraps his arms around her.

"They frighten me so much...I'm so relieved you're here with me." Staring into his eyes, she suddenly wraps her arms around his neck and begins kissing him with an explosive passion. The privacy of the deserted old house ignites both their emotions, and Mario pulls her tightly against himself. Their kisses become more heated as they succumb to the joy of touching one another. Antonella whispers,

"I love you, Mario. But...but I've never been with a man before. I'm afraid to stay here for very long."

"You don't have to do anything you don't want too, Antonella. I love you, too, and I don't want you to be afraid or upset when you're with me."

"Thank you for understanding. I...I just need more time. You are so kind and gentle. What will happen to us, Mario?" she says, kissing him tenderly.

The same question has been haunting Mario for several weeks now. He gently brushes her hair to the side of her face.

"I'm not sure. But I know I don't want to lose you."

"But someday you will have to go back to America, yes?"

"Yes, but I'll either stay or come back after the war. I don't really know. All I know is I'll do something." The sobering dose of reality tempers their emotions for the moment, and he says,

"Let's go back to Napoli before it gets too late in the day."

They leave the farmhouse, return to the harbor and board the ferry for the return passage to Napoli. After the most extraordinary day of his life, Mario realizes he cannot leave Italy without Antonella. His mood is quiet and reflective during the short trip to Napoli. He knows he will ship out for home sometime soon. He realizes that the only way he can be with her is to marry her. His head is full of questions. What would she say? Would the Army allow him to marry? Where would he live? He has a twinge of panic over the thought of leaving without her. He is already looking ahead to getting answers to these important questions when he returns to base. Noticing his distant stare, Antonella asks,

"Mario, you are so quiet. Is there something wrong?"

"No, I was just thinking of some things I must do when I get back to the base."

Several days after his visit to Capri, Mario decides to speak with Sergeant Thompson regarding his situation with Antonella. Finding him in his office, he knocks on the door jamb and asks,

"Hey Sarge, ya got a minute?"

"Yeah. Give me a second to finish up this report. Have a seat." Mario sits patiently while the sergeant stuffs the papers into an envelope. Sergeant Thompson looks up and groans,

"There…this goddamn paperwork…it never ends in this man's army. What's going on with you, Mario? I haven't seen too much of you lately."

"Yeah, I know. I've been spending a lot of time with that girl I met…you know the one that fixed my clothes for me."

"Yes, I remember. What did she do? Dump ya or somethin?"

"No, not yet. But I got a serious question ta ask you."

"You aren't in any trouble are you? Did you get this girl pregnant or something?"

"No, Sarge. It's nothing like that. But I'm thinking of getting married, and I want ta know what to do. Can you help me out?"

Sergeant Thompson freezes for a second and looks directly at Mario.

"Did you say you want to get married?"

"Yeah, Sarge. I want to marry Antonella. I'm in love with her."

"Jesus Christ, Mario. You're not bullshitin me are you?"

"No, Sarge. I'm serious. Can I get married if I'm in the Army?"

"I've heard a lot of guys stationed in Britain married girls there, so I'm sure it can be done. But it's a big pain in the ass. You have to get approvals from all kinds of big brass in the Army Command. Are you sure you want to do this?" Mario thinks over the question for a moment and says,

"I've never been more sure of anything in my life, Sarge."

"Okay, Mario. I'll start working on the details for you, but it's going to take some time. Give me a couple of weeks. She must be one helluva woman to put you through the hell you're going to have to go through to marry her. I can hardly wait to meet her."

Mario continues to visit Antonella, but says nothing of his intentions. Since their day on Capri, the question of their future together has remained troubling and unanswered, but he's certain they both feel a powerful commitment to each other. He wants to be sure the army will allow him to marry before he proposes to Antonella. Calling Mario into his office several weeks later, Sergeant Thompson holds up a stack of documents.

"I've finally been able to get some information for you. You have to fill out these request forms and return them to me. Once you get those back to me, I'll submit them to the camp commander." Mario takes the papers from Sergeant Thompson and quickly flips through them.

"What happens after that?"

"As your NCO, I have to advise the camp commander's office that this marriage won't prevent you from performing any of your assigned duties. You have to list personal information about the woman you intend to marry and submit it all for security checks. Once that's complete, you'll be given approval to marry. Oh, and one last thing. Your spouse can't live on base, so you'll have to find a place to live in Naples."

"Sarge, that won't be a problem, will it? You know...that part about advisin the commander's office that I can carry out my duties?"

Sergeant Thompson smiles at Mario. Speaking more as a friend than his superior, he says,

"Mario, you've bailed my ass out of more hot water in this war than anyone else in this outfit. If this is what you really want, then you've got it."

Mario stands, and shakes the sergeant's hand.

"Thanks Sarge, I've made up my mind, and I wanna to do this…very much. Can I ask ya one more favor?"

"What's that?"

"Do ya mind not sayin anything to the guys until I get this all figured out?"

"I won't say anything until you do. You have my word."

Following his discussion with Sergeant Thompson, Mario is confident his friend will help him get through the enormous stack of military regulations he faces. What he is most nervous about is his next visit with Antonella. How will he ask her to marry him? Remembering their remarkable day on Capri, he decides to return to the tiny island with her and propose. When he arrives at her apartment, he quickly climbs the stairs and knocks on the door. Antonella welcomes him with a hug and a light kiss.

"Hello, Mario. I didn't expect you until later."

"I know…but I…ah, I thought we'd go out for dinner, and I was thinking how nice it would be to go back to Capri. If we leave early, we can make the midday ferry. Do you want to go there again?"

"Of course, I love Capri. What a wonderful surprise."

"I remember seeing several nice cafes along harbor road. Why don't we stop at one of them?"

"If we are going to eat in one of those places, I must change into a nicer dress. I will return in a minute." Antonella enters her bedroom and closes the door. Waiting patiently, Mario watches the busy street below the window until she returns. A few moments later, the door reopens and she asks,

"Do you like this dress, Mario?" Mario turns to look at her and is speechless. She is wearing an exotic, summer dress made of bright, yellow silk. It's bare at the shoulders, with only two small straps, no bigger than shoelaces, holding it up. Perfectly sized, the brightly colored dress highlights her attractive figure, her long black hair and olive skin. In awe of her appearance, he simply utters,

"You...you look just fine." She's never looked more stunning and, while on the way to the ferryboat, Mario is more certain than ever of what he must do. Unlike the previous trip aboard the ferryboat, there are many more customers and several more crewmen. After boarding, Mario and Antonella climb to the open, top deck to enjoy the short ride to the island. The warm breeze tosses her hair about wildly and occasionally lifts her dress well above her knees. Antonella laughs playfully while trying to prevent her dress from flying up too high.

"Mario, I must lean against you to keep my dress down."

"I don't mind, but some of the crew and passengers are going to be disappointed."

He notices many passengers staring at her. To find such a beautifully dressed woman in this war-ravaged country is still extremely rare, and he sees how much Antonella enjoys the attention. She also notices and tells him with a giggle,

"Before the war, I found many customers by wearing my clothes out in public. It's so much fun for me. Maybe someone will want a new dress today." Soon after the ferryboat arrives at Capri, Mario and Antonella are strolling along the wharf together.

"There...that one, Mario. Let's stop there."

Overlooking the harbor, The Hotel Belvedere & Tre Re is a beautiful, old building which offers a ideal setting for what is about to take place. He quickly agrees, saying,

"That looks perfect. Let's go." A jovial looking man approaches them.

"Boun giorno, Signor e signorena. Voi gradiscono una tabella?"

"Do you have one overlooking the harbor?"

"You speak Italian, signor? How very nice...come. I have a lovely table for you and the beautiful lady." He leads them through the main floor of the hotel and out to a veranda facing the harbor. Standing next to a table against the stone and wood railing, he asks,

"Will this do, Signor?" Mario looks to Antonella for her approval.

"Do you like this one?"

"Oh my God, Mario. Yes…of course…it's wonderful."

Pulling a chair away from the table, the man extends his hand to Antonella, inviting her to be seated.

"May I bring some wine signor? I have a delicious white from Tuscany I'm sure you will enjoy."

"What is your name, signor?" asks Mario.

"Dominic."

"Dominic, can you please bring a bottle? This is a special occasion." As Dominic leaves, Antonella is puzzled by Mario's last comment and asks,

"Mario, what do you mean this is a special occasion? I don't understand."

"I'll explain soon."

While Antonella speaks to him, he can only partially listen. He wonders what powers of fate have somehow led him here. When he left Detroit three years earlier, it was impossible to conceive of sitting on a warm, Mediterranean island and asking the most fascinating woman he has ever met to marry him. His mystic trance is broken when Dominic returns with the wine. The proprietor pours a small taste into one of the crystal glasses and hands it to Mario.

"Tell me if you like this, signor." Mario sips it lightly, nods his head in approval and Dominic fills both glasses.

"Please enjoy. I'll return to take your dinner order when you are ready. You just call me over." On the verge of asking the most

important question of his life, Mario is starting to feel very nervous. His heart is pounding so hard he's certain Antonella will hear it at any moment. His breathing becomes short and choppy, forcing him to gently take several deep breaths to help him relax. Drinking some of the wine with her eases the tension, but then Antonella asks,

"Mario? Are you going to tell me what the special occasion is?" He surprises her by taking the wineglass from her hand and placing it on the table next to his. Unsure of his peculiar behavior, she asks,

"Why did you do that? Are you feeling alright?" Saying nothing, he reaches across the table and takes her hand in to his. She can feel him trembling slightly and is afraid something might be wrong.

"Please...please tell me what's the matter. You're scaring me, Mario." With his emotions dancing somewhere between raw fear and sheer excitement, he forces a weak smile.

"I...I'm fine. But I have something important to talk to you about...something I need to ask you." Having rehearsed this moment in his mind numerous times, he's chosen his Italian words carefully. But now, his thoughts remain entangled somewhere between the two languages he speaks so fluently. His mouth is suddenly dry, and he takes a sip of wine before he proceeds. In a slow and deliberate voice, he begins to propose.

"Antonella, mai ho conosciuto, I mean...I've never known a woman like you. I love you and want to marry you...I want you to

come to America. Oh no...I'm so sorry. I am speaking English, excuse me. *O non amato alcua donna come voi ed io desiderate sposarli e portarmeli con vivere in America.* Will you please be my wife? I...I mean, *Volontà siete la mia moglie?"*

Antonella is nearly in shock. She begins trembling, pulls her hand from his and covers her mouth as she gasps in disbelief. She becomes flushed, her face reddening as her heart races wildly. Her thoughts flash back to the many dark nights of the war, when she and Lucia each fantasized about an intense romantic affair with a handsome man and now, it seems her fantasy has come true. Tears immediately come to her eyes.

"You...you want to marry me, Mario? I...I can't believe you've asked me that. I don't know what to say. I love you...very much."

"Then just say yes Antonella...say yes. I can't imagine my life without you." She hesitates momentarily, then leans across the small table and kisses him. In a voice choked with emotion, she whispers,

"Yes...yes, Mario. I want to marry you very much."

They spend the rest of the romantic day enjoying dinner and wine and talking of the extraordinary events that have brought them together. Antonella asks Mario endless questions about his family and life in America, and she enjoys the next few hours listening to him tell her all about what a wonderful world America must be. There will be much to do to make this dream a reality, but for tonight,

Mono V. D'Angelo

they want nothing more than to enjoy their love and passion for each other during the first few hours of their engagement.

CHAPTER 16

Following Antonella's extraordinary day with Mario, a disturbing uncertainty begins to creep into her fairy-tale experience. The joy and excitement of his proposal is being slowly undermined by the reality of what price she will have to pay for his love. Sitting alone in her little room, she replays the magical events on Capri in her mind. The beautiful hotel, the spectacular view of the ocean, and Mario's endearing nervousness are the romantic images she's found only in her dreams, until now. They are the elements of the fairy tale that have convinced her to say yes to him. She is troubled, however, by one aspect of his proposal. His words, "I want you to live in America with me," keep repeating in her mind. The thought of living anywhere, other than Napoli, has never occurred to her. But now, she faces the real possibility of leaving her family and the only life she has ever known.

Mario's vivid descriptions of large homes with many rooms and land to grow gardens have increased her curiosity about life in America. Even when Pirrone lived, they could never afford such opulence. After living in apartments her entire life, homes such as Mario describes seem like mansions to her. His talk of big cars, radios and movie houses everywhere simply adds to the fascination. She cannot conceive of such luxuries in Napoli. She believes Mario's promise of a better life, but the chilling reality of leaving Lucia, Assunta and Giancarlo forever lingers in the shadow of her fantasy like an unwelcome guest. She struggles to overcome what she imagines will be the consequences of marrying him, but cannot resolve her conflicting feelings alone. She decides to tell Lucia everything and ask her advice.

The following day, she anxiously waits for Lucia to return from a trip to the local markets. Feeling impatient and nervous, Antonella rushes from her bedroom when she hears Lucia entering the apartment. With Assunta in the kitchen preparing her bag of supplies to deliver another baby, Antonella quietly asks her sister,

"Lucia...I'm so glad you're home. I must talk to you. It's...it's very important."

"Fine. Let's talk. Is something wrong?" Grabbing Lucia's hand, Antonella whispers,

"Let's go for a walk. I don't want Mama to hear this yet. Mama, Lucia and I are going out for a short time." After leaving the apartment, Antonella leads Lucia down the street until they are a short

distance away. Troubled by her sister's mysterious behavior, Lucia stops on the busy street. Becoming somewhat angry, she asks,

"This is far enough, Antonella. I will go nowhere until you tell me what this is about. You're not in trouble are you?"

"No...no, it's nothing like that. It's Mario. When we went to Capri...yesterday, and he...he asked me to marry him. He wants me to...live in America with him, Lucia." Antonella can feel tears welling up in her eyes, while waiting for her sister to say something. Astonished by the news, Lucia places her arm around Antonella's shoulder and directs her to a nearby bench.

"Oh, dear God, Antonella! Why didn't you tell me it was so serious with him? What...did you say?"

"Lucia, it was the most...the most beautiful moment I've ever known. We were sipping wine before dinner...at one of the hotels on Capri...next to the ocean. He suddenly took my glass from my hand and...and then he asked me. I said yes, Lucia. I said yes. He said he loves me and doesn't want to lose me. Lucia, no man's ever said that to me before." Antonella knows that Lucia's upset. She can feel her tears trickling down her cheeks, as Lucia asks,

"And do you love him? Really love him? Enough to leave Napoli?" Antonella weeps softly at the pointed question, while placing her hand over her mouth to muffle her crying.

"I...think so. I want to be with him all the time. That's love, isn't it?" While wiping the tears from Antonella's face, Lucia's own misgivings begin to mount.

"I don't know. I've never been in love, but that doesn't matter. You must decide for yourself if you love him enough to leave Italy. I...I don't understand, Antonella. How could this happen so fast? Are you sleeping with him? Is that why you feel this way?"

"No...no, I'm not. But I want to be with him...for the first time since the sailor's attack...I..." Stopping before she finishes her thought, Antonella realizes she has unintentionally divulged her long kept secret.

"What? What attack? What in God's name are you talking about, Antonella?" shouts Lucia.

"It was many years ago. I met a sailor...while I was swimming. I went on a large ship with him and...and he tried to...rape me. I've been afraid to be with any man ever since...until now."

"Why didn't you tell me, Antonella? I'm your sister. You're supposed to tell your sister these things. I'll always love you...no matter what you do."

"I was afraid you...you would scream at me. I wasn't hurt, but I...I was frightened...and ashamed. That's why I didn't want to go out with any of the boys who asked me." Overwhelmed by Antonella's frightening revelations, Lucia hugs her tightly while they sit in silence.

The shocking news renders Lucia speechless for several minutes, but after finally regaining her composure, she asks,

"Antonella, do you really understand what you'll have to give up? You'll be alone...in a place you know nothing about. How much do you really know about Mario? Antonella...I'm very afraid for you. We've never been apart from each other before. We've survived this horrible war, but now I...could lose you, for...forever." Her voice fades, as the thought causes her to weep. *"We were supposed to walk...with our children...on the beach, but...now,"* Wiping tears from her face, as if embarrassed, she tries to remain calm. *"What of Giancarlo? How will you tell him of Giancarlo?"* she asks, after another discomforting moment of silence.

"He knows about Giancarlo. I told Mario everything about him."

"But how will you tell Giancarlo? And what if our brother objects to this marriage? What will you do then?"

"I...don't know, Lucia. I just don't know. Please don't be angry with me. What should I do?"

Antonella's plea for help tears at Lucia's heart. The fifteen-minute conversation creates a great deal of anguish for Lucia. To help Antonella is to lose her, but to turn her back on her is selfish and unthinkable. Her profound love will not allow it, no matter how sad the consequences. She makes the most difficult decision of her young life.

"If this is what you truly want, Antonella, then I...will help you tell Mama and Giancarlo." A weak smile brightens Antonella's

face.   She hugs Lucia and kisses her cheek in an intense show of affection and gratitude.

"Oh, Lucia, thank you, thank you...I don't know how I would do this without you. I love you so much." Hiding her fear beneath a layer of devotion, Lucia tries to console Antonella regarding the difficulties that lie ahead.

"I think Mario...is a good man. He's always kind to Mama and respects her very much. I can see how much you love him and...I want to share in your joy, Antonella. I don't know how I will live without you, but I want to see you happy. Promise me we'll always love each other...that you will never forget your family...promise me that, Antonella."

"I promise, Lucia.   You know we will always be together...somehow."

They return to the apartment to face the ultimate paradox: a family marriage that will ultimately lead to a separation destined to haunt them forever.

It has been only two days since Mario's proposal, and Antonella paces about the apartment in a nervous quandary over his absence.   Having told Lucia everything, she's anxious to tell her mother as well, but she waits for Mario to return before doing so. Why hasn't he returned by now? Has he changed his mind? Her insides ache and her heart rate multiplies, as she fears the worst. At last, she hears the sound of his Jeep on the street below the apartment, and Antonella rushes to the window to be certain it's Mario. After waving at him wildly, she dashes out of the apartment and down the stairs to greet him. Throwing her arms around his neck, she gives him a gentle kiss and says,

"Mario, where have you been? I was so worried about you. There is nothing wrong is there?"

"I'm...a little nervous, that's all. I've been trying to think of how to tell your family the news."

"Lucia knows everything. I...I told her yesterday."

"You did? What did she say? Is she upset...or angry with me?"

"She was very unhappy when I told her of our plans to leave...Napoli. But she promised to help me...if I need her. I was so afraid yesterday, Mario. Are you sure we're doing the right thing? Do you still feel the same way...about me?" Taking her into his arms, he holds her tightly.

"I'm afraid too, Antonella, but I'm sure of one thing. I'm very much in love with you and want you for my wife. I'll do anything to make that happen," he says as he kisses her, *"and I've come here to ask your mother's permission to marry you. Are we ready to do that tonight?"*

"Si, amore mio. Si."

After following Antonella up the stairway and into the apartment, Lucia greets him the moment he enters the room.

"Boun giorno, Mario. It's nice to see you once again." They exchange the traditional embrace and light kiss on the cheek with

417

each other, and she says, *"Antonella has told me about Capri...I'm happy for you both. But I am her only sister and I always worry about her. I have never thought I would have to live without her. It frightens me to think of being so far apart from each other."*

"Antonella told me how you feel, and I just want to thank you for offering your help. It will be hard to do this alone. I've come to talk to your mother tonight...to ask for her permission." Mario's gesture of respect brings an uneasy smile to Lucia's face, and she lightly holds his arm.

"Mama likes you very much. I am sure she will give you her permission, but she is not the only person who will judge you." Lucia's reference to Giancarlo rings clear and ominous. Mario understands that he will eventually have to deal with their brother, but for tonight, he must convince Assunta that he will take good care of Antonella. His conversation with Lucia is suddenly halted, when Assunta enters the room.

"Mario...I didn't hear you come in. Have you been here long?" asks Assunta, while taking his hand.

"No, not very long. I got here a few minutes ago. Lucia and I were just talking."

"Look, Mario. I have something to show you," she says, while pointing to a settee in the apartment. *"It's not new, but it's in very good condition, don't you agree? A woman's husband gave it to me for delivering his son. He was so excited about the baby, he offered it to me as payment."*

"It looks nice. Can I sit on it?"

"Of course. Please, sit down. I'll go and make some coffee. You do want some coffee, don't you?"

"I'd love some, Signora." Mario is pleased to see Assunta so excited. The settee permits guests in her home to sit comfortably while they visit, and he can see it's brought her a step closer to the normal life she once enjoyed.

With the delicious aroma of fresh-brewed espresso permeating the air, Antonella joins Mario on the settee and nervously holds his hand. Sitting at the dining table across the room, Lucia looks at Antonella and Mario and holds her finger to her lips, signaling Antonella not to say anything to their mother. When Assunta returns with the coffee, she is quick to notice the unusual tension between her daughters and Mario. After filling the cups, she looks at the three of them and asks,

"Why are you all so quiet? Is there something wrong?" Lucia glances at Antonella once again and says,

"No Mama. But Antonella and Mario...they have something exciting to ask you. Don't you Antonella?"

"What are you talking about, Lucia?" Assunta asks. Turning to Antonella, she then asks, *"What does she mean, Antonella? What exciting news?"* Lucia's unexpected comment prompts Mario to react quickly. He rises from the settee and sits next to Assunta at the dining table.

"I have something to ask you, Assunta...something very important. That's what Lucia means." Sitting with her hands folded on her lap, Assunta looks first at her daughters and then at Mario.

"What is it, Mario?" she asks. His nervousness is apparent, as he clears his throat and fidgets with the tops of his pant legs.

"First, I want to thank you for letting me into your home like this. You treat me like...one of your family. Napoli, it is like a second home to me." Feeling somewhat embarrassed by Mario's sincerity, Assunta kindly replies,

"You are a kind man, Mario, and I can see how much you love Napoli."

"I love more than just Napoli, Signora. I...think you know that I care a lot about Antonella. I love her...very much. More than I could ever imagine." Mario's comment unsettles Assunta, and she shifts nervously in her chair while glancing at Antonella. As mother and daughter stare silently at each other, Mario is certain Assunta knows what he is about to say. Mario breathes deeply, trying to calm himself.

"Signora Cappodanno. I want to ask for your permission to...to marry Antonella."

Assunta's chin begins to quiver and tears begin to appear in the corners of her eyes. Saying nothing, she stands and goes to Antonella. Assunta sits next to her daughter on the settee and takes her into her arms. Then sitting back, she holds Antonella's hands in hers and asks,

"Is...this what you wish to do? To marry Mario?" Wiping away her own tears, Antonella looks at Mario for a second before answering her mother.

"Yes, Mama. I do. I love him as much as he loves me and I...I want to be his wife," she answers, in a trembling voice. Placing her hands upon Antonella's cheeks, Assunta lightly kisses her forehead. Turning to face Mario, she says,

"I think you are a good man, Mario, and Antonella is fortunate to have someone who loves her as you do. If this is what you both want, then you...have my blessing." After giving her consent, she stands before Mario, gives him a gentle hug and asks,

"Mario. You...you must promise me...that you will always take care of her. I love her dearly, but...but her life...it becomes your responsibility now."

"I promise you that I will, Assunta. I promise." His commitment to Assunta brings a smile to her face. Having received her mother's blessing, Antonella rushes to Mario and throws her arms around his neck. She kisses his cheek and then turns to her mother and sister to share tearful hugs. They delight in the exciting news and begin looking forward to the first marriage in their family.

After receiving her mother's consent to marry Mario, Antonella and Lucia spend the following weeks planning the details of the wedding.

"Lucia, I love the beautiful light inside Maria Santissima. Do you think they will let me be married there?" asks Antonella. Maria

Santissima Dosolata, her favorite church in Napoli, had been spared from destruction during the war. Having made her first communion there, she has adored the old cathedral since she was a little girl.

"Yes...yes, that's the perfect place to be married. The frescos on the ceiling have always been my favorite. I'm sure if we ask the Father soon, he will reserve a date for us," replies Lucia. Soon, their thoughts turn to the most delightful detail of all. *"What will you do about a dress, Antonella? Can you design your own wedding dress?"*

"I don't know, but I think so. I already know what it will look like."

"You do? How is that possible?" Laughing loudly at Lucia's question, Antonella explains.

"I've never told you this before, but when we hid in the attic for days...I used to imagine the design of my dress many times. I saw every stitch and detail, and...now I just know how it will look."

"Well, don't tease, Antonella. Tell me. What will it be like?" Antonella begins to laugh once again at Lucia's curiosity. She stands to better illustrate her vision.

"It will be very tight at the waist...with a two or three layered skirt touching the floor," she says, while sculpting the imaginary gown with her hands. *"The top will have an open neckline and it will be covered with embroidered patterns...and it will have a long, flowing train. I would love to have many little flower girls to help me hold it."*

"You really can see the dress. I will help you with it, but we must start to look for material right away."

The search for the fabric begins immediately. After several futile days of scouring the local merchants and traveling to neighboring towns, the reality of a war-zone economy defeats them. Suitable white fabric with which to make her gown is nowhere to be found. Even peddlers in the black market cannot find anything Antonella can use. During one of Mario's visits, her frustration makes her unusually irritable, and he's aware something is troubling her.

"You look upset, Antonella. What's the matter?" he asks.

"Lucia and I have shopped everywhere for some white fabric, but we can't find any. I want...to design my own wedding dress, Mario. It's something I've dreamed about. But without material...I can't do anything. I'm sorry for being so unpleasant. I'm disappointed, that's all."

"What kind of material do you need?"

"White linen is what I want. Why? Do you know of some?" she responds with growing interest.

"No, but some of my friends on base know how to find a lot of different things. I can ask them for some help." Antonella's temperament changes instantly, as Mario hints at the possibility of finding some fabric for her.

"Do you really think they can find some? That would be wonderful, Mario. When will you know?"

"Don't get too excited, yet. I'm not sure they can do anything. But when I go back to the base tonight, I'll ask them."

It's well past midnight when Mario returns to Pomig. As he enters the barracks, most of its residents are fast asleep. When passing Hank's bunk, he notices some movement and stops at the foot of his bed. He whispers,

"Hey, Hank. You awake?" Pulling the blanket from over his head, he looks up at Mario with a puzzled expression.

"What the hell? Wh…what time is it?"

"It's around 12:00 o'clock. Put on some clothes and come outside for a minute. I need ta talk to you about something."

"Jeesus Christ, Carlucci. This better be important," grumbles Hank, groping for his pants and shoes. The two men slip quietly from the barracks and sit on the steps of the entrance porch. Mario lights a Pall Mall and then offers one to Hank. After taking a long puff, Mario slowly exhales the smoke skyward and gazes at his still-groggy friend.

"Hank, I need another favor. You know, something like the coffee and sugar you got for me a while ago."

"You mean you rousted me outta my bunk ta tell me ya want more coffee?" replies Hank, incredulously. Mario begins chuckling over his misunderstanding.

"Naw…it's nothing like that. Look, I'm gonna tell ya something I only told the Sarge so far, then you'll understand. I'm gonna get married. I asked Antonella to marry me." Snapping out of his sleepy pall, Hank sits up straight and stares at Mario in astonishment.

"What? Are you serious?"

"Yes, I am. I asked her a few weeks ago, and she said yes. I'm really gonna do it."

"Holy shit! I don't believe it. You're the last guy I woulda ever guessed ta git hitched. This Antonella must be a hellava gal. I can't wait to meet her."

"She is…I never met a woman like her before. I didn't say much to anyone until I knew for sure. But now, I can tell you guys about it. I'm gonna have everyone out for dinner to meet her soon."

"So, what's this favor you need?"

"Oh, yeah. I damn near forgot why I got you up. Look, she needs some white material…to make a wedding dress. It's real important to her, but she can't find any in town. I figure if anybody can find something like that, it's you. Whatta ya think? Can ya do anything?"

"I don't know for sure, but I got an idea where ta start lookin. Let me work on it tomorrow, and I'll let ya know. Son of a bitch! You're getting married. I still can't believe it," replies Hank with a laugh. "Wait till the guys hear this one." He shakes Mario's hand and they return to the barracks, knowing their wartime friendship of the last few years is about to change.

A few days later, Mario spots Hank entering the barracks, lugging a large, paper sack over his shoulder. The wide, ear-to-ear grin plastered across Hank's face suggests that he's met with some success in his search for the elusive white fabric. Throwing the bundle onto Mario's bunk, he says,

"Will this stuff do?" Hastily opening the neatly-wrapped package, Mario discovers a large bolt of white, silky material. It's nearly three feet wide, and certainly contains enough fabric for a dress. The extent of Hank's ability to locate the impossible continues to amaze Mario.

"Where in the hell did ya get this stuff?" he asks. Hank's bellowing laugh echoes through the empty barracks.

"Me and Frankie? We was playin craps with your dice one night. There was this Sergeant Kowalski, and he was having a bad night, till we showed up. Anyway, he ended up winnin some of his money back, and he thinks we had something to do with it."

"What's that got to do with this stuff?"

"Will ya wait a goddamn minute and let me finish what I was sayin? Kowalski's a supply sergeant for the infantry boys, including some of the Airborne divisions. This is the stuff they make parachutes outta. When I told him what I needed, he gave me the whole damn roll. He says they'll never use all of it and he was happy ta get rid of it." Picking up the roll, Mario slides his hand along its length and smiles.

"This is great Hank. You're amazing. I don't know much about this kind of stuff, but I'll bet Antonella will go crazy when she sees it." He makes plans to surprise her with the rare fabric on his next visit, but he doesn't realize there's a surprise waiting for him as well.

*   *   *

Antonella and Lucia have left the apartment in search of items for the wedding. Deciding to remain home, Assunta busily prepares vegetables for the evening meal. Hearing the sound of heavy footsteps on the outside stairway, she assumes it is Mario and goes to the door to greet him. There is no usual knock, however, and the mysterious visitor is apparently standing outside her apartment door, saying or doing nothing. Remaining ever cautious, she asks,

"Sì? Chi è là?"

"It's safe, Mama. Please open the door." Giancarlo's voice pierces her being like a summer's thunderbolt. In the seconds it takes to unlock the door, her heart begins racing wildly, and her tranquil emotions explode into a combination of joy and disbelief. Her hands begin to tremble, and tears fill her eyes, as she fumbles with the familiar lock. After throwing open the door, the reality of her son standing before her totally overwhelms her senses. Sobbing uncontrollably, she rushes to him and throws her arms around his neck.

"Gian...Giancarlo. Oh, dear God. You're...you're home. My...my son is home." With one hand gently cupping the back of her

427

head, he hugs her tightly and kisses her forehead, as their nearly five years of separation come to an end.

"It's over, Mama. It's all over, now. I'm home for good. Please Mama...don't cry, anymore." Their tearful embrace lasts for minutes, with the thrill of their reunion flooding them with sheer joy. Assunta releases Giancarlo from her arms, as the shock of his return slowly diminishes.

"Dear God. I...still cannot believe you've come home. Let's go inside. Let me make you something to eat. You must be starved."

"I've dreamed of this moment...of having a meal at home, so many times," he replies with an emotional voice. *"Where are Lucia and Antonella? Are they not home?"*

"They have gone to the market, but will return soon. They'll be so excited to see you, Giancarlo," she answers, preparing a plate of fresh fruit and cheese for him. Placing the dish before him, she watches contently as he enjoys the simple meal. Studying his face while he eats, she notices disturbing differences. His boyish smile has been replaced by the fatigued expression of a defeated warrior. His eyes, once bright, sit deeper in his face, surrounded by the dark circles that accompany fear and worry. His tired expression makes him appear older than his years. Her heart aches over the living hell his life must have been while he was away, but she is elated that her entire family has survived the war and is reunited again.

Numerous questions regarding his confinement come to her mind. Still unsure how comfortable he is discussing such details, she limits her initial inquiries to less sensitive subjects.

"How were you able to find our apartment?" she asks. Reaching into his shirt pocket, he pulls out her letter written to him months earlier, and says,

"After arriving in Napoli on the train, I took the bus to Bagnoli. I showed your address, here on this envelope, to the bus driver and he told me how to find this area. Then, I simply asked on the street until I found someone who knew the Cappodanno family."

"We did not expect you...until the war is over. Did the Allies release you early?"

"Yes. There is no reason to keep us any longer. The war in Italy has been over for many months now...and they want to go home as much as we do."

"The young soldier...the one from Rome. He told us what you did there. Is it true you speak English now?"

"Yes, I can speak a little. I became an interpreter for the British and Americans. They treated me well, but the Americans...they're very arrogant and rude. The last few months there, I did very little...there were no new prisoners coming into the camp, so when I told them I had a family living alone in Napoli, they allowed me to leave." After finishing his meal, his fatigue from the long journey catches up with him. While rubbing his tired eyes with the back of his hands, he asks,

"Is there someplace I can lie down and rest for a while, Mama? I've not slept for over twenty-four hours."

"Here...on the settee. You can sleep here. Take off your shoes while I go find you a blanket." Exhausted, Giancarlo reclines on the settee and closes his eyes. He is fast asleep before Assunta returns. Standing over her son as he enjoys a much-needed rest, she feels tears trickling down her cheeks once again. She gently covers him with the blanket, brushes his tangled hair away from his forehead and then anoints herself with the sign of the cross in a thankful prayer for his safe return.

Although a free man, Giancarlo remains an emotional captive of his long imprisonment. Despite his total exhaustion, he is unable to turn off the memories of the past four years. In his half-conscious world of haunting nightmares and blurred reality, deep sleep is a rare occurrence...,

Drifting off, he once again, finds himself sitting in the familiar pilot's seat of his Piaggio P108 bomber. The drone of its four powerful engines reverberates throughout the aircraft. The only lights visible are those of a myriad of instruments housed in the console before him. Unsure of the target for the plane's brutal mission, he asks his co-pilot,

"Do you have co-ordinates for the drop?" There is no answer. Turning to question the co-pilot again, he discovers Pirrone sitting there, dressed in his usual black hat, tie and coat.

"Papa, what are you doing here?" he asks. Starring straight ahead into the blackness, Pirrone neither looks at him nor says anything. Radioing the bombardier, Giancarlo, asks,

"Lieutenant, are we over the drop zone yet?" Again, there is no answer. He then radios the remainder of the six-man crew, saying,

"This is Captain Cappodanno. Report your readiness to complete the drop, immediately." Receiving no response from any of them, he suddenly realizes there is no crew aboard, only his father. Concentrating on the mission, he opens the bomb bay doors and prepares to deliver the plane's deadly ordinance by himself. But Pirrone reaches out and grabs his hand before he can pull the release handle. Turning to face him, Giancarlo says,

"Papa, don't try to stop me. This is my job. I must do this." Pirrone remains silent, but he slowly shakes his head from side to side with a sorrowful expression of disapproval on his face. Ignoring his father's objections, Giancarlo pulls the release handle. The plane shudders violently, as it disgorges its rain of death. Watching through his windshield as the plane rolls through a turn, he sees billowing plumes of red and yellow flames silently dot the night sky below from the bombs finding their mark. Then, without warning, voices of playing and laughing children begin to echo into his headset as the final five hundred-pound bomb plummets toward them.

"Run...run fast," he shouts, while turning to Pirrone once again. *"It's my job, Papa. I'm sorry,"* he says, trying to explain his vile action. As the laughing grows louder, he tears the radio headset

431

from his ears and throws it into the rear of the plane, only to hear the voices increase to a deafening roar. When they continue unabated, he covers his ears with his hands, closes his eyes and cowers in the darkness as the bomb zeros in on the innocent children.

Jolted awake by the intensity of the dream, Giancarlo is covered in a cold sweat. He attempts to focus his eyes on the ceiling. Drifting in and out of his restless state of mind, he hears the same laughing voices coming from the street below. Disoriented by the nightmare, he climbs from the settee and rushes to the window to see if the children are safe. After standing there for several seconds, he realizes he's experienced another one of his hellish dreams. Gazing down onto the street, he recognizes Lucia and Antonella mingling and laughing with several of the neighbors. Seeing them, for the first time in almost four years, sends a chill through his body. He is tempted to call out their names, shout to them that he has returned, but he says nothing for the moment. At the time of his enlistment, they were frightened, young girls who depended on him for a father. But watching them now, he is astounded by what beautiful young women they've become. He stares at them for several minutes, without saying anything, watching them with great pride as they enjoy their early morning conversations. For all of its terror and brutality, the war appears to have left them physically unharmed. Admiring them from his secluded position, his thoughts return to Pirrone, and he thinks of how proud of them he would be. He watches as they say goodbye to the neighbors and begin to climb up the stairway to the apartment. They are still laughing and talking as they open the apartment door and find him standing there.

For the first few moments, Lucia and Antonella remain frozen in place, shocked by his presence. They cover their faces with their hands and scream in disbelief. His emotions cripple his ability to speak, and he welcomes his sisters by extending his arms to them. With tears streaming down their faces, Lucia and Antonella rush to him together, each wrapping their arms around him and touching his face as they all embrace one another. Grabbing them by their waists, he lifts them completely off the floor in his exuberance.

"Giancarlo! Oh Giancarlo, I don't believe you're home. I'm so happy to see you...to see you've returned safely," cries Antonella. After putting them down, he kisses each of them on the cheek.

"When...when did you...you get here?" asks Lucia, as she wipes her eyes with her bare hands.

"I came home early this morning. Mama said you and Antonella were out to the market," he replies. Stepping back a few steps, he says, *"Look how beautiful the both of you are. I can't believe how much you've both grown. It's so wonderful to be together again...like when we were children."* Joining her children in their joyous reunion, Assunta says,

"Lucia and Antonella, please. Let Giancarlo sit down and rest. He's traveled many miles."

"I'm fine, Mama, really. You don't know how I've missed their attention and the way they used to spoil me," he replies with smile.

"And we shall spoil you again, dear brother. We will prepare a wonderful dinner and make you eat until you can no longer walk. Can we do that, Mama? Can we?" asks Antonella excitedly.

"Yes...of course. We'll spend the entire evening together...as a family, again."

Sitting comfortably at the dining table, Giancarlo watches his mother and sisters prepare the family meal, with the joy they shared so many years ago. Antonella brings him glasses of wine, while Lucia serves him fresh bread and hard sausage. The apartment is filled with laughter, as they rebuild the weakened bonds that once held them tightly together. With dinner served, they sit at the table, join hands and bow their heads, as Giancarlo offers a simple prayer of thanks.

"Dear God, we thank you for protecting this family during our terrible ordeal and for bringing me home to them once again. Amen."

"Amen," repeat his mother and sisters. They enjoy a simple meal of pasta with seafood sauce, fresh green salad and homemade bread, while reliving many wonderful moments of their lives before the war.

"Giancarlo, please remind Antonella how much trouble she used to get into...she would never listen to anybody, isn't that right?" teases Lucia.

"Oh Lucia, stop. You were always so concerned about everything I did. Tell her, Giancarlo. She was like another mother to me," replies Antonella with a sarcastic giggle. He smiles at his sisters' loving way of annoying each other in jest.

"I'm sorry, but I refuse to take sides in that argument," he says, sounding much like an older brother. The evening dinner helps to reacquaint them, but they talk very little about the war at first. Eventually, however, Giancarlo speaks of his experiences, as the mood becomes more somber.

"I can't even tell you how terrified I was for your safety after the war broke out. I would go for days...many days, with little or no sleep. My insides hurt from worry...every day I felt sick...about not being here."

"It...it was horrible, Giancarlo. The bombs, the fighting...so many people died here. The city, it was nearly destroyed. We prayed for you everyday," admits Antonella.

"I prayed too, Antonella. For all of you...and the poor souls I dropped bombs on. I'll never forget the fires...as the cities burned. It was a terrible feeling for me."

Even as their emotions swing wildly, from child-like giddiness to terror-filled memories, Giancarlo is able to reclaim his place in the loving family he left years ago. He is home, at last.

Antonella's joy over her brother's return is brief. Lying awake in her bed, long after everyone has fallen asleep, she worries how she will tell Giancarlo of her plans to marry Mario. She is thankful that neither Lucia nor Assunta have said anything to Giancarlo regarding Mario, but she knows it is her responsibility to do so right away. Realizing Mario will be visiting at anytime, she cannot allow him to confront her brother before she tells Giancarlo everything. She decides to speak to him immediately after breakfast the following morning. Pans banging gently against the small stove in the kitchen wake Antonella. She can hear her mother softly humming an unintelligible tune, while preparing breakfast for them. Returning to their shared bedroom after bathing, Lucia sits on the edge of the bed and dries her hair with a large towel.

"Lucia, is Giancarlo awake yet?" asks Antonella in a whisper.

"No, I don't think so. I'm sure he will sleep late. He was very tired last night."

"I plan to tell him today, Lucia. About Mario...and about the wedding. I know Mario will return soon, possibly today. What...do you think Giancarlo will say?" Crumpling the towel into a wrinkled ball on her lap, she stares at Antonella with a look of great concern on her face.

"I think it's too soon, Antonella. He returned home only yesterday. Can't you tell Mario to stay away for several days?"

"That's not possible, Lucia. Even if I wait for him on the street, Giancarlo will find out. I...must do this today. I have no other

choice. *Will you help me, Lucia? Please?"* Lucia bows her head and nervously folds the damp towel.

"I promised you I would, Antonella. What do you want me to do?"

"Just be there with me. I want him to go for a walk with us...after breakfast, and I'll tell him then. I'll do it, Lucia, but maybe you can tell Giancarlo what you think about Mario...how he's different than the other Americans." Lucia holds Antonella's hand. With a serious expression tone in her voice, she replies,

"I know you're scared, but we knew this would happen. I will tell Giancarlo about Mario, and that he's not like the others. We'll tell him that, Antonella, and hope that he understands."

"Thank you, Lucia. How would I ever do this without you?" Kissing Lucia's cheek, Antonella springs from the bed. She goes into the bathroom to bathe and think about the difficult task ahead.

Antonella and Lucia are at the dining table with Assunta, sipping orange juice and eating sweetbread when Giancarlo awakens. Sitting on the settee, he rubs his eyes, stretches his arms and combs his fingers through his hair.

"Ah, Giancarlo. I see you have finally decided to wake up. Did you sleep well?" asks Assunta.

"I haven't slept well in many months, Mama. It will take some time, I'm afraid, but it feels good to be home. That will help."

"Come and have some breakfast. I'll go find something for you," says Assunta, as she hurries into the kitchen. While Giancarlo

437

sits at the table and tries to wake up, Lucia glances at Antonella, then nods in his direction to encourage her to say something to him.

"Giancarlo, Lucia and I thought you might like to join us for a walk today. You can meet some of the neighbors, and we can talk some more."

"That's a wonderful idea. I'd enjoy spending some time with my beautiful sisters," he replies with a smile. *"Will you join us, Mama? We can spend the entire day together."*

"No, but I would love nothing more. I must visit a woman who is going to deliver a baby any time now. I told her I would check on her every day until the child is born. But you children go and enjoy yourselves."

A short time later, Antonella and Lucia are proudly escorting their brother along the busy streets and through the local market place, introducing him to friends and acquaintances. The late morning sun warms the day quickly. Hoping to find a quiet place to reveal her secret, Antonella makes a suggestion,

"It will be cooler near the ocean. Why don't we go there? Maybe we can find someplace to have lunch." Tall shade trees line the street opposite the beach. Finding an old park bench facing the ocean under one of them, Antonella nervously clears her throat and says,

"Can we sit here for a while, Giancarlo? I...have something important I must tell you." Sitting between his two sisters, Giancarlo notices Antonella's voice becoming unsteady, and her manner uneasy.

"What is it, Antonella? You look so serious. Is something wrong?"

'No, but what I'm about to say will...oh, I...I'm not sure how to begin."

'I don't understand. What are you talking about?" he asks, looking to Lucia for help.

"Antonella, it's going to be all right. Go ahead and tell him," says Lucia. Now visibly anxious, Antonella takes a deep breath to calm herself before speaking.

"Giancarlo, I...I'm getting married." He pauses for a second, first looking at Lucia and then turning back to her with a smile. After putting his arm around her shoulder, he pulls her toward himself.

"That's wonderful, Antonella. But, I'm not at all surprised. What is the lucky young man's name?"

"It's...Mario. Mario Carlucci," she answers, with even greater hesitation.

"Carlucci? I don't recognize that name. What part of Napoli is he from?" Her breathing becomes shallow, as her anxiety is rapidly replaced by fear. Her eyes dart back and forth between him and Lucia. She is preparing to answer the question she dreads the most.

"He's not from Napoli, Giancarlo. He...he's an...American. A soldier. I started repairing some clothes for him and...and." Giancarlo's personable reaction from only moments earlier vanishes, and he quickly interrupts her. His mood suddenly turns darker.

Mono V. D'Angelo

"What are you saying? You are going to marry an...American? How can this be?" he responds angrily. Turning to Lucia, he asks, *"Lucia, what do you know about this? Is this really true?"*

"Giancarlo, please. Listen to us...before you become too angry. He is not like the other Americans you have met. He speaks our language...his family is from Sicily. He respects us...and treats us with great kindness. He even came to Mama...to ask her permission to marry Antonella. She likes him very much. Once you meet him, I'm sure you will too." Lucia's pleadings do little to dull the sharpness of Giancarlo's temperament, and he remains highly skeptical.

"I don't know what to say, Antonella. I...should be happy for you, but instead, I'm very upset. This American is going to take you away from us. We will...lose you forever, Antonella. How can I accept that? How can I welcome this man, this man who wants to destroy my family, into our lives?" On the verge of tears from Giancarlo's painful comments, Antonella fights her emotions and tries to remain poised.

"I know this news must shock you, but I love him, and he loves me. Mario...is not only kind to Lucia and me, but he is very generous to Mama. He's brought her wonderful gifts of coffee and sugar, when it was impossible to find any in the city. He didn't have to do that, but he did. He's more Italian than American, Giancarlo; he is. You cannot avoid him...he will visit again soon. I've told him all about

440

you, and he wants to meet you. Please tell me you will wait until you've met him before you start to hate him. Will you do that for me, dear brother?"

Remaining quiet and sullen, Giancarlo ponders Antonella's request while desperately trying to understand how she could have fallen in love with an American soldier. Puzzling questions race through his mind. Is this American like those he's known in Sicily? Although his sisters' descriptions of this man bear no similarity to the Americans he's met, he is deeply troubled by this disturbing news. His feelings are complicated by his love for his family and the unthinkable consequences of losing one of them. Holding his sisters' hands in his, he says,

"While I was away, I never stopped worrying about all of you. I would lie awake...praying that all of you would not be hurt or killed. That...that would have been unbearable. I often thought of coming home, of deserting my command, so I could protect you. That's how much I love you. I cried when Mama's letter arrived, knowing everyone had survived the war." He stops talking for a moment and carefully considers what he is about to say. *"Antonella, I love you so very much that it's difficult for me to imagine losing you. But I will meet this American, if that is what you want me to do. I only hope and pray you are right about him."*

"That's all I ask, Giancarlo. Thank you...thank you. I love you very much, too," she replies.

"Are you certain that this is what you want, Antonella?" he asks, once more.

"Yes, I am, Giancarlo. I am sure," she answers, nodding her head up and down.

While reluctantly agreeing to meet Mario, Giancarlo harbors serious reservations about his sister's marriage. Having become familiar with the Americans during his captivity, he thinks very little of them. He disapproves of the way they flaunt their money and equipment, look down on their own allies with indignance, and he considers them far too demanding. He will judge Mario harshly, and if he proves to be no different than the other Americans he's known, he will use his powerful influence within the family to prevent his sister from making, what he believes, is a terrible mistake.

Leaving Pomig with the roll of white material in the Jeep, Mario is looking forward to watching Antonella's expression when he surprises her with it. Arriving at the apartment, he parks in his usual place, tucks the bolt of white silk under his arm and bounds up the stairway two steps at a time. Knocking loudly, he hears some commotion inside, and then the door slowly opens. Antonella greets him as she usually does, but she is plainly distraught. Forcing a smile through her pursed lips, she greets him with uncharacteristic coolness. Standing in the doorway without speaking, she nervously looks over her shoulder, as if searching for something behind her.

"You look worried. Is there something the matter, Antonella?" he asks.

"It's...it's my brother. He's come home, and he's here now," she replies, in a muffled voice. Mario glances into the apartment but can see no one.

"What have you told him?"

"Everything, Mario. I told him about the wedding plans and...about you. He knows you're an American." Mario is surprised by Giancarlo's unexpected return, and his plan to give Antonella the gift of white fabric is lost to the initial meeting between the two men. He sets the package down on the stairway landing, lightly kisses Antonella on the cheek and says,

"Why don't you introduce us, then? I'm sure he's curious about me."

"Yes, he...is. He said he wants to meet you. But Mario, I must warn you, he's very upset over this." She re-enters the apartment, and Mario follows. With a clear view of the dining table, he sees her brother sitting there. Giancarlo is wearing a military shirt adorned with pilot's medallions on each collar.

When he notices Mario, he promptly stands and faces him. He is taller than Mario had imagined and appears thin. With Giancarlo's glaring attention riveted on him, Mario begins to take Antonella's warning seriously. His fierce expression forewarns Mario of the resentment Giancarlo holds for him. They are joined by Assunta and Lucia, and the tension-filled moment tests everyone's nerves. The two men stare silently at one another. Taking Mario's arm, Antonella cautiously leads him to Giancarlo. Her voice quivers slightly, as she introduces them to one another.

"Giancarlo, this is...Mario. He's been looking forward to...meeting you."

Extending his hand to greet him, Mario uses his flawless Italian and says,

"Ciao, Giancarlo. Sono soddisfatto di venirlo a contatto." Continuing to stare directly into Mario's face, Giancarlo hesitates for several seconds before reluctantly accepting Mario's greeting gesture.

"So you do speak Italian. My sisters told me that you know our language," he says coolly.

"Yes, I do. My father made my brothers and me use it all the time. I never knew how important it would become." Giancarlo's staunch demeanor remains unchanged by Mario's friendly comments.

"You must be relieved to be home. Antonella has told me you've been away for a few years," says Mario, trying to find some level of conversation in which to engage him.

"Yes, too long. I'm thankful the war is over for us. My family has been through a terrible ordeal."

"I know. They have told me how hard it's been for them." Mario senses no willingness by Giancarlo to talk openly about what is bothering him.

"I know you don't approve of the way I've come into your family, but they didn't trust me at first either, especially Lucia," he says, with a smile. *"After we spoke to each other, they gradually*

realized there was nothing to fear from me. *They've been like a second family to me. I'm willing to do whatever is needed to show you I mean your family no harm. Do you think we can talk about this honestly?"* After expressing himself as sincerely as possible, Mario detects a slight lessening in Giancarlo's rigid attitude.

"Why don't we take a short walk? Maybe if we talk, as one soldier to another, I can tell you what I want," he replies.

"I'm ready. Let's go," answers Mario.

Away from the women who are so important to each of them, Mario patiently listens to Giancarlo speak of his family.

"When my father died, Antonella and Lucia were very young, and Mama, well, she was devastated. I had to care for them...like a father. I had no choice. I've protected them ever since. I even helped Antonella run her business before the war. I don't intend to stop protecting them now."

"But your mother and sisters have changed. They are strong women now. Talk to the neighbors; they will tell you how Assunta helped them to survive the war...how brave and careful she is. I know she's happy you've come home, but they learned how to take care of themselves while you were away. You...don't have to protect them like that anymore," replies Mario. His comments cause Giancarlo to stop in the middle of the roadway. Mario can see by Giancarlo's rigid posture and grim expression that he refuses to accept these facts about his family as the truth. After thinking over what has just been said, Giancarlo replies,

"*I cannot simply stop worrying about them. The Americans I've met...they are not the kind of men I want my sisters to marry.*" Mario starts to feel his dormant temper reemerge, and he abruptly interrupts him.

"*Don't you think your sisters should have something to say about that?*"

"*What do you know about my family's needs? Nothing! That's the trouble with you Americans; you all want to interfere where you don't belong. How dare you come into my family and try and buy their loyalty. I know about the gifts you bring to my mother. You might fool them, but not me. I know what you're after,*" he shouts.

"*Is that what you think? Look, if all I wanted was a woman to sleep with, there are plenty of street girls in Napoli to chose from. I love Antonella, and I plan to marry her. You'll have to accept that.*"

"*I do not have to accept anything that's not right for my family. My sister doesn't know the Americans like I do. She will eventually see that marrying one is a mistake.*"

Mario can no longer tolerate Giancarlo's obstinate behavior. Feeling threatened and angry by Giancarlo's overly protective attitude, Mario paces angrily while searching for a way to resolve this unexpected impasse. With his heart pounding madly, he's feeling flushed from the growing rage he is experiencing, but he knows he cannot turn the conversation into a shouting match.

"I've heard enough. I can see you've already made up your mind before giving me a chance. I'm going back to the base. You'll have to tell Antonella and your family what you did here today. But I'm telling you one thing...this is not over yet." Mario runs up the stairway, grabs the package of material he'd planned to give Antonella and climbs into his Jeep. Sitting there for a moment, he looks at Giancarlo once more and says,

"I'll be back in a few days to talk to Antonella about this. She will have something to say about this."

Giancarlo says nothing before Mario races away. Returning to the apartment alone, he startles Antonella, who questions him with great concern.

"Giancarlo, where's Mario? What did the two of you say to each other?"

"He's returned to his base," he replies with a surly voice.

"But...why? That's not like him to leave without saying anything. What did you tell him, Giancarlo?" she asks.

"Antonella, you must understand something. I know the Americans well and I told him...I said it's not good for you to marry him. It's a big mistake, and you will see that someday."

Antonella is shocked by what her brother has just said. Still not fully believing his intentions, she stands directly before him and asks,

"Do you mean...you told him we cannot get married? Is that why he's gone?"

447

"You're making a serious mistake, Antonella. One day you will thank me." After he acknowledges her worst suspicions, she turns away from him and rushes to the window, searching the street below for Mario. When she sees he is gone, she struggles with a flood of conflicting feelings for her brother and what he's just done. She's never experienced any hatred toward him, but as a result of his actions, she feels powerful resentment over his attempt to control her life. Turning away from the window to face him, she shouts out with a rare anger in her voice.

"How...can you do such a thing? I'm not a little girl anymore. I know what I want, and you have no right to decide that for me. I can't believe this...this has happened. Why didn't you say anything to me?"

"I know what's best for our family, Antonella. You must not question me about this."

"Giancarlo, you cannot stop me. I will run away and marry Mario if I have to. Do you understand that? You're only my brother, not my father."

Giancarlo stands silently as Antonella breaks down in tears and rushes into her bedroom. Lucia follows and closes the door. Lying face down on the bed, her face buried in a pillow, Antonella can feel her sister's touch on the back of her head. Rolling over, she asks Lucia,

"Why is he doing this, Lucia, why? What can I do?"

"I don't know. I've never seen him like this before."

CHAPTER 17

Following the confrontation with Giancarlo, Antonella remains in her room for most of the next morning, rethinking her relationship with him. She's never before raised her voice at him in serious anger, and the guilt she feels because of it troubles her deeply. She understands that the war has changed him, and she is compelled to try and comfort him any way that she can. But the loving brother of her childhood, the man who became her father and watched over her poor business habits, has become a victim of the conflict. In his place stands a tired and angry man, one she must learn to know and love all over again. However frustrating she finds his attempt to control her life, she regrets what she's already said to him. She thinks perhaps Lucia is right. Maybe it is too soon to tell him of her marriage plans. Tortured by the thought of having to choose between Mario and her brother, she desperately searches for an answer.

449

A short time later, the bedroom door swings open and Assunta enters. Sitting on the bed beside her youngest daughter, she quietly asks,

"How are you feeling? Do want something? Some water or juice?"

"No thank you, Mama, not now. Mama, what can I do about Giancarlo? I've never seen him act so stubborn."

"I know, my darling; it's not like him. But we must remember what's happened here. We've been apart for a long time. The war...it's changed everyone. We all need time...to get over that."

"Will you speak to him, Mama? Can you make him understand how I feel about Mario?"

"I already have. I told him he must talk to you again. To listen carefully to what you have to say. He knows that he cannot really stop you from getting married. That to try will only drive the two of you...further apart."

"What...did he say?"

"Very little, but he's aware that he's causing you a lot of unhappiness. Give him some time...to think this over. Don't forget, Antonella, he's only doing this because he loves you." Assunta's intervention offers Antonella a glimmer of hope.

"Should I say anything...right now?"

"He's gone out. I think he wants to be by himself for a while. But, I'm sure when he returns, he will be less angry. You talk to him then."

"I will. Thank you, Mama," she says, hugging her affectionately.

Several more hours pass before Antonella hears Giancarlo return. Leaning against the small countertop in the kitchen, she watches as he enters the apartment, removes his coat and carefully hangs it on the back of a dining room chair. He does not notice her at first, choosing instead to stand at the window and stare out at the street while deep in thought. With her arms folded across her chest, she steps into the living room and greets him.

"Buono sera, Giancarlo. Come sta?" Surprised by her presence, he turns and faces her. She can see worry on his face. There are deep creases across his forehead and around his eyes, creases that were not there before the war. Before speaking, he approaches her and takes her into his arms. While he holds her tightly for a few moments, Antonella notices a difference in his attitude, a difference that causes him to tremble slightly.

"I'm sorry for hurting you the way I did, my dear sister. I've been thinking about all that was said...the harsh words we used. We've never talked like that to each other, even when we were young. You know I only said those things because I want what's best for you, don't you?"

"It's all right, Giancarlo. I know you didn't mean..." He interrupts her, as if his need to explain himself cannot wait any longer.

"Antonella, I've done many terrible things while I was away, things I can never tell you about. But I thought that if I protected you again, like I used to, it would somehow make those awful memories...go away. But I've made a mistake. Your Mario, he told me how strong you've all become, and he's right. Can you forgive me...for the way I've behaved?"

"There's no need to ask my forgiveness, Giancarlo. I said some very mean things to you...and I am sorry for that. I just want my loving brother to come home again." With her arm around his, they sit together on Assunta's settee and discuss their differences calmly.

Hoping Giancarlo will consider talking to Mario once again, Antonella cautiously approaches the subject with him, saying,

"Giancarlo, I want you to be happy. You have earned the right. During the worst days of the war, Lucia and I would cry for hours at a time because we thought we'd never find someone to love. When I met Mario, falling in love with him was the last thing I expected, but I did. I can't remember being this happy since we were children. I DO understand what I will have to sacrifice to marry him, but it's what I want. Can you ever see that?" He listens intently, realizing she is reaching out to reconcile their bitterness over her marriage plans.

"Yes...I do now. I was so upset over your plans to marry an American that I didn't give him a chance to tell me very much about

himself. The three of you cannot all be wrong about him. If he's won your hearts, he must be very different than the Americans I've met."

"Will you meet with him again?"

"Yes, and I promise to talk, really talk, to him this time. I want to know how this man has won your love."

"That's wonderful, Giancarlo. When you get know him, I'm sure you'll understand why I feel the way I do."

With their painful argument behind them, Antonella and her brother take the first steps toward restoring their damaged trust. But, despite Giancarlo's willingness to meet with Mario, she worries whether they will get along any better than the last time they spoke. She waits in nervous anticipation for Mario to return.

It's been over forty-eight hours since Mario drove away from Antonella's apartment in a silent rage. During that time, his constant complaining and short-tempered behavior attract the attention of Sergeant Thompson. After Mario has another pointless argument with one of the supply officers, the Sergeant grabs him by the arm and says,

"Let's you and I have a little conversation, Carlucci. In my office, right now!" Sergeant Thompson leads the way and waits next to the open door until Mario enters the room. Mario has seen his stern expression before and, as the Sergeant slams the door closed, Mario expects to be chewed out. Sergeant Thompson does not disappoint him.

"What the fuck is going on, Mario? You've been sulking around the barracks for the past two days, just looking for someone or something to pick on. It's time to knock it off." Mario stares at the floor, embarrassed by his own annoying behavior.

"Sorry, Sarge. I guess I've been kind of a asshole lately, ain't I."

"Yeah, you have. It's not like you to be so miserable. What's wrong?"

"It's Antonella's family. She's got a brother who just got out of a POW camp in Sicily. He was a pilot...in the Italian Air Force. I just met him the other day, and...and well, it didn't go very good."

"What's that mean?"

"He's a real hard ass, Sarge. Before the war, he took care of everything for her family, and now he's sayin that Antonella and I can't get married. I tried to talk to him...to reason with him some, but he just doesn't like Americans. I'm not sure what's gonna happen now."

"Christ, no wonder you've been working with such a short fuse. When are you going to go back there? You are going back, right?"

"Yeah, sure I am. I'm not giving up that easy. But he's sure gonna mess things up if I can't get him to change his mind. You got any suggestions how to handle this?"

"I think you have to talk to Antonella first. Find out what she wants. If she lets her brother do this, then I think you're going to have a hell of a fight on your hands."

"That's what I been thinking too, Sarge. If she still wants to get married, I don't think he can legally stop us, can he?"

"Probably not, but that's asking for a lot of trouble. You're best bet is to try and make him understand how important this is. If anyone in this man's army can pull this off, it's you, Mario," says Sarge with a smile.

"Thanks a lot. I wish I was as sure as you are, though. Guess there's only one way to find out." After shaking Sergeant's hand, Mario leaves his office and heads for his Jeep. As he climbs behind the wheel, he sees the bundle of white silk in the rear seat and wonders if he'll ever be able to give it to Antonella as he'd planned. Pushing the ignition switch, he fires up the engine and heads for Bagnoli, wondering if this may be the last of his many trips there.

Arriving at the apartment, Mario stares up at the window and sees Antonella rush up and shout,

"Mario, wait there for me." Moments after vanishing from view, she appears on the street and runs to him. After greeting him with a hug and a kiss, she says,

"I'm so glad to see you again. I've been sick with worry that you wouldn't come back right away."

"Did your brother tell you...about our argument?"

"Yes...and I had a fight with him, too. But Mama and I have both talked to him since then, and I think he's calmed down. He's agreed to meet with you again and promised not to be so rude. Will you see him? He's in the apartment right now." Antonella's encouraging news bolsters his confidence, and Mario becomes optimistic about resolving this matter completely.

"If he's willing to try this again, then so am I." With that said, they return to the apartment.

When Mario enters the apartment, he can see Antonella's brother standing there waiting. Assunta and Lucia are sitting on the settee, but after a brief greeting, they withdraw to the back bedroom, leaving Antonella, Mario and Giancarlo alone. Mario nervously waits for Giancarlo to say or do something. After giving his sister an affectionate hug, he turns to Mario. The two men stare at each other for several seconds. Mario finds much less intensity in Giancarlo's face this time, as they extend their hands to greet one another.

"I feel I owe you an apology...for the way I treated you the other day. It's been very difficult for me...to be away, knowing that I could not help my family when they were in such great danger. But I can see that you are right, that they are much stronger now than when I left. They have said many good things about you." Mario glances at Antonella and sees a slight trace of a smile on her face, as Giancarlo continues, *"And I don't want my poor judgement to come between my family and me. I realize I must listen to them. Is it possible to forget what has happened between us and try again?"*

"I'd like that, Giancarlo," replies Mario, *"because there have been a lot of surprises for both of us."* The second chance suits Mario perfectly.

"Why don't we sit at the table and talk?" asks Giancarlo.

"You two sit while I make some coffee for us," adds Antonella.

Pulling the small wooden chairs away from the table, the two men sit across from each other and try to overcome their awkward silence. Mario expects to be thoroughly questioned, but to his surprise, Giancarlo sits in silence with his hands clasped together. Mario ends the tension, and says,

"I know you think all the Americans are like the ones you met, but they're not...I'm not."

"After listening to my sisters and mother, I don't know what to think anymore."

"Your family is very careful, especially your mother. I'm sure if I acted like the Americans you met, I wouldn't be here right now. But, I'm not like those men. My father, his name is Giuseppi, he lived only a few hundred miles from here. When I walk through the streets of Bagnoli, the neighbors...they treat me like I've lived here all my life. I don't know how to explain it, but coming to Italia has been the most important thing that's ever happened to me. It's too bad it took a war to bring me here."

Antonella returns with fresh coffee. Giancarlo takes a spoonful of sugar and gently stirs it into his cup. The clinking of the spoon is the only sound they hear for a brief instant. Gazing into the steaming cup of coffee, he seems lost in his own thoughts for a moment.

"This war!" he exclaims with a deep sigh. *"It's so hard to find any good in it. But you are fortunate. I almost envy you. To discover your family's homeland and learn to love it...well that's a small miracle. I've misjudged you badly, Mario."* Antonella joins them at the table, taking Mario's hand as Giancarlo's admits his rush to judgment. Mario and Antonella share in the feeling of relief, and then Mario faces Giancarlo again and says,

"I promised your mother that Antonella will have a good life in America. My family is Italian, and she'll never feel like a stranger there. Giancarlo, she is the first woman I've ever wanted to marry. I have a good job waiting for me when I return home, and I promise you that I will take care of her...forever." Mario's heartfelt commitment seems to erase any lingering distrust Giancarlo might have. He leans over to his sister, kisses her cheek and says to her,

"I'm sorry for making you so angry with me. I will not try to stop you from getting married." Rising from his chair, he shakes Mario's hand and, with a subtle smile, says.

"I musta compliment you. You Italian, it'sa very good."

"You...you speak English?" asks a startled Mario.

"Yes. I learna to speak inna the Allied camp. I was an interpreter," he replies. "I thinka you are right abouta my family. And a they are right about you. I see why they trusta you. I lova my family very much, Mario, and I believa your promise. It'sa hard for me to accepta that my young sister, she hasa grown up, but I will not stand inna the way of a her happiness."

"*Grazie, Giancarlo.* And I must return the compliment. You speak very good English. The surprises never seem to end, do they?" replies Mario with a smile of his own.

After listening to the conversation from the back bedroom, Assunta and Lucia enter the dining room and exchange emotional embraces with Giancarlo. Everyone shares in a welcomed sense of relief, as the two men put their differences aside.

Having settled the most serious of their issues, Mario and Giancarlo continue to explore each other's personalities. What began as a crisis only hours before has become a light lunch, rich in conversation ranging from personal taste to family details. Mario speaks proudly of his two brothers and father, even describing Joe's seafood business and how his brother would love to have the great variety of fish found in Napoli. Giancarlo talks of his love of flying and of his long struggle to become a pilot. He expresses remorse for his role in the war, and it becomes clear to Mario what a painful experience the war has been for him. Mario avoids any further discussion of the subject unless Giancarlo brings it up. Their progress toward some level of respect moves slowly but steadily forward, and Mario is pleased. As the mood of the afternoon continues to become more relaxed, Mario remembers Antonella's package in the rear of the Jeep. He stands and says,

"I'll be right back. I forgot something in the Jeep." He dashes out to the street, grabs the bundle of material and returns to the apartment. With an anxious grin, he hands the mysterious package to Antonella, saying, *"This is for you...from my friends at the base. I hope you can use it."* Excited and curious, she carries it to the dining table and carefully opens the brown paper wrapping.

"Mario, what...oh my God, where did you get this? Lucia, look. It's white fabric...like we have tried to find. There must be enough here for two dresses." Her excitement rapidly mounts, as she hugs Mario.

"This...is such beautiful cloth. Isn't it wonderful, Lucia?"

"Yes, it's perfect. You must thank your friends for us, Mario," replies Lucia, laughing with delight. With Lucia's help, Antonella grabs the bolt of cloth, unwraps the end and begins waltzing around the room, the silky fabric billowing up behind her. Draping it around herself, she models the cloth into the shape of a floor-length dress.

"It will make a beautiful wedding dress, don't you think, Lucia? Thank you so much, Mario."

"You're welcome. I'm just happy that you can use it. I wasn't sure."

While her daughters buzz with excitement over Mario's surprise gift, Assunta slips into the kitchen and brings out a bottle of wine she's been saving for a special occasion.

"Giancarlo, will you open this wine while I find some glasses?" she asks.

"You have wine, Mama? Find a corkscrew and hand the bottle to me. I think we can all use some wine right now," he answers.

The early afternoon gives way to an evening of simple celebration. Sharing wine and food, Mario and Giancarlo slowly discover a fondness for each other. What began as confrontation between adversaries begins to evolve into a fragile friendship, one centered around the love of a woman who shares their lives. There will be many more evenings like this in the days ahead, as plans for the wedding can now be made without reservation.

The weeks gradually become more hectic. Devoting up to eight hours a day to creating her bridal dress, Antonella finds little time for any outside repair work. She draws patterns on old newspapers and then uses them to cut out matching sections of her gown. Lucia helps to cut and organize the many patterns for her, and she compiles a list of friends and family to invite to the wedding. Arriving home from one of her daily trips to the market, Lucia hurries to Antonella and says,

"I saw Father Bertulucci today, and I told him of your wedding plans. I hope you don't mind."

"No, Lucia, I don't mind. What did he say?"

"Well, he suggests that you and Mario go see him together to reserve a day for the wedding. He wants to talk to both of you. He seemed surprised that you are marrying an American."

"Well, he's known us from our first communions, and I'm sure he must be very curious. I'll tell Mario that he wants to see us."

461

"He said you could come to the church at any time. He's there every day."

Not having discussed where to be married, Antonella plans to use the meeting with the priest to show Mario the beautiful cathedral of Maria Santissima Dosolata and reveal her wish to be married there.

During Mario's next visit, Antonella bubbles with excitement. As he enters the apartment, she rushes to him, giving him a kiss and smiling brightly. Taking his hand, she leads him to the settee and says,

"Let's sit down, Mario. I have some wonderful news."

"I can see you're excited over something. What is it?"

"My priest wants to meet with us...to make sure we reserve the church for the day we want. I also think he's very nosy...about you. Lucia told him you are American, and he wants to talk to you."

"I hope he doesn't try to talk us out of this," Mario says with a laugh, *"but if he wants to see us, then let's go there today."*

"I was hoping you would agree. Besides, I want you to see what a beautiful cathedral Maria Santissima is. Ever since I was a little girl, I've dreamed of being married there."

"Is it very far from here?" he asks.

"No. We can walk there in a few minutes."

Antonella leads Mario through the local neighborhood until they arrive at the church. Having escaped damage during the air raids and combat, the cathedral is the religious center of the neighborhood and an ideal setting for a wedding. It's a small church, with six towering columns standing majestically at the entrance. Hand-crafted from large blocks of quarry stone, it appears to Mario to be very old, and he's reminded of ancient Greek ruins seen in pictures at Enzo's restaurant. A large, sculpted relief of Christ's descent from the cross occupies the triangular façade atop the columns. Standing on terraced steps leading to the arched doorways, Antonella asks,

"Do you like it, Mario? Isn't it lovely?"

"Yes. It's very old...isn't it?"

"Mama told me it was over two-hundred years old. Let's go inside," she replies.

Entering the cathedral, they enjoy how its interior is illuminated by brilliant beams of colored light passing through the stained glass windows near the ceiling. Pious, marble statues both large and small are everywhere, and paintings or frescos adorn virtually every wall. The seating pews are plain oak and highly polished from many years of use. Stepping inside the main hall, Antonella dips her fingers into a basin of holy water and makes the sign of the cross while she genuflects before the alter. Although he was born Catholic, Mario has not practiced his own religious beliefs. Since he rarely attended church as a child, he suddenly feels out of place in this holy shrine. Not wanting to admit his lack of religious knowledge, he follows Antonella's example, and they walk quietly up the center aisle toward one of the side entrances off the main alter.

"I made my first communion right here," she says, gazing at the altar.

"I've never seen a place like this before. It's like a living museum. I see why you love this church so much."

"Antonella? Antonella Cappodanno? Is that you my child?" echoes a voice from the rear of the church. Strutting briskly up the center aisle is Father Bertulucci, his vestments sailing in all directions. A rotund man with a flushed face, the result of drinking too much communion wine, he extends his arms out to greet her, saying, *"It is you. I'm so pleased to see you here. Lucia told me of your marriage plans. How wonderful for you."*

"Thank you, Father. It's nice to see you again," she replies, as they exchange courteous hugs. *"Father, this is Mario Carlucci, my future husband."* Directing his attention to Mario, Father studies him with a whimsical grin on his face before blurting out,

"Carlucci? I know of Carluccis on Sicily. Do you know them, Mario? You don't mind if I call you Mario, do you?" Mario smiles, shakes the Father's hand and says,

"No, I don't mind. My father and mother are from Sicily. I came through Sicily on my way to Napoli, but I couldn't find any of my relatives there. I know my family in America wants to know how they are doing."

"Ah, such a shame. What a thrill that would have been for you to meet them. Did your mother and father teach you to speak Italian so well?" he asks while patting Mario on the shoulder.

"My father speaks it all the time, and I learned from him. My mother died when I was young."

"Oh I'm sorry. So, you have come to Italia and found a beautiful bride, eh?" Father Bertulucci's frankness is both refreshing and amusing to Mario. Smiling at Antonella, he answers,

"Yes, I'm a very lucky man, Father."

"Sometimes, God's gifts arrive when they're least expected. I assume you are Catholic, Mario?"

"Yes...but I don't go to church too often, since the war and all." .

"That's understandable. I only ask so I can plan a mass for your ceremony. You do want a mass, don't you, Antonella?" asks the priest, abruptly shifting his attention back to Antonella.

"Yes, Father. Of course I do."

"Excellent. I'll arrange to have altar boys and an organist. You do want an organist, don't you, my dear?"

"Yes...yes, Father. That would be very nice. Can I ask him to play something...special?"

"Certainly. Just be sure to tell me ahead of time. We must give him time to practice," says the priest with a smile. *"Let's walk through the garden. We can show Mario what a special place this is to have a wedding celebration."*

Leading the way, through a maze of smaller sanctuaries, Father pushes open a heavy, plank door and rushes into the garden. Standing in the center of the grounds with his arms stretched out to his side, the priest's jovial pose causes both Mario and Antonella to snicker at his boundless enthusiasm.

"What do you think, Mario? Is it not perfect?" asks the priest. Turning slowly to view the entire garden, Mario agrees completely. A cobblestone footpath winds its way from the cathedral around the outer perimeter and converges into a larger courtyard surrounded by huge, clay flowerpots. The air is rich with the scent of lilacs and roses. Graceful, old shade trees protect the garden from the intense afternoon sun, providing a comfortable environment for any gathering. A small footbridge straddles the tiny creek running through the garden and completes the picturesque setting.

"You're right, Father. It couldn't be more perfect," replies Mario.

"Very good, then. Now, you must tell me what day you plan to be married. You have decided on a day, haven't you?"

Realizing they have never discussed an actual day to be married, Mario looks at Antonella with a puzzled expression. He tells the priest,

"We don't have a date picked out yet, do we Antonella?"

"No...we have had so many other things to worry about...we haven't decided," she admits with some embarrassment.

"The entire month of July is available. July is a wonderful month for a wedding," says Father.

"That's three months, Antonella. Is that enough time for you?" asks Mario.

"I...I think so. What do you think, Mario?" she asks nervously. For the first time since Mario proposed, they are about to select the day that will change their lives forever.

"Is the seventh a good day for the both of you?" asks Father Bertulucci.

"It's good for me. Seven has always been good luck for me," replies Mario, *"Do you like it, Antonella?"*

"Yes...that's fine," she answers, with a hint of apprehension.

"Then it's settled. July 7 it is. Congratulations to the both of you. Contact me the week before, and we'll discuss the details."

Returning to the apartment, they share the news of the wedding day with Antonella's family. Assunta and Lucia are excited now that an actual day has been selected.

"We have to start planning a meal for the party, and we must begin buying wine now, to be sure we have enough," exclaims Assunta.

"I have a partial list of guests already started, Mama. But we must all look it over to be sure we don't forget anyone," adds Lucia.

For the first time since Capri, the many difficult obstacles concerning their marriage now seem resolved. With the wedding day identified, Antonella and Mario are finally confident their plans will no longer change. As the family joyfully attends to the list of details, Antonella and Mario look forward their new future. They will be married on July 7, 1944.

Sergeant Thompson calls out to Mario from his barrack's office,

"Hey, Mario. Got a minute? I need to talk to you."

"Sure, Sarge. Be right there." Mario joins the Sergeant in his quarters.

"Have a seat. I've got some good news for you." Handing Mario an envelope, he explains, "The C.O. has signed all the approval forms, and you're officially permitted to get married. There are your copies of all the paperwork." Mario opens the envelope, removes the documents and studies the signatures at the bottom of each one.

"Thanks, Sarge. I guess there's no turning back now, huh? That reminds me...I better start looking for somewhere off base to live," adds Mario, with a nervous laugh.

"Yes, I guess you should. So when are you going to tie the knot? Do you know yet?"

"July 7. We just decided a few days ago."

"July, huh? Wow, that's only a few months away. How are you feeling about all this?"

"I'd be lyin if I said I wasn't a little scared, but I want to do this. Her brother and I got our differences, but we're getting along better now. Sarge, you and the guys, well, you're the only close friends I have here, and I want you ta meet Antonella."

"It's about damn time, Carlucci. You been hiding her from us long enough," replies Sarge with a loud chuckle.

"Yeah, since you guys are gonna have to stand up in the wedding for me, I figured it was about time," adds Mario with a laugh. "There's a little trattoria in Bagnoli, called LaPalicio. It's on the north end of the Via Pozzuoli, not far from the harbor. It's not hard to find; it's the only one on the beach. Why don't we meet there tomorrow night about seven?"

"Sure, seven's good. I'll let the other guys know. They wouldn't miss this for anything."

"Okay, great. Is it all right if I take off today? I wanna check on some apartments I saw near here."

"Yeah, no problem. There's not much going on around here, anyway. I'll see you tomorrow."

"Thanks, Sarge. And tell the guys the wine's on me," adds Mario on his way out.

Returning to Antonella's apartment the following day, Mario flies up the stairway, opens the door without knocking and calls out,

"Antonella? Where are you? I have some good news." From her bedroom, she replies,

"Mario? I didn't expect you so soon. Don't come in here...I'm working on my dress. I'll be there in a minute." Pacing through the living room and kitchen, his patience is worn thin by the time Antonella joins him.

"I have some exciting news to tell you. The Army approved my request to get married and live off base. Sergeant Thompson told me yesterday." Sharing in his exhilaration, she kisses him and says,

"Mario, that's good news. Did you tell him that we've picked a date?"

"Yes. He was surprised when I told him it was July. But there's more I want to tell you."

"There is?"

"After we're married, I can live off base, so I looked at some apartments for us. They're not too far from here, and buses go right by there. I want you to go with me and look at them soon."

"Our own apartment? When can we go see it? Can we go today?"

"We can go there before we go out for dinner tonight."

"Dinner? You didn't say anything about dinner. How nice...we can celebrate."

"We...uh, won't be eating alone, though. Sergeant Thompson and the other guys I work with, they been dying to meet you, so they're going to join us. I hope you don't mind."

"Mind? Of course not. It will be fun to meet them. We can make it like a party. I must wear something nice, yes?"

"Yes. I've told them all about you and your business," says Mario with a laugh, *"but I don't think they believe me."*

"Well then, I'll try not to disappoint them," she replies with a flirtatious wink.

Frankie looks at his wristwatch again and thumps his fingers on the table.

"It's damn near 7:30. Where in the blue Jesus is he? Are ya sure he said seven o'clock, Sarge?" *LaPalicio* is crowded, and Mario's four friends are seated around the last large table available, awaiting his arrival.

"Relax, will ya? He'll be here," replies Hank, "Ya always get so damn itchy."

"Hank's right. He'll show up. He's looking forward to this as much as we are," adds the Sergeant. While pouring everyone another glass of wine, George notices a Jeep slowly cruising along the Via Pozzuoli toward the trattoria. Standing upright for a better view, he says,

"Is that him? It must be...there's a woman in it." The four GI's stop talking and shift their attention to the Jeep as it comes to a stop in front of the trattoria. Mario turns off the engine and raises his hand, signaling to his friends that he sees them. Turning to Antonella, he says,

"There they are. I hope they're not mad at me because we're late."

"You have a good reason. They will understand, won't they?" she asks.

"Yes. And after they meet you, they'll forget all about it, anyway. They're good guys, and I know you'll like them." Hopping out of the Jeep, Mario runs around to the other side and helps Antonella step out. Standing there, she brushes her hair back with her hands, tugs the waist of her dress back into place and asks,

"How do I look, Mario?" She wears the same yellow dress she wore the night he proposed, and her wild beauty is still alluring to him. His pulse quickens every time he sees her dressed in one of her stunning gowns. Smiling broadly, Mario says,

"You look wonderful. The guys are really going to enjoy meeting you. Are you ready?"

"Si, amore mia. Andiamo."

As Mario and Antonella make their way across the street, Frankie stares at them wide-eyed and with his mouth wide open.

"Jeesus! Will ya look at that? I don't think I ever seen a prettier gal," he exclaims. Navigating through the congested dining area, Antonella causes many patrons to stop and take notice. Sarge, Hank, George and Frankie are also momentarily silenced by her appearance. Approaching the table, Antonella takes Mario's arm in her hands and smiles warmly at them. Mario shakes each of their hands and says,

"Sorry, we're late, but we looked at an apartment before we came here and decided to rent it. I want you guys to meet Antonella. She doesn't speak much English, so I'll have to translate for her." Rising from the table in unison, the four soldiers stand speechless and fidgety, behaving more like intimidated schoolboys than grown men. Mario begins to introduce Antonella to his four friends.

"Il Antonella, questo è Sergeant Thompson." Extending her hand to the Sergeant, she politely shakes it.

"I'm happy to meet you, Antonella."

"Ciao, Sergeant Thompson." Then she's introduced to Hank, George and Frankie, and she wonders why they smile so little and seem so nervous when shaking her hand.

"Mario, why are they acting so strange?" she asks. Mario laughs and says,

"They're just a little shy, that's all. They'll get over it soon."

Frankie suddenly bolts from the table, grabs an unoccupied chair from another table and slides it up behind her, saying,

"Here ya go, Antonella. Why don't you sit down right here? How about some wine...uh *vino? Si?"* His charming antics amuse her. She flashes a wide smile at him and says with a giggle,

"Si, *Frankie, grazie*...ah...thanka you?"

"You're welcome. Ya see, we'll have ya speakin more English in no time," replies Frankie with his typical screeching laugh. Although understanding little of what he's saying, she continues to find his behavior flattering. Noticeably flustered by Antonella's charm and beauty, he repeatedly clangs the wine bottle against her glass while trying to fill it for her. Watching Frankie fumble with a full bottle of red wine so near to Antonella instantly drives Hank crazy. Unable to restrain himself any longer, he stands and yanks the bottle from Frankie's hand.

"Gimme that, will ya?...before ya spill something on her expensive dress."

"I ain't gonna spill anything. And if ya keep grabbin at me like that, you're gonna be wearin the wine." Ignoring Frankie's

473

threat, Hank fills a glass with wine and carefully hands it to Antonella.

"There you go. Better safe than sorry," says Hank while glaring at Frankie.

"Will you two guys give it a rest for a while? We're here to have dinner with Mario and his future bride, not listen to both of you carry on," scolds Sergeant Thompson.

"Why don't we order some food? Maybe if we feed them, they'll start to behave. What would you like, Antonella?" asks George. Lost in the English conversation, Antonella takes Mario's arm and asks,

"Mario, I don't understand. What are they saying?" Laughing over how to translate some of what's just been said, he finally tells her,

"The boys are having one of their normal arguments. It's not important. They want to order dinner, and George asked what you would like."

"Can we have the bruschetta? Do you remember how good it was the last time we ate here?"

"George, Antonella would like some bruschetta. And you better check with the waiter to see what else they're serving...they have a short menu here."

"I already did. They speak a little English here...guess cause a few GI's eat here once in a while. I'll order it special and tell them to start bringin some pasta."

Sipping her wine before dinner arrives, Antonella quickly makes friends with Mario's army buddies. With Mario serving as translator, she begins to hear where they are from and what they did in America. She answers questions about herself, telling them she's never been to America, but she loves to hear all about the big cities and movie houses. Antonella sits with one leg casually draped over the other, and the men find it difficult to ignore her shapely figure. After the waiter places dinner on the table, they are soon stumbling over each other to help serve Antonella her dinner. Flattered by so much attention, she leans against Mario and says,

"Mario, your friends are so nice. I'm having a wonderful time."

"So am I. I'm glad you like them. They can get a little wild sometimes, but they're on their best behavior tonight," he responds with a smile. After they finish the meal, Mario orders a round of coffee and Amaretto for everyone, then makes an important request of his close friends.

"I want you guys to stand up in the wedding with me. It'll be great to have ya there to make sure I don't forget something," he says with a grin.

"Just try and keep us out," responds Hank. Sarge stands, lifts his glass of Amaretto and proposes a toast.

"To Mario and Antonella's wedding." They all stand, down their drinks and shake hands with each other in anticipation of the special event.

"Hey, Mario. Who gets to be the best man?" asks Frankie, with his usual bluntness. The question has been troubling Mario. Unable to decide which of the four will serve as his best man, he answers,

"I don't know. How can I choose one of you guys over the others? If someone wants to volunteer..." Frankie immediately jumps up from his seat and shouts,

"I'll do it! I'll volunteer." Hank grabs him by his belt, pulls him back down in his seat and says,

"Frankie, don't ya get it? We all want to volunteer. We'll have to decide ourselves. Is that ok, Mario?"

"That's not exactly what I was thinking, but it sounds like a good idea to me. Whatta ya got in mind?" After reaching into his pants pocket, Hank holds up Donnie's dice bag between his two fingers and says,

"Highest roll gets to be the best man."

"You gotta be jokin, right?" replies Mario.

"I'm dead serious. Anybody got any better ideas?" asks Hank. The others look at one another, but no one suggests anything else. "Then that's it. Let's find someplace to roll em."

Watching the conversation with great curiosity, Antonella asks,

"Mario, what are they saying? What's in the little bag?" Feeling embarrassed by the idea of rolling dice to choose his best man, Mario tries to explain.

"There are dice in the bag. They are going to roll dice to decide who'll be my best man."

"Roll dice to be your best man? How can they decide something so important that way? I've never heard of such a thing."

"I know it's hard for you to understand, but those are my dice, and we've had good luck with them since the beginning of the war. If they want to do this, that's up to them." Finding an empty corner at the end of the trattoria, Hank pours the dice from the purple bag and says,

"Well, we gonna do this or not?" Soon, everyone is crowded into the small space, and they begin the strange contest.

"Who wants ta go first?" asks Hank.

"Gimme those things. I'm gonna get this over with in a hurry," bellows Frankie. "Come on, box cars!" Throwing the dice with a vengeance, they crash and bang around the corner until finally landing on a four and a five.

"Nine. Okay, who's next?" barks Hank. Sarge steps up, takes the dice in his hand and gently shakes them a few times before tossing them into the corner. Bouncing wildly, they come to rest on a six and a three.

"Another nine," says Hank. "Come on, George; you're up." Scooping up the dice from the floor, George holds them between the palms of his hands, rolling them back and forth for good luck. Curling one hand around them, he blows into his closed fist and hurls the dice into the corner. The result is a pair of ones. Disappointed, George moans,

"Snake eyes. Looks like I'm out." Being last to roll, Hank knows all he needs is to beat a nine and he's Mario's best man. He feels as connected to the dice as Mario does, and he holds them in his hand with a comfortable confidence. Shaking them a few times for good luck, he flings the ivory cubes into the corner and watches them dance around. When the rolling stops, the dice show a three and a one.

"Damn, a four," he says with great disappointment. "Looks like Frankie and Sarge gotta go again." This time, Sarge goes first. He throws the dice and holds his breath until they come to rest.

"Yes!" he shouts, "A lucky seven." Handing the dice to Frankie, he smiles confidently and says,

"Hard to beat a seven, Frankie. Why don't you just give up now?"

"Forget it Sarge. Jus git outta the way." Rolling the dice from one hand to the other, he takes a deep breath and slams the dice into the corner again. One of the dice flies from the corner due to the force of the throw and ends up near the center of the dining floor. The one remaining in the corner lands on a two. Frankie rushes to locate the other, only to find it's rolled a three, giving him five points. When Sarge realizes he's won, he slaps Frankie on the back, saying,

"That was close. No hard feelings, right?"

"Naw…ya won fair and square, Sarge. But for someone who never shot craps before, ya sure did win a good one," replies Frankie with a half-hearted smile. Sergeant Thompson goes to Mario and shakes his hand.

"Mario, I know you have two brothers at home, and I'm sure you'd like one of them to do this for you. But, I'm honored to be your best man. I'll try and fill in for them as best I can. Tell Antonella I'm very happy to be able to do this."

"Thanks, Sarge. I figure I'm pretty lucky to have a guy like you to fill in for them," replies Mario. Turning to face Antonella, he says,

"Sergeant Thompson will be our best man, Antonella. He wants you to know he's proud and happy to do this." Standing on her toes, she reaches up and gives Sarge a light kiss on the cheek. Smiling at him, she combines her limited English with her Italian.

"Grazia, tante, Sergeant. I'ma verry happy, too."

Returning to the dinner table, Antonella gestures for everyone to sit while she walks around the table, pouring wine in each man's glass. Giving each man a hug, she thanks them for spending the evening with her and Mario. Amid more toasts and laughter, the evening draws to a close. After taking one last moment to thank Mario's friends for their help, Antonella tells Mario,

"It's getting late, Mario. I must go home or Mama will start to worry."

"I know. I'll tell them we must leave."

After Mario explains he and Antonella must leave, the men all jump up and demand one last hug from her. Her charm and beauty have completely won them over, and they say goodnight with reluctance. Returning to the Jeep, Antonella waves to them as Mario starts the engine. They wave back.

"You are fortunate to have such good friends, Mario. I like them very much. I think they like me too, don't you?" As he drives off, he smiles at her.

"Yes, Antonella. I think they like you very much."

CHAPTER 18

It's less than two weeks until his wedding day, and Mario's time is filled with handling an endless list of details. After renting the apartment, he discovers that furnishing it with bare necessities is an unexpected challenge. With help from Frankie and Hank, he scours the city looking for used furniture that is both clean and serviceable. Eventually locating a couch, a dining table with four chairs and a lightly used bed, he's able to convert the stark little apartment into a comfortable home for Antonella and himself. Sergeant Thompson gives him the freedom to come and go, as his needs demand, but he spends more time off base than on. He's satisfied with the apartment and begins to move some of his clothing and other personal belongings into it.

On one of the rare days when nothing needs his immediate attention, he sits alone in his apartment and writes a long overdue letter to his father. With so much happening to him, he wonders where to begin. After thinking about the incredible events taking place in his life, he writes to his father with the amazing news.

Dear Pa,

I hope everyone's doing ok. I'm doing good. After I left North Africa, I went to Sicily. I met some nice people in Palermo and, when they found out I was Sicilian, we became pretty good friends. Knowing how to speak Italian has made things pretty easy for me. I do a lot of translating for my sergeant, and I can talk to anyone here. I'm in Naples now, and it looks like I'll be here until I come home. I'm sorry for not writing for so long, but something very special is happening. Since I been stationed here, I met an Italian girl named Antonella Cappodanno. I've been seeing her for more than six months, and I even met her family. They are wonderful people and we get along very good. Antonella is really special. I've never met anyone like her. She's beautiful and talented and we are in love. I guess this will come as a shock, but I asked her to marry me, and she said yes. The wedding is going to be July 7. By the time you get this letter, I'll be married.

I sure wish John and Joe and you could be here. I'm going to miss having you guys around for this. But I have some good friends who will be standing up with me during the ceremony. I know it won't be the same, but we been together since Fort Dix and they are great guys, so I won't be doing this alone. Pa, we are having a formal wedding in this beautiful old church, and I'm sure you would approve. I'll bring home plenty of pictures for you. I'm sure this is one hell of a surprise to you, but it's a surprise to me, too.

With the war over in Italy, Sergeant Thompson says we'll start shipping out sometime next year. I can't wait to get home and have you meet Antonella. You're going to love her. Tell John and Joe the exciting news and that I miss everyone a lot. I'll write again after the wedding and send you some pictures. Take care of yourself, Pa. See you soon,

Mario

Mario folds the letter, stuffs it into an envelope, and licks the flap to seal it closed. Returning to the camp, he drops it in the mailbox just outside the camp post office. He wonders what his family will think when they discover he's coming home with a war bride.

Antonella and her family have also been busy. After countless hours of cutting patterns and sewing the delicate puzzle together, Antonella has nearly finished her bridal gown. In order to add the finishing details more easily, she often enlists Lucia's help to model it for her.

"Lucia, come over here...close to the window. I need more light."

"There, how's this?" replies Lucia, stepping up onto a small footstool.

"That's much better. This way I can be sure the hem is straight."

"Don't you think you should be wearing this, and I should be sewing the hem?" asks Lucia with a laugh.

"What difference does it make? We're the same size, aren't we? Besides, I've seen how you sew, and I'd rather do this myself."

Laughing over Antonella's teasing, the two sisters find this special time together a precious gift. Their joy in sharing the creation of this beautiful dress has fulfilled one of the many fantasies they've dreamed of from their childhood. They frequently laugh and cry at almost the same time, further strengthening the powerful bond between them. With so many details to attend to, they say little of the day when Antonella will have to leave for America. They choose to ignore the painful subject and try to make her wedding day as beautiful as possible.

When they are not busy working on the dress, Antonella and Lucia help Assunta with the preparations for the wedding party. Returning to the apartment from a visit to the bakery, Assunta calls out,

"Antonella, guess who I saw today? Theresa Minelli! She got very excited when I told her about the wedding and she offered to cook something for the party. Isn't that kind of her?"

"Theresa is so sweet to help that way. I must go and thank her."

"And Senora Tucci, from two apartments over, she promised to bring something, too. The neighbors are so happy for you, my dear." Antonella cannot recall her mother being so overjoyed. Working tirelessly to insure they will enjoy a traditional wedding celebration, Assunta has seen to many details, such as arranging for

flowers and guest candy. She has even ordered a small wedding cake. Antonella's wedding is the most jubilant event the family has enjoyed since the days when Pirrone was still alive. Giancarlo, too, has become more supportive. In the time he's been home, his angry nature has calmed, and Antonella can see the good man he once was. He's completely accepted Antonella's decision to marry Mario, and she's grateful the two men have become friends. Although taking his own apartment nearby, he visits daily to assist her in any way that he can. During one such visit, Antonella says,

"Giancarlo, please sit for a moment. I have something I must talk to you about."

"You look very serious. What is it?"

"I've never asked you to...to escort me to the altar during the wedding. Will you do that for me, Giancarlo?" He smiles and takes her hands into his.

"You know there's no need to ask such a question. I won't have it any other way."

"I know. But I feel it's important that I ask you. I'm so thankful you've come home to do this. I know Papa would be pleased." She then gives him a hug and a kiss.

"Thank you, Giancarlo. I love you." It is now only days until she is to marry Mario. With her wedding day so near, Antonella is both eager and afraid. Her churning emotions will not subside quickly.

Father Bertulucci has requested a rehearsal of the wedding ceremony and, on the eve of the marriage, Mario's friends will be meeting Antonella's family for the first time. While checking his dress uniform one more time to insure there are no unexpected spots or stains, Mario hears Sarge calling out his name.

"Hey Mario, I'm a little worried about something."

"It's getting sorta late for that, ain't it, Sarge? You're not going to spring some Army surprise on me or somthin are ya?"

"No. Everything is all set that way. But it's Antonella's sister, Lucia."

"Yeah? What about her?"

"You said she can't speak English. Well, if I can't speak much Italian, how are we going to get through this wedding ceremony together?"

"It'll be ok. The priest's gonna give everyone instructions today, and I'll make sure you know what's going on. Besides, I don't think you have to say too much during the ceremony."

"What about the dinner tonight?"

"I'll introduce you to her brother. He speaks pretty good English. He can help you translate, too. Don't worry, it'll all work out," Mario says with a chuckle. Sharing a nervous laugh with Mario, Sarge adds,

"Then the only problem we have will be keeping Hank, Frankie and George from offending your future brother-in-law."

"I'm leaving that up to you, Sarge. I got enough to worry about," replies Mario, smiling.

"I'll go round them up so we can leave," says the Sergeant.

"Yeah. We should get going. We gotta be at the church in an hour."

Antonella and her family arrive at Maria Santissima a few minutes ahead of the scheduled 4:30 appointment. Father Bertulucci is waiting for them at the front entrance. After exchanging friendly hugs with Antonella and Lucia, Father takes Assunta's hand and says,

"How very nice to see you again on such a joyous occasion, Assunta. You must be very excited over Antonella's marriage."

"Oh yes, Father, I am. It's still hard to believe that my youngest child will be the first to marry, but no one can predict such things."

"God's ways are often difficult to understand," he answers. Then, looking at Giancarlo, he asks, *"Don't tell me this is your son?"*

"Yes, Giancarlo returned home several months ago. I'm so thankful he's safe. All of our prayers have been answered." Shaking Giancarlo's hand, the Father says,

"Welcome home, my son. I assume you will be escorting your sister in the ceremony?

"I will, Father. I told her she could not hold the ceremony unless I'm allowed to walk her down the aisle."

"And so it should be," laughs the Father. Looking up and down the street, he asks, *"Where is the groom, Antonella?"*

"He should be arriving any time now. Can we wait here for a few minutes?"

"But of course. We have plenty of time." Moments later, they hear the familiar muted rumble of Mario's Jeep in the distance.

The high-pitched squeal of the Jeep's brakes attracts everyone's attention, as Mario parks it along the curb. Followed by Sergeant Thompson, Frankie, Hank and George, he climbs out and proceeds directly to meet Antonella's family and the priest. After greeting Antonella with a gentle embrace, he begins speaking in Italian to introduce his friends to her family.

"This is Sergeant Duane Thompson. He will be the best man, Father. Next, here is George Pinkerton, and that's Frank Erskin and Henry Forrester." Easily switching to English, he identifies the members of Antonella's family.

"This is Assunta, Antonella's mother. The pretty woman standing next to her is Lucia, her sister. And this is Giancarlo, her brother, and that's Father Bertulucci." Except for Giancarlo, the language difference reduces the introductions to a series of awkward handshakes, accompanied by polite smiles. Sergeant Thompson is the first of Mario's friends to speak directly to Antonella's brother. Having been informed of Giancarlo's language skills, Sarge shakes his hand and says,

"It's a pleasure to meet you, Giancarlo. Mario's told me you speak some English."

"The pleasure isa mine, Sergeant. I looka forward to talking witha you during dinner later."

As each of the other men meet Giancarlo, he greets them with a similar, warm-hearted reaction. In spite of the language difference, the mood of the group is upbeat and energized. When Father Bertulucci leads them into the cathedral, Mario's heart beats a little faster. Father begins giving instructions to everyone, controlling the rehearsal like a policeman directing traffic. Explaining each part of the ceremony through the use of word and gesture, he instructs them exactly where to stand and when to move. The final component of the rehearsal is the bridal walk to the altar. Smiling and laughing during the entire procession, Antonella repeatedly pulls on her brother's arm to try to throw off his cadence. Her innocent prank and infectious joy bring a smile to even the Father's face, as he declares,

"Well, I think we've done enough for tonight, Antonella. Maybe a glass of wine or two will help us all relax." Antonella kisses her brother's cheek, and he can no longer keep from laughing with her. She rushes to Mario, takes him by the arm and says,

"It's impossible for me to believe we'll be married at this time tomorrow. Isn't it wonderful, Mario?"

"I hope you'll be nicer to your poor brother tomorrow than you were tonight," jokes Mario.

"Poor Giancarlo," she says with a giggle. *"Lucia and I used to pick on him like that all the time when we were children. He knows*

I was teasing him only because I'm nervous." With the rehearsal finished, she reminds everyone,

"We are going to a small café at the end of the street for dinner. I hope everyone will join us."

The eatery is a short walk from the church. Several large tables in the outdoor dining area are available. Antonella and Mario sit there together and the others gather around them. Having arranged the dinner party with the proprietor, Giancarlo signals to a waiter. Moments later, he brings a tray of glasses and an assortment of sweet and strong liquors. The waiter fills a glass for each of the women with her choice of sweet liquor and pours each of the men some of the stronger drink. Antonella watches with pride as Giancarlo stands and taps one of the bottles with his table knife to get everyone's attention. After the loud clinking quiets everyone, he says,

"Desidero fare un pane tostato a Mario ed a Antonella." With his arm extended toward Antonella and Mario, he raises his glass and offers a simple, Italian toast.

"La buona moglie fa il buon marito. Anda for our American guests, thisa means, 'a good wife makes a good husband.' *Salute,"* he shouts, and downs his drink. There is a chorus of laughter and cheers from one and all, and they follow Giancarlo's example and finish their drinks. The staccato sound of the empty glasses slamming onto the wooden table echoes through the small restaurant.

The waiters quickly refill the glasses and serve dinner, consisting of small pizzas and fresh salads. As the food is passed around from one person to the next, Antonella holds Mario's hand tightly in hers beneath the table. On this warm July evening, she's reluctant to let go of him, even to feed herself. Smiling and flirting with him openly, she enjoys sharing her love while surrounded by her family and friends.

While holding a bottle of wine and two glasses in his hand, Giancarlo joins Sergeant Thompson.

"May I pour soma wine for you, Sergeanta Thompson?" Pulling an empty chair out from the table, Sarge replies,

"Sure. Have a seat right here." Giancarlo takes a seat and fills both glasses full of wine. Handing one glass to the Sergeant, he hoists the other and they tap them together.

"To a good night and a happy tomorrow," says Sarge.

"*Salute*," responds Giancarlo with a smile. "Do you hava family, Sergeant?"

"I'm not married, if that's what you mean. But I have a younger brother living at home with my mother and father. That's all the family I have."

"How long hava you been away froma them?" Sarge sips his wine while thinking over the question.

"I guess it's been almost four years now. I'm looking forward to seeing them again. How long were you away from your family?"

"Abouta four years, like a you. You were inna North Africa, like Mario?"

"Yeah. I left the U.S. with Mario and these guys, and we've been in the same unit ever since. Mario tells me you are a pilot."

"I was a pilot. I hava no desire to fly anymore. I'ma happy to be home again." Without warning, Frankie and Hank interrupt the conversation. With his usual bluntness, Frankie asks,

"Hey, you guys got any more wine?" Giancarlo holds the bottle up to the light, checking its content with a grin, and says,

"I thinka there'sa enough for two glasses." After emptying the bottle into their glasses, he says,

"Why don'ta you sit and talk with us?"

"Sure, that's a great idea," answers Hank. Dragging a chair from another table, Frankie plops down in it and asks Giancarlo,

"So where'd ya learn to speak such good English?"

"I study English inna school, but I learned froma the Americans inna Sicily after Italia surrendered."

"Oh yeah? We were in Sicily, right Sarge?" chirps Frankie. "That place was great compared to North Africa. Did Sarge tell ya the one about the Nazi flag?" he continues. Puzzled by Frankie's disconnected thoughts, Giancarlo looks at Sarge and asks,

"I'ma not sure I understand. What isa he saying, Sergeant?" Before Sarge is able to answer him, Frankie blurts out,

"Ya didn't tell him? Let me, Sarge." Knowing he couldn't keep Frankie from repeating the story anyway, Sergeant shrugs his shoulders, laughs and says,

"Go ahead, Frankie. Seems you're going to turn that story into a legend all by yourself."

Sitting squarely in front of Giancarlo, Frankie begins to retell the story yet another time.

"We met some Brits in Tripoli, ya see, and they was sellin war souvenirs. Nazi pistols and flags, stuff like that. So I bought this here flag from em. Well, we asked em if they had any booze for sale, cause ya can't get nothin to drink in that damn country." Apparently caught up in Frankie's tale, Giancarlo asks,

"Did a they hava something for you to buy?"

"Yeah, they told us to go to this old warehouse and we could buy some gin there. Remember that mean-lookin SOB that met us there, Hank?"

"Yeah, I'd a like to a seen his face the next morning," chuckles Hank.

"After we give em money for some booze, we start winnin it back in a crap game, and they git all pissed off and kick us out empty-handed. Well, I fixed em. Before we left, I run that Nazi flag up the flagpole in front of the place and, the next morning, the joint was surrounded by tanks and troops, ready ta blow em ta smithereens. It was the funniest damn thang I ever saw," says Frankie, now roaring with laughter. Giancarlo, along with Sergeant and Hank, begin laughing at Frankie's reaction to his own story.

"Sergeant, I thinka you are right. In Italia, we calla that a *storia di Guerra,* or a war story. Frankie willa tell thata story forever," adds Giancarlo with a grin.

"Antonella! Assunta! Oh how exciting to see you tonight," calls a voice from the darkened street. Antonella quickly finds herself in the embrace of Theresa Minelli. *"I can't believe you'll be married tomorrow."*

"Hello, Theresa. Please join us. We had a short rehearsal tonight and just finished eating. Will you drink some wine?" asks Antonella.

"Yes, that would be very nice, thank you. And how are you, Assunta?"

"I'm still a little nervous, but it's a wonderful time for us." Holding her glass of wine in the air, Theresa says,

"God has smiled on you and your family, Antonella. May he smile on your marriage, as well." A wonderful buzz of activity surrounds them during the evening, as many more friends and neighbors stop to offer Antonella and Mario their congratulations. Amidst all the good wishes and sincere toasts, Antonella glances at Mario. They feel completely alone as their eyes lock together. It is in the brief privacy of these exchanges that Antonella conveys the depth of her pure and honest love. Neither of them doubts that this marriage is their destiny.

Standing behind Mario, a smiling Assunta places her hands on his arms. She leans over and says,

"I'm sorry, Mario, but I must take her from you now. It's close to midnight, and in our family, it's bad luck for the groom to see the bride before the ceremony on her wedding day."

After giving Antonella one last kiss, Mario watches her leave for home. Finishing the last of the wine and liquor at the table, everyone feels the affect of the powerful liquors.

"Come on, Mario. Let's get you back to the base tonight," advises Sarge.

"Sure, Sarge. Ya know, it's hard to imagine this is the last night I'm going ta spend with you guys there. We've had one helluva time since we left Fort Dix, ain't we?"

"It ain't over yet, buddy. Let's go," warns Hank with a smirk. Returning to the barracks, Hank charges ahead and stands at the door. Smiling mischievously, he says,

"You guys wait here. I'll be right back. No sense in wakin up the whole damn squad."

"Does anyone know what he's up to?" asks Mario. Hank's intentions are quickly revealed when he returns with a bottle of expensive cognac. As the four good friends sit on the barracks' steps, he twists off the cork top, takes a long swig and hands the bottle to Mario.

"Here ya go, Mario. Your last drink as a single man." Taking a long drink, he feels the potent cognac burn with an unexpected intensity.

"Thanks, I think," replies Mario with a choking laugh. Handing the bottle to George, Mario watches him take a drink and pass it on, until each man has tasted it at least twice. Although noticeably drunk, Hank says,

"Mario, I just want to…tell ya how happy I am for ya. We been through a lot of shit, the four of us…and it's just great that we can do this with ya."

"That goes for all of us," adds George.

"You guys, you're like brothers to me. I know we're all kinda drunk, but I'm glad we all got here. It's really important to me," replies Mario.

"Let's get some sleep. You got a big day, tomorrow," says Sarge. Mario is the last to climb into his bunk, but he is unable to sleep. He pulls on his trousers and steps out onto the landing again. Lighting a cigarette, he stares into the quiet night, wondering what his family would be doing now if they knew what would happen the next day.

"Can't sleep, either?" asks Sergeant Thompson. Holding out the pack of Pall Malls, Mario answers,

"No, I guess I'm still pretty nervous. Wanna a smoke?" Lighting up, Sarge says,

"I've never been married, but something tells me that being nervous about it is part of the deal. And of all the places this damn Army could have sent you, you end up in the one place where you can speak the language. That's some pretty good luck, Mario."

"I know, Sarge. I wonder about that a lot."

"Maybe those dice of yours are luckier than you think."

"I keep thinkin about my old man and what he's gonna say when he gets my letter. I'd love to see his face when he reads that I'm gettin married."

"I'm sure he'll approve. Antonella's beautiful, talented and she seems to be crazy about you. What more could he ask for? I hope you two have a busload of kids."

"I never thought much about havin kids, but I'd like to have some one day." Sarge drops his cigarette and snuffs it out with his boot.

"It's been a long night. I'm goin to sleep. Don't stay up all night, ya got it?"

"Sure, Sarge. Whatever ya say."

After a restless night, Mario is finally able to fall asleep. The few hours of rest seem like only minutes to him, and the morning arrives quickly. Frankie is the first to greet him. Yanking the covers from Mario's bunk, he shouts,

"Up and at em, buddy. Time ta hit the showers. Ya got a big day ahead a you." Still groggy and suffering with a mild headache from the night before, Mario climbs from his bunk. Frankie pushes him to the showers, and the rest of the squad stands and applauds his last morning in the barracks.

"Take it easy, will ya? I got a headache this mornin," jokes Mario, in mock anger. Having already turned the shower on, Hank snickers as he strips off Mario's underwear and shoves him into the steaming water.

"That outta take care of that headache for ya."

The hot shower is therapeutic and begins to clear Mario's head. Within a few minutes, he's fully awake. While he's shaving, Hank, George and Frankie hover about like mother hens.

"Don't you guys have something else to do besides watch me shave?"

"We're only tryin to help. Whatta ya want us to do?" asks George.

"If you guys really wanna help, my boots could use some polish and you could check my dress uniform and make sure its not all wrinkled." To his surprise, all three of them exit the shower room and do as he's asked. Smiling at himself in the mirror, he continues to shave while feeling thankful for having them as friends today.

As Mario and the others are dressing, Sergeant Thompson enters the barracks. He's been gone for several hours, and Mario asks,

"Where ya been, Sarge?"

"I called in a favor and got the C.O. to let me use a couple of officer staff cars today. Me, you and George can drive one to the church, and Hank and Frankie can use the other one to pick up Antonella's family. It's a little surprise I've been working on for you."

"Two sedans? Thanks, Sarge. That's great. I think they were going to use a taxi. I'll bet Antonella will be shocked when she sees one of em pull up. And before I forget, I got something for you." Opening his locker, Mario retrieves a small box and hands it to Sarge.

"I guess it's your job ta take care of this until the ceremony." Sergeant opens the lid and finds a simple gold band inside. "I bought it in town not too long ago. It's supposed to be fourteen carat gold."

"It's real nice, Mario. I'll take good care of it."

Within the hour, each man is dressed in his best uniform and ready to leave for the church. Mario stops for a moment and shakes hands with each of them, one last time. They can sense finality in their three-year journey, knowing that their friendship will take on a much different kind of importance after today. As his buddies all pat him on the back, Mario leaves the barracks, and the only life he's known with them, for the last time.

Sergeant Thompson hands the key to one of the sedans to Hank and asks,

"You have the address I gave you, right?"

"Sure Sarge, her place ain't far from the church. I checked it on a map. I'll pick em up and see ya there." With that, Sarge, Mario and George climb into the other sedan and begin driving to the church. After leaving Pomig, however, Hank speeds along the main road leading to Naples. He studies the roadside as if searching for something. Suddenly slamming on the brakes, he throws Frankie forward into the dash panel, where he lands with a hard bump.

Backing up to a small, unpaved road, Hank steers the sedan off the main highway and up into the surrounding hills.

"What in blue Jesus ya tryin ta do? Break my neck?" squeals Frankie. "Where the hell are ya goin, anyway?"

"Don't worry, this won't take long. Sarge ain't the only one who's got a surprise for Mario today," Hank says with a loud laugh. Driving wildly down the rutted path, he stops in front of an old stable. With the engine still running, he leaps from the sedan and charges up to the tattered farmhouse. Frankie watches in confusion. Hank pounds on the door several times, and a stocky, little man appears. Pointing to some horses standing in the fenced yard, and using what little Italian he knows, he gets the man to nod his head in agreement. After handing him an envelope, Hank shakes his hand and rushes back to the car.

"What the hell was that all about?" inquires Frankie.

"It's a little surprise for Mario and his bride. Somethin special. Wait till ya see it. It's gonna be great."

"How'd ya find this damn place, fer Christ's sake?"

"One of the guys in the infirmary knows a girl who lives around here. He told me about it."

"You ain't gonna tell me what the surprise is?"

"Nope. You'll just have ta wait and see," shouts Hank with an impish laugh.

Antonella is feeling very anxious. Lucia carries one of the dining chairs into their shared bedroom.

"Why don't you sit here while I brush your hair?" Far more interested in trying to calm her sister down than actually doing her hair, Lucia speaks in a relaxed, steady voice.

"Do you remember how many times we talked of this day, when one of us would get married? It's so hard to believe you'll be a bride in a few hours. I'm so happy for you. Everything is ready, so you have nothing to worry about except looking pretty for Mario."

"I...know, but I can't help feeling a little scared. Thank God I have you, Lucia. I would be frantic if I didn't." With Lucia gently stroking her sister's hair, Antonella's tense shoulders drop slightly, and she no longer fusses with the hem of her nightgown. Lucia leans over her sister's shoulder and gives her a tender kiss on her cheek.

"You're going to be the most beautiful bride, ever." Antonella's eyes glisten from the tearful moment. She stands and embraces Lucia. Knowing how different their lives will be after today, she whispers,

"I love you so much. How...will we ever live...without each other?" Unable to answer her sister's poignant question, Lucia holds her more tightly, as the haunting thought intrudes into this special day. Moments later, Assunta enters the room and ends the disturbing mood. Holding Antonella's hands, she says,

"We haven't much time before me must leave for the church, my dear. Do you want something to eat before you get dressed?"

"No thank you, Mama. I'm too nervous to eat right now."

"Then I'll prepare your dress while Lucia finishes your hair."
Taking her daughters into her arms, Assunta kisses them lightly on their cheeks and her own emotions begin to show. On the verge of tears, she goes to the closet and begins to remove the linen sheet protecting Antonella's gown. Carefully smoothing its many layers with her hands, she sits on the edge of the bed and watches as her daughters share the final few hours of the only lives they've ever known.

Antonella's talent and skill have worked magic with the material Mario gave her. True to her vision, the wedding gown is a series of shortening layers from the waist to the floor. Its tight, form-fitting waist highlights her athletic figure, and the crescent-shaped neckline is low enough to reveal her tanned complexion. The upper half of the gown is embroidered with a delicate floral design, the result of many hours of sewing by hand. A wispy train, nearly six feet in length, completes the dress. Of all the beautiful clothes she's designed, her own wedding dress is the most spectacular. Holding the dress, Assunta says,

"Lucia, why don't you help keep the back open, so Antonella can step into it."

Carefully stepping into the gown and pulling it up over her shoulders, Antonella waits patiently as her sister buttons up the back. While Lucia is adjusting the fit of the gown, Assunta goes to the next room and returns with a floral tiara, which she places on Antonella's head. It is the crowning detail to compliment the magnificent gown. Holding a small hand mirror in front of her sister, Lucia says,

"See how beautiful it looks, Antonella."

"Thank you, Mama. It's perfect," says Antonella, hugging her mother once again.

During the excitement of the morning, Antonella doesn't notice Giancarlo arrive. Fully dressed and finding it difficult to move through the small apartment, she stands near the window as Lucia and Assunta ready themselves. She turns toward the door as he enters the apartment. The reflections from a bright morning sun sparkle against her pure, white dress, and Giancarlo is speechless as he gazes at her. After a few moments, he takes her into his arms, saying,

"You look so very beautiful, Antonella. I've never seen such a lovely wedding dress. Mario is a very fortunate man to have someone like you to love him." He gently kisses her forehead.

"Thank you, Giancarlo. I'm so happy you're home to see it."

"Papa would be so proud if he only knew how talented you have become." The mention of Pirrone touches Antonella deeply. Holding Giancarlo in a loving embrace, she says,

"He would be proud of all of us, Giancarlo. Especially you."

After parking the large, green sedan in front of Antonella's apartment, Frankie and Hank scamper up to the apartment. Hearing them arrive, Giancarlo opens the door before they can knock and greets them.

"Gooda morning. I see you founda the apartment," he says.

"Yeah, it was no problem. How'd ya know we were comin?" asks Frankie.

"Sergeant Thompson, he tella me last night. It's a very nice for him to do this. Antonella willa be very surprised. Come in. We are almosta ready to go." Entering the apartment, their first view of Antonella in her wedding dress gives them pause to stare for several seconds.

"My goodness. Look at you, will ya? You're gorgeous," exclaims Frankie, *"Bella...very bella.* Do ya understand?" he asks, humorously mixing the two languages. Laughing over Frankie's clumsy Italian, Antonella laughs and says,

"Grazie tante, Frankie. Thanka you. You arra verry pretty, too." Her misplaced English makes Frankie laugh. His piercing squeal and high spirits bring a smile to everyone's face, as Antonella forgets her anxious mood for the moment. Signaling to his wristwatch, Giancarlo says,

"Andiamo. We musta go." The difficult task of descending the stairway in her wedding gown concerns Antonella, until Assunta and Lucia step in to help. While lifting the floor length gown in the air, Assunta instructs Giancarlo to take Antonella's hand and guide her down the stairs. Frankie and Hank hold the long train off the floor. Moving step by step, they reach the street without incident, and Antonella climbs into the back of the sedan. Assunta and Lucia join her in the rear seat, and Giancarlo sits with Hank and Frankie in the front.

"Everyone ready?" shouts Hank. He speeds away before anyone has time to answer.

With little more than an hour to go before the ceremony begins, Mario is chain-smoking in the back of the sedan. Sergeant Thompson parks it in front of Maria Santissima. Jumping out, Mario asks,

"How do I look, George? My uniform okay?"

"Ya look fine. You know, this'll be a whole lot easier if you relax a little."

"I know, but I can't help it. You got the ring, Sarge?"

"Yes, Mario. It's right here," answers the Sergeant, tapping his shirt pocket.

"I'll sure be glad when this is all over. Man, I never been this nervous before."

"Let's go inside and tell the priest you're here," advises George. They climb the terraced steps leading to the doorway and enter the church, but they find no one inside the main hall. They make their way toward the main altar and hear Father Bertulucci's voice echo through the cathedral.

"Hello, Mario. Congratulations on this glorious day." Appearing from a small doorway at the side of the cathedral, he rushes to Mario and shakes his hand.

"Thank you, Father Bertulucci. I still can't believe today's the day. We were coming to find you," replies Mario, *"Where do you want us to go?"*

"You can wait in the small sanctuary just to the right of the altar. That doorway, there," he answers, pointing to the small side altar. *"How are you feeling, my son?"*

"Nervous, Father. But I suppose every groom feels that way."

"That's true, Mario. You're expected to be nervous. This is the biggest day of your life," replies the Father. Mario finds little comfort in the priest's comment. He can only respond with a weak smile before following the altar railing to the sanctuary.

Sitting between Lucia and Assunta, Antonella holds their hands tightly. Staring straight ahead, she is spellbound by the final moments leading up to her marriage. After parking the big sedan directly behind the first vehicle, Hank opens the rear door for her. Antonella climbs out and waits nervously while her mother and sister pull and fluff her dress to restore its shape. Giancarlo takes her hand, and they proceed to the small chapel at the front of the church. Father Bertulucci joins her there. With the mass only minutes away, he's dressed in his ceremonial vestments. As her childhood fantasy is about to come true, the Father's readiness to perform her wedding mass gives her goose bumps.

"Good morning to everyone," greets the Father with a cheery smile. Taking Antonella's hand, he says, *"Congratulations, Antonella. Such a beautiful dress for a beautiful bride."*

"She made it herself, Father," announces Lucia proudly.

"I've been told of your talent, and I can see it's all true. How are you this morning, my dear?"

"I'm excited and happy...and a little afraid, too. I keep thinking something will go wrong," Antonella replies with a soft laugh. The Father offers a reassuring hug.

"God wants you to be all those things today. Everything is prepared. We're going to have a wonderful mass, so you needn't worry. We'll begin shortly."

Friends and neighbors take their seats inside the cathedral. Frankie extends his arm to Assunta and escorts her to the front of the church. After genuflecting and anointing herself with the sign of the cross, she sits in the first pew with a clear view of the altar. A hush comes to the cathedral as all the guests are finally seated. Altar boys scurry about, carefully lighting the many candles to be used during the ceremony, and the pipe organ begins to play a melodic hymn, filling the cathedral with a soft, delicate sound. Father Bertulucci enters the sanctuary where Mario waits and says,

"We're ready to begin, Mario. You can all join me on the main altar." After a last round of congratulatory handshakes from Sarge and George, Mario and his friends join the priest at the front of the main hall. The organ music comes to an immediate stop, and the Father instructs the guests to stand by raising his upturned palms to the ceiling. After Frankie and Hank join him, Mario can see Assunta daubing her eyes with a small, white handkerchief. Father nods his head, and the great organ explodes with the music of *La Traviata*, Antonella's favorite opera.

With his heart pounding wildly, Mario faces the entrance of the cathedral, and the bridal procession begins. Lucia is the first to appear. Using careful, measured steps, she approaches the altar and smiles at Mario. She takes her place alongside the priest, and the guests turn their attention to the front of the cathedral. Mario takes a deep breath and gently rubs his sweating hands against his trousers. Antonella and Giancarlo begin to march to the altar in slow, matching steps. She moves gracefully down the center aisle, holding tightly to her brother's arm. Mario watches in quiet amazement as she draws nearer to him. Seeing her for the first time in the magnificent gown she's created, he believes she is more beautiful than he can ever recall. Antonella finds it impossible not to look at Mario. When their eyes meet, this moment they have been anticipating for all these months feels so very right. She smiles at him ever so slightly, and his nervous anxiety quickly melts away, replaced by a love far deeper than he ever thought possible. In those few seconds, she is the only thing he can see. He's wondered many times what this exact moment would feel like, but even his most optimistic expectations failed to equal the reality. To marry someone so beautiful, in a place as spectacular at this, seems almost miraculous to him. She approaches the altar with Giancarlo, and they stop just short of the two steps leading up to Father Bertulucci. The priest gestures for Mario to move directly in front of him. As Mario steps forward, he never turns his eyes away from Antonella.

Raising his hand, Father Bertulucci silences the music and begins the ceremony. Antonella stares nervously at Mario. The priest asks,

"Antonella, will you and Giancarlo please step up before me?"

"Giancarlo, do you give Antonella's hand in marriage to Mario, this morning?"

"Yes, Father, I do."

"Will you please place her hand in his, then?" With a small tear glistening in the corner of his eye, Giancarlo gently kisses his sister on the cheek and gives her hand to Mario. He shakes Mario's hand and joins his mother in the front pew. Father Bertulucci then signals the altar boys to join him, and the mass begins.

With the organ playing quietly in the background, they take their place, Lucia standing to Antonella's left and Sergeant Thompson to Mario's right. Father Bertulucci's tense and anxious behavior during rehearsal is replaced by a soothing, professionalism that soon calms Antonella's nervousness. With Mario by her side, she follows the familiar steps of the mass from recital of the gospel to the serving of communion. Following communion, the Father shares some of his personal thoughts with Antonella and Mario.

"How are you holding up?" he asks with concern. They simply smile, as he continues, *"Antonella and Mario, in just a few minutes, you will become husband and wife. We have not had a wedding in our church in a very long time, and I am thrilled to be*

here today. One of the most enjoyable parts of the priesthood is being the first to wish you both a lifetime of happiness and the blessing of many children. I must remind you that with marriage come responsibilities to God, your families and each other. I know that Mario is from another part of the world, Antonella, and that one day you will join him there. You and Mario have made this courageous decision together, but only you, Antonella, will have to leave one life and start another. While you have accepted this sacrifice to be here today, I can see by Mario's love for you that you will not have to face this new life alone. As man and wife, you shall more easily resolve even the most frightening of life's surprises. May God bless the both of you. There now, shall we complete the ceremony?"

With hearts pounding, they nod in agreement. Father directs Lucia and Sergeant Thompson to stand close and witness the exchange of vows. Father looks at Mario and asks,

"Mario. Do you take Antonella for your wife in the eyes of God and before your friends and family present here today? Do you pledge to love and protect her, for better or worse, until only death separates you?"

"I...do, Father."

Shifting his attention to Antonella, he asks,

"Antonella. Do you take Mario for your husband in the eyes of God and before your friends and family present here today? Do you promise to bestow the precious of gift of children to him and

pledge to love and honor him, for better or worse, until only death separates you?"

Antonella glances at Mario for a brief second and in a quiet, quivering voice, replies,

"Yes, Father. I do." Father Bertulucci points to his ring finger and asks Sergeant Thompson,

"Avete l' anello?" The Sergeant pulls the small gold band from his pocket and hands it to the priest. Holding the ring in his left hand, Father blesses it with a sign of the cross before handing it to Mario.

"Mario, place the ring on Antonella's finger and repeat after me." With trembling hands, Mario struggles for a moment before the ring slides gently over the knuckle and onto her finger. With Father Bertulucci's prompting, Mario says,

"With this ring, I devote my love and my life to you forever." Facing one another, Antonella and Mario lock their hands tightly together, and Father completes the ceremony.

"By the authority of the Catholic Church, I pronounce you man and wife. Congratulations to you both. You may kiss your beautiful bride, Mario." Antonella stares into Mario's eyes with love, finding it difficult to believe they are truly married. With their hands still clasped, they share their first kiss as husband and wife.

Antonella becomes aware of the delicate touch of Lucia's hand on her shoulder. She turns to her, and their joyful emotions spill over in a tearful embrace. The essence of their childhood dreams is now a reality.

"I'm so happy for you, Antonella. I...I'm going to cry like a baby if you say something. Just let me hold you for a few moments," whispers Lucia. After kissing her sister on the cheek, Lucia wipes the tears from Antonella's eyes with a small kerchief.

"It's time for you to walk down the aisle with your husband. I love you."

Taking Mario's arm, Antonella proudly waits at his side until the pipe organ begins to play. All the guests rise to their feet. With all eyes focused on them, they begin the traditional stroll down the aisle to the front of the church, followed immediately by Lucia, Sergeant Thompson, Giancarlo and Assunta. The daylong celebration begins amid a sea of laughter, tears and kisses. Giancarlo and the Sergeant kiss Antonella and shake Mario's hand. Assunta rushes to Antonella, gently places her hand on her daughter's cheek and says,

"Your father would be so proud of you today. You look so happy."

"I am, Mama. And I'm sure Papa is watching and smiling."

Surrounded by friends and neighbors on the steps of the church, Mario and Antonella thank the many well-wishers, including Frankie, Hank and George. Hank intentionally waits to be the last of the three to greet them in order to deliver the surprise he's arranged. After hugging Antonella, he shakes Mario's hand and says,

"I hear they got a custom in this town that the bride and groom have to ride through their neighborhood in a fancy carriage, so I got ya one."

Hank's surprise has arrived. On the street in front of the church sits a carriage, complete with a pair of matching white horses. Recognizing the driver to be the same man Hank had talked to earlier, Frankie shouts,

"Ya son of a gun. That's the little guy from the stable, ain't it?" Now, however, the little man is dressed in a black, driver's uniform, complete with top hat and white gloves. The black carriage sparkles in the bright July sun. It is decorated with highly polished brass lamps and hardware. The passenger's seats are covered in tufted, red leather, burnished to a lustrous sheen from many years of service. Hank grabs Mario's arm and nudges him toward the carriage.

"Come on, buddy. Time ta take your gal for a carriage ride through town."

"How...I mean where...did you find this guy?"

"I'll tell ya some other time. Get goin; all these people want ta throw a lot a rice at ya," Hank replies with a loud laugh. Under a shower of flying rice, Antonella and Mario dash to the waiting carriage. With help from Mario and Hank, Antonella is able to climb into the carriage with her dress intact. Smiling playfully, Antonella leans over the edge of the carriage and takes Hank's hand.

"Thanka you, Hank. *E bella.*"

"Wait one second. George needs to take some pictures." Armed with a used Brownie Hawkeye, George carefully aims the viewfinder and clicks several shots of Mario and Antonella in the carriage.

"Okay, go enjoy the ride," he shouts after taking the last photograph.

The driver suddenly cracks his whip in the air, and the horses lurch forward. Waving to the gathering of family and friends, Mario and Antonella move away from the church and enjoy the leisurely ride through the neighborhood. The time-honored tradition draws friendly cheers and applause from even complete strangers. Mario and Antonella delight in their first moments alone as husband and wife.

Returning to the church after the forty-five minute carriage ride, Mario and Antonella enjoy another round of cheers from the waiting guests. The wedding celebration gradually moves to the church garden. With help from his altar boys, Father Bertulucci has placed many wooden chairs and several tables around the courtyard earlier in the day. Mario and Antonella stroll through the pristine grounds arm-in-arm. Now that the ceremony is complete, they are more relaxed and able to sit and talk with their guests. George continues to take more photographs, and a familiar voice calls out to Antonella.

"Your dress is gorgeous, my dear. And you look so beautiful in it. Such talent," states Theresa Minelli. Turning to Mario, she

adds, *"Do you realize how fortunate you are to marry such a lovely and talented girl, Mario?"*

"Yes, Signora Minelli, I do. She's very special."

"I'm so very happy you're here today, Theresa. Thank you for coming," says Antonella.

"There's no need to thank me, me dear. You're like a daughter to me, and I'm so thrilled to see you get married. I couldn't stop crying during the entire ceremony," she admits with a smile. *"You go and talk and enjoy your wedding day. I'm going to help your mother."* Antonella watches Theresa and her mother embrace each other. She can hear them laughing from across the garden. Together, they make sure the final details for the evening are attended to, while sharing several glasses of wine together.

Mario escorts Antonella to the small bridal table set up in their honor. Decorated with fresh flowers and ornate candelabras, the table provides enough seating to accommodate Lucia, Sarge, Giancarlo and Assunta. After assisting Antonella into her seat, Mario pours a small glass of wine for each of them, and they take a few minutes out of the exciting day to catch their breath. Slowly drinking his wine, he quietly observes the amazing events unfolding before him. Sergeant Thompson and Giancarlo, sitting in a nearby corner of the garden, are engrossed in conversation. Mario is pleased his good friend and his new brother-in-law get along so well. He's amused by Hank and Frankie's efforts to flirt with the politely attentive Lucia. He can only wonder what she must be thinking, as the two men wave their hands

515

wildly through the air in an effort to communicate with her. He's grateful for George's willingness to take pictures of this day. They will be the only record of this remarkable event he'll have to share with his family in Detroit. Although supported by his Army friends, he suddenly feels deeply disappointed that his father and brothers could not be here to witness this incredible place and meet the people who have become his family. Momentarily lost in his thoughts, he stares at a distant statue on the opposite side of the courtyard.

"Mario? Mario, are you not feeling well?" asks Antonella. Startled by her question, he collects himself.

"I'm fine. I was just thinking about my family...how they would enjoy this day." Antonella kisses him.

"It's sad that you and your brothers have missed each other's weddings, but there's nothing we can do. You have wonderful friends here who care about you, and that's something to be thankful for."

"I know. There're the best friends I ever had. I couldn't be happier."

As midday turns to early evening, a large table in the middle of the courtyard offers bowls of pasta, seafood, fresh-baked bread, and an ample supply of wines and liquors. Mario and Antonella are the first to fill their plates. Returning to their table, they realize how hungry they are from the excitement of the day. While Mario and Atonella enjoy their meal, guests seat themselves along the outer edge of the cobblestone court, surrounding them in anticipation of the festivities to come. Juggling their plates on their knees and wine glasses in their hands, no one seems the least bit concerned about the lack of table space. They view it as simply another inconvenience of the war, and they are simply glad to share in Mario and Antonella's happiness. Before long, the faint sound of knives and forks clinking against wine glasses grows to a loud crescendo, demanding that the bride and groom kiss. Laughing, Lucia gently pushes Antonella against Mario.

"Kiss him, Antonella. You must kiss him right now." Needing little encouragement, Antonella places her arms around Mario's neck and gives him a long, passionate kiss. Howls of laughter and suggestive comments fill the air.

"You must save those kinds of kisses for later," shouts one of the guests. *"Keep your hands on the table,"* hollers another. Staring at Mario after the sensual kiss, she sees a passion in his eyes. She smiles at him seductively, and her thoughts drift ahead to sharing their first night together. The delightful tradition of kissing each other when the guests demand is repeated many more times during dinner. After everyone enjoys servings of wedding cake and coffee, Assunta presents a colorful, woven basket to Antonella. Its contents are covered with a white napkin, and a long-handled, silver spoon lies on top of it.

"It's time to give away the bomboniera. Go...you must be sure not to miss anyone. That's bad luck," says Assunta with a laugh.

Holding the basket by its handle, Antonella moves gracefully through the courtyard, spooning out several of the candy-covered almonds to each of the guests. Required to give each male guest a kiss with the candy, Antonella playfully teases Hank, Frankie and George by rushing back to Mario after giving them their candy and refusing to kiss them. Pointing to their lips, the three Americans demand their kisses and begin chasing Antonella around the courtyard, trying to collect. The sight of her long gown billowing out behind her, as she dashes in and out of tables and chairs, brings delirious laughter from everyone. Finally stopping in the middle of the courtyard, she affectionately kisses and hugs each of Mario's good friends, to the applause and delight of all the guests. Watching her behave with such wild exuberance, Mario's reminded of why he was drawn to her in the first place. He finds her more alluring than ever. When she returns to her seat, he smiles and says,

"*I think my friends are in love with you, too.*"

"*They are so sweet, Mario. I think they enjoy when I tease them.*" As the wonderful celebration draws to a close, Giancarlo surprises Mario and Antonella with a toast. Standing in the center of the courtyard, he lifts his wine glass.

"*To the bride and the groom. May your lives be rich and full, your regrets few.*" Joined by the guests, a last round of well-intentioned cheers fill the garden. Mario kisses his new wife once again.

The long shadows of night begin to reach across the church garden, and Mario's promise to return to Capri for their wedding night requires that they leave soon. In order to be aboard the last ferryboat departing from Napoli, Sarge has offered to drive Mario and Antonella to the pier. After saying goodnight to many of the guests, Mario and Antonella join her family to thank them for their help on this special night. Following a tearful embrace with her sister, Lucia reaches into a small bag she's kept hidden under the table and retrieves a flower vase. Handing it to Mario, she smiles.

"You and Antonella must throw this on the ground. Breaking the vase is good luck. The number of pieces will be the number of years you'll be happily married." Unfamiliar with the practice, Mario questions Lucia to be sure he has not misunderstood her.

"Lucia. We are to smash it on the ground? Right here in the garden?"

"Yes, Mario. Both of you must do it before you leave." Each with one hand on the vase, Mario and Antonella raise it high above their heads and bring it crashing down onto the cobblestones. Exploding into many pieces too numerous to count, the shattered vase lies scattered at their feet. They all cheer at the ancient custom. Sergeant Thompson checks his wristwatch and reminds Mario,

"If you want to be on that ferryboat, you need to get going, Mario." After a final exchange of hugs and handshakes, Mario and Antonella hurry from the garden, climb into the waiting sedan and drive back to Antonella's apartment to change clothes for the trip to Capri.

Arriving at the apartment, Mario leans forward and informs the Sergeant,

"We won't be very long, Sarge. Antonella wants to change and grab a small bag we've packed. Be back in a few minutes."

"Okay, Mario. I'll wait right here." Holding her dress well above her knees, Antonella scrambles up the staircase effortlessly. After entering the apartment, she turns her back to him and asks,

"Mario, can you unbutton the back of my gown for me. It's impossible for me to reach it." When he releases the last button, she carefully steps out of the dress and places it on a waiting hanger. Dressed in only her underclothing, she runs to Mario without warning, throws her arms around his neck and gives him a long, sensuous kiss.

"I love you so much, my darling," she whispers. Wrapping his arms around her and pulling her tightly against himself, Mario can feel Antonella's hands clawing at his back as she curls her leg firmly around his. They exchange fiery kisses, as they are consumed by their own passion for each other. There is electricity in their love now, and he can think of nothing else except to be with her. Resisting the temptation, however, Mario releases her.

"We'd better go or we'll miss the ferry."

"I have something very special I want to wear for you." Mario follows her into her bedroom, where she searches through her collections of dresses until she finds the one she wants to wear. The dress she selects is pale turquoise. Its high, modest neckline appears more like a short collar. With short sleeves and a skirt slit to the

middle of her thigh, it fits her superbly, as all her creations do. Modeling the sensuous gown for him, she asks,

"Do you like it? It's one of my favorites." He answers the question by holding her tightly and kissing her once again. With their sexual appetite for each other no longer restricted, they enjoy the anticipation of their first night together. Mario picks up the travel bag and leads Antonella by the hand, back to the waiting sedan.

The Sergeant speeds them away from the apartment and within minutes he is dodging an assortment of old trucks, piles of fishing nets and several startled dockworkers as he hurtles along the pier toward the Capri ferry. Stopping the big sedan alongside the boat, he jumps out and opens the door for Antonella. She steps from the rear seat, waits and watches as Mario pulls the small suitcase from the trunk. The telltale clunking sound of the ferry's engine indicates it is ready to depart within minutes. While shaking Sarge's hand, Mario says,

"Sarge, I don't know how to thank you for all you've done for us."

"I'm glad I could help, Mario. You're a good soldier, and you turned out to be a better friend. I'm happy...for the both of you." With little time before they must board, Antonella gives the Sergeant a final hug and kisses his cheek. In her combined English and Italian, she says,

"Thanka you, Sergeant. *You are a very good man."*

"Grazie, Antonella. Buon viaggio," he responds in his limited Italian.

Picking up the suitcase, Mario takes Antonella's hand, and they hurry to board the waiting boat. Sergeant watches from the shadowy pier. Standing on the lower deck of the dimly lit ferry, Mario raises his hand to his head and salutes the Sergeant before the darkness descends on him completely.

Clearing the harbor, the ferryboat plows its way across the Mediterranean, as Mario and Antonella make their way to the top deck. The ocean breeze swirling around the rolling ship cools the warm July evening. Although the sun has already fallen below the horizon, it continues to cast an orange-colored tint through the high clouds that linger above the blackness at the ocean's edge. Soon, the first stars of the evening become visible, and Mario and Antonella drink in the colorful magic of the twilight sky.

"Tell me what you are thinking, Mario?"

"I'm not sure how to explain it. I just never imagined I'd get married like this and be spending my wedding night on an island like Capri. These things just don't happen to someone like me. I keep thinking I'll wake up and find out it's all a dream." Antonella wraps her arms around his waist and pulls herself against him. After giving him another passionate kiss, she looks into his eyes and says with a warm smile,

"When you wake up in the morning, my love, you'll know this is not a dream."

Alone on the empty deck of the ship, they openly begin to express their love. Their kisses become more erotic, and they begin to explore each other's bodies. The short ride to Capri raises their desire to be together to a feverish pitch, and the remaining hours before they can sleep together will be full of sweet anticipation.

Approaching Capri, the rumble of the ferryboat's engine fades, and the boat's speed slows to a crawl. The brightly-colored lights along the docks of Marina Grande are now clearly visible as the boat enters the harbor. Sliding into its berth along the seawall, the small ship gently thumps the dock pilings, and the crew casts mooring lines ashore to waiting dockhands. Securing the ship, they lower the gangplank, allowing the ship's few passengers to disembark. Carrying the small suitcase containing their personal belongings, Mario holds Antonella's hand. They stroll along the Via Spiaggia and return to the Hotel Belvedere Tre Re. The street is busy with local residents and a small number of U.S. military personnel enjoying a Saturday evening in one of the many trattorias along harbor road. When they arrive at the hotel after the short walk from the ferryboat, Mario asks the proprietor to seat them at one of the outdoor tables overlooking the harbor. Noticing the suitcase Mario is carrying, he asks,

"Will you be spending the night with us, Senor?" Still holding Antonella's hand, Mario smiles.

"Yes. We were just married today. Do you have a nice room with a view of the ocean?"

"You are newlyweds? How wonderful. Congratulations to you both." A kindly man with a welcoming smile and bubbly manner, the proprietor is excited and calls out to his wife,

"Franca, come quick. We have newlyweds staying with us." Bursting through the free-swinging doors leading from the kitchen, the proprietor's wife scurries out to the dining area, still wiping her hands on her apron.

"Welcome, I'm Franca. So you were just married today, and you have come to Capri for your honeymoon? How romantic. Isn't that romantic, Dominic?" Too impatient to wait for his reply, she continues, *"It's so nice to see young people in love again."*

"Thank you, Franca. I'm Antonella and this is Mario. He asked me to marry him in this very hotel. It's such a beautiful place, we had to return," explains Antonella.

"Of course! Now I remember. The two of you were here several months ago...is that not correct?"

"That right, Dominic. You have a good memory," Mario responds with a chuckle.

"How could I forget such a beautiful woman with an American soldier?" asks a perplexed Dominic.

"Well, we have a lovely room for you. It's on the second floor and has a balcony overlooking the ocean. It's very quiet and private.

I'll have a maid prepare it for you while you have something to eat," says Franca before she disappears behind the kitchen doors.

Returning with a small platter of grilled vegetables and fresh bread, Franca places the appetizers on the table.

"I brought you a little something to eat. Would you like anything else?"

"This is fine, thank you. We had dinner several hours ago," answers Antonella. Moments later, Dominic arrives at the table with a freshly opened bottle of wine and four glasses. After pouring a bit of wine into each glass, he hands them to everyone and keeps the last one for himself. Raising his glass, he says,

"We are honored to have you as our guests. Thank you for returning to our hotel for your honeymoon. May your stay here bring you only the fondest memories." Touching glasses with their gracious hosts, Mario and Antonella politely drink the wine and sample the food on the table. Keenly aware that Antonella and Mario did not come for dinner tonight, Franca hands Mario the room key.

"You must be exhausted from such a long and exciting day. Your room is ready for you. If you want or need anything, please let us know." After thanking them for their kindness, Mario and Antonella climb the narrow staircase leading to the second floor. He compares the key number to those on the doors and finds a match.

Unlocking the large, mahogany doors, Mario swings them open. The room is large and spacious, with a formal seating area furnished with a sofa and chair. Fine, linen curtains hang over glass-paneled doors leading to the balcony, and several large ceiling fans whirl silently overhead. Charging into the room, Antonella begins to explore what lies hidden behind the other doors. Mario places the suitcase on a table and removes his tie. Antonella calls out to him from another room.

"Mario, come quickly. You must see the view from here."

Entering the bedroom, Mario finds two more glass doors swung wide open. While the sea breeze lifts the curtains high in the air, he sees Antonella standing outside on the adjacent balcony, staring at the ocean.

"Look at the sky...it's so full of stars. They light up the ocean. Isn't Capri beautiful, Mario?" Joining her on the balcony, Mario slips his arms around her waist, kisses the back of her neck.

"I think you're the most beautiful view on Capri tonight," he replies. She turns to face him. Throwing her arms around his neck, she gives him another long, sensuous kiss.

"I love you, Mario and I want to be with you," she murmurs. Their embrace grows more heated and their kisses more aggressive. Mario caresses her breast, and Antonella pulls him tightly against her. She guides him into the bedroom, steps away for a moment and unbuttons her dress. Letting it drop to the floor, she stands before Mario wearing only her sheer underclothes. Seeing his beautiful wife with so little on fuels his desire even more. With his heart pounding madly and his breathing short, he takes her into his arms and continues kissing her.

"Let me take off your shirt," she whispers. She unbuttons his shirt, and he lightly licks her neck and shoulders, enjoying the moist, delicate taste of her skin. Encouraging him to remove all of her underclothes, she pulls him onto the canopy-covered bed. They caress and kiss each other wildly, while Mario removes the rest of his clothes. They embrace once again, feeling their bodies against one another for the first time.

"I want to make love to you, Antonella," he whispers.

"Oh yes, Mario. I want you, too."

With an insatiable appetite for one another, their repeated lovemaking makes the next several days the most incredible time of their young lives.

CHAPTER 19

After moving into their tiny apartment, Mario and Antonella enjoy their new life as husband and wife. With the war in Italy at an end, Mario is allowed away from the base more often, and he is able to be with Antonella for days at a time. During these first magical months, the thrill of discovering each other's likes and dislikes, of learning to live life as a couple, bring them even closer together. Sharing breakfast on leisurely mornings after making love, searching through the local markets for an evening's meal, or finding a new café or trattoria's food to sample are simple pleasures that serve to strengthen their love for each other.

This carefree time in their marriage brings about noticeable changes in Mario. Truly happy for the first time in his life, he finds that much of the anger and combativeness he knew as a young man no longer agonizes him. The violent thug who had brutalized Roberto

Lucci in a nightclub men's room has fallen victim to the war. In his place stands a man whose future has purpose, a future that includes the responsibilities of caring for another person. He has grown in many ways during the war, and his most remarkable change is the ability to love this woman. He feels compelled to give of himself rather than take advantage of whatever opportunity a woman may present. A calming self-assurance is the reward for this newfound maturity.

Returning to Pomig on one of his assigned workdays, Mario checks in with Sergeant Thompson. Finding him in his office at the back of the barracks, he joins him there.

"Morning, Sarge. We got anything ta work on today?"

"Not too much. A couple of transports and a some banged up half-tracks."

"Sure is getting slow. What do ya hear from the combat guys?"

"Sounds like the Normandy invasions are pushing Jerry back to Germany, but it's pretty rough up there these days. I hear they're bombing Berlin every day. We're too far south of the front, so I doubt we'll get much to do down here. Oh, by the way, you got a letter from home. I got it here in my drawer," replies Sarge, handing the letter to Mario.

"Thanks. I've been waitin for this. I wrote home and told my family I was gettin married. Looks like they finally wrote back. I'll see ya later, Sarge. I want to read this right now." Mario sits on his old bunk and opens the letter. Looking quickly at the signature on the bottom, he sees it's from John.

> Dear Mario,
>   We got your letter and no one can believe you got married. Pa called me and Joe and kept shouting for us to come over right away. He was too excited to tell us over the phone. He showed us the letter when we got to his house, and all he could do was run around the dining room laughing and shouting. I think he's in shock. We are all surprised by the news and can't wait to meet your new wife. She sounds terrific. Pa is already planning to have a big party when you get home. Do you know when you are coming home? The papers are saying the war could be over early next year. Everybody here is doing fine. The store is doing good, and I'm still busy at the plant. We'll be starting to build cars again soon, so it looks like your job will be waiting for you when you get back. I guess you are going to need one now. We're all happy for you. Write back when you can.
>
>   John

Mario folds the letter, puts it back in the envelope and stuffs it into his shirt pocket. Hearing from home is always a treat, but this letter brings an especially good feeling with it. The image of his father traipsing all over the house after receiving the letter causes him to laugh out loud as he heads for the repair center. He's looking forward to seeing his family again.

On the days Mario reports to the base, Antonella usually visits her mother and sister for lunch. During one of her visits, she doesn't eat the meal Assunta has prepared. Pushing the food around with her fork, she stares blindly at the plate in obvious discomfort.

"Antonella, why are you not eating?" asks Assunta.

"I'm not hungry early in the day. I feel sick, like I'm going to vomit."

"How long have you been feeling like this?"

"For two, maybe three weeks now. By the end of the day, I feel fine. I'm sure it will pass." Assunta is not so quick to dismiss her daughter's symptoms as a mere annoyance. She asks more personal questions.

"Are your still having your periods?"

"I didn't last month. Why are you asking such things?"

"I've seen many women with these same symptoms, my darling. I think you are going to have a baby." Her mother's suspicions strip away Antonella's denial. She is excited and afraid at the same time over the possibility of being pregnant. Assunta holds her daughter's hands to ease Antonella's sudden nervousness.

"Mama, are you sure?"

"Yes. I'm quite sure, Antonella. You are young and healthy, and such morning illness usually means only one thing." Slumping back into her chair, Antonella smiles at her mother. With her anxiety relieved by Assunta's gentle confidence, she says,

"Mama. You're going to be a grandmother."

"This is such a wonderful surprise, Antonella. I'm so happy for you. A grandchild...I never thought I'd have a grandchild so soon

after you were married. Have you said anything to Mario yet?" asks Assunta.

"No, not yet. I wasn't sure what to say until now. I'm going to tell him tonight. Maybe I'll ask him if we can go to a trattoria this evening...to celebrate. And...and don't say anything to Lucia and Giancarlo yet. I want to be sure Mario is with me when we do that. I must go back to our apartment. He'll be home from the base soon," she answers, as she rushes out the door.

Returning home earlier than expected, Mario discovers Antonella is away. Assuming she is visiting her family again, he pours a small glass of wine, kicks off his boots, and sits on the small veranda overlooking the street. While sipping his wine in the late day sun, he sees Antonella step from the bus at the nearby corner. When she looks up and notices him standing there, he raises his arm and waves to her. Waving back at him wildly, she sprints the short distance to their apartment. Laughing out loud at Antonella's never-ending enthusiasm, Mario steps inside the apartment to await her return. Opening the door, he hears her charging up the stairs, shouting,

"Mario...Mario! Where are you? I want to ask you something." Leaping into his arms when she reaches the top of the stairway, she squeals, *"Can we go out to eat tonight...someplace special? I have some wonderful news to tell you."*

"We can go out if you like. Did you enjoy Piccola la Cucina?"

"Yes. That's good. Hurry and change so we can go."

"What is it? Why are you so excited?"

"No, no, no, Senor Carlucci. I'll tell you nothing until we get to the trattoria."

Piccola la Cucina is located only a short walk from the apartment. Small and intimate, it's become Antonella and Mario's favorite local café. Arriving there, she takes Mario by the hand and guides him to a secluded table at the rear of the dining room. Bewildered by her mysterious conduct, Mario cannot wait any longer for her to reveal her secret to him.

"Will you please tell me what this is all about, Antonella?" Saying nothing at first, she takes his hand and gently places it onto her belly. Her broad smile and joyful expression stun Mario for a moment, as he realizes what she's trying to tell him.

"Antonella. Are...are you pregnant?" Wiping tears of joy from her eyes, she nods her head.

"Yes, Mario. We're going to have a baby. Mama says I have all the signs. Isn't it wonderful?"

"Are you...sure? I mean...is she sure?"

"Mama's delivered many babies, Mario. She's very certain about this."

Momentarily numbed by the unexpected news, Mario sits upright in his chair, holding Antonella's hand. The prospect of becoming a father so soon is both overwhelming and exciting. Bringing her hand to his lips, he kisses her tenderly.

"A baby! I...I can't believe it. I'm going to be a father? I never though we'd start a family so fast...it's such a surprise. When...I mean...do you know how long...it's been?"

"Mama thinks I'm about six weeks, so we have time to get ready."

"No one's ever given me such a...wonderful gift. I...I can't even find any words to tell you how...how I feel. I love you, Antonella."

"I love you too, Mario." During dinner, they laugh and kiss like new lovers, as their remarkable journey continues to shower them with happiness. Remembering John's letter, Mario smiles.

"I got a letter from my brother John today. The first one since I told my family about getting married."

"What did they say, Mario? Were they...surprised?"

"Pa was shocked. They all were shocked. Everyone's looking forward to meeting you," he says with a laugh, *"but wait till I tell Pa about this...that he's going to be a grandfather. I'd sure like to see his face when he hears the news."*

Thinking about the birth of his child raises some important questions for Mario. He returns to camp the following day and seeks out Sergeant Thompson's assistance once again, hoping he can answer some of them. After checking the Sergeant's office and not finding him there, he asks around the barracks to see if anyone knows where he is.

"Try the mess hall. I saw him in there a few minutes ago," one soldier replies. Hustling over to the hall, he spots the Sergeant sitting with several other men. As he approaches the table, Sarge sees him coming.

"Hey Mario, you're here bright and early. What happened? Did that pretty wife of yours kick you out?" Chuckling at Sarge's friendly teasing, Mario joins him at the table. Sarge introduces him to the other men sitting there.

"Mario, this is Sergeant Mahoney and Sergeant Bremmer."

"Nice ta meet you guys," replies Mario, shaking their hands.

"Mario just got married a few months ago…found himself a great little gal," says Sergeant Thompson. "What's on your mind this morning, Mario?"

"I need some information. Maybe we can get together later when…"

"We were just leavin, Mario. He's all yours," says Sergeant Mahoney. After they're gone, Sergeant Thompson asks Mario,

"When you come looking for me, there's something important going on," kids the Sergeant. Shifting around in his chair, Mario smiles.

"It's Antonella. She's going to have a baby. Can ya help me figure out what to do…as far as the Army is concerned?"

"Holy shit, Mario! That's great! Congratulations. When did you find out?"

"Last night. We went out for dinner and she told me then."

"Well, that didn't take very long."

"I know. I guess I didn't expect this to happen so soon, but I'm pretty excited. Do ya know what I need to do, Sarge?"

"Not entirely, but I do know that the baby is considered an American citizen. I think the Army will issue you a birth certificate so you can apply for a U.S. passport."

"How do I make all that happen?"

"I think it's pretty automatic. When the baby's born, just report his name and birth date to the C.O.'s office. I can handle that for you, if you want. In the meantime, I'll check on anything else you need to do."

"That'd be great, Sarge. I don't know what lucky straw I drew ta get hooked up with you back in Jersey, but I really appreciate all ya been doin for me." Sarge rises from the table and shakes Mario's hand.

"That's okay. It takes a lot of nerve to do what you've done. There's going to be some rough road ahead for you and Antonella, and if I can help in some way, I will. Now let's tell the guys what you've done," he adds with a smirk.

Searching the barracks, they find no sign of Frankie, George or Hank.

"Let's check the repair center. I think they were working on a couple of big generators some Navy guys brought in." As expected, they locate Mario's three friends there.

"Take a smoke break, you guys. I have something to tell you," announces the Sergeant.

"If ya tell us we gotta pack this place up and move out again, I'm goin AWOL," shouts Frankie.

"No, it's nothing like that. It's Mario here. He's going to be a father." Bursting out in a howling laughter, Mario's friends swarm around him. While shaking his hand and slapping his back, their expected teasing and taunting begins.

"What the hell took you so long? Ya been married for almost two whole months already," razzes Hank.

"See what a coupla years in the desert will do, Mario? Didn't anyone tell ya how that happens?" teases George.

"Hell, if I was hitched to a good looker like Antonella, she'd be havin kids left and right," shouts Frankie.

"Thank God, we ain't gotta worry about that. One a you is bad enough," jokes Hank.

"Aw, screw you, Hank. I don't see any women linin up around yer ass," replies Frankie.

"Knock it off, will ya?" says George, "Mario's got enough to worry about without listenin to the two of you yappin at each other. Congratulations, Mario. How's Antonella feeling?"

"She's really excited, too. She gets a little sick in the mornings, but I guess that's normal."

"Well, tell her I should be getting your wedding pictures back from the PX soon. That'll make her feel a little better," says George with a laugh.

"Seriously, Mario. This is great. We all left Fort Dix together and we're gonna get ta see one of us go back with his own family. That's somethin pretty damn special. I'm real happy for you and Antonella," adds Hank.

"Thanks. Everything's happenin so fast, it's a little scary. Going home with a war bride and a baby was not in the cards when I enlisted. I'm still a little shocked."

"Don't this make us temporary uncles or somethin?" chirps Frankie.

"Yeah. I guess it does," replies Mario with a beaming smile.

Several days have passed since she last saw her mother, and Antonella is anxious to share the news of her pregnancy with Lucia and Giancarlo. When Mario returns to their apartment, she greets him with a kiss, then asks,

"Mario, can we go to Mama's tonight? I want to tell Lucia and Giancarlo about the baby. I asked Mama not to say anything...until we can tell them together."

"That's fine. I told the guys about the baby and they're calling themselves uncles already, so we better hurry up and tell your sister and brother," replies Mario with a smile. Antonella waits anxiously for Mario to change into a fresh set of fatigues. As he steps

538

from the bedroom, she grabs his hand while he's still buttoning his shirt and pulls him out the door.

"Let's go, Mario. I'll do that for you while you drive. I can't wait any longer."

Laughing at her impatience, he follows her down the stairs, two steps at a time, and into the Jeep. After the short ride to Bagnoli, Mario parks in his usual place below Assunta's apartment and Antonella immediately climbs out. Hearing her name being called out by several of her neighbors, she waves at them. Stopping to talk as she crosses the street, she wishes she could share her exciting news with them, but she waits to tell her sister and brother first. She knows her mother will soon tell all the neighbors anyway. Entering the apartment, they find Assunta and Lucia sitting at the dining table enjoying an early dinner.

"Antonella...and Mario. What a nice surprise. Come and sit. Are you hungry, Mario? I have some nice fish left if you want it," asks Assunta.

"I'd love something to eat. Your daughter rushed me from our apartment so fast, I barely had time to change my clothes."

"How are you feeling, Antonella? Can I get something for you?" Assunta's innocent inquiry draws Lucia's attention, and she asks her sister,

"Antonella, have you been sick?" As Antonella's eyes dart from Assunta to Mario, she smiles at Lucia.

"Only in the mornings...sometimes I feel sick to my stomach and throw-up."

"Mama, do you know about this?" asks a startled Lucia.

"Mama knows, Lucia. I talked to her several days ago. I'm going to have a baby, Lucia. You're...you're going to be an aunt."

"You...are pregnant? Oh my God, I can't believe it," she screams. *"How long have you known?"*

"Only a few days. We think I am only four or five weeks." The thrilling news has Lucia ecstatic, and she rushes to Antonella. Embracing her tightly, she realizes that another of their childhood fantasies will become a reality.

"We must start making baby clothes right away...and...and find a crib and even diapers," says a giggling Lucia.

"Yes...yes, of course. But we have time. You'll be the baby's godmother. Isn't that a wonderful idea, Mario?"

"I can't think of anyone more perfect."

"Mama, do you expect Giancarlo tonight? I can't wait to tell him, too," asks Antonella.

"I'm sure he'll be here any time now. You know how your brother hates to cook for himself. Sit and eat something until he arrives."

The family sits at the dining table enjoying dinner together. Giancarlo arrives a short time later, as Assunta has predicted. After kissing Antonella and Lucia and shaking Mario's hand, he joins them, and his mother prepares a plate for him. Placing a bottle of wine on the table, he calls out to Assunta,

"Mama, can you please bring the corkscrew and some extra wineglasses?" Giancarlo opens the wine, and pours a little into all the glasses.

"I see I'm not the only one who comes home to Mama for dinner."

"We love her cooking too, Giancarlo. But that's not the only reason we're here tonight. Mario and I have some exciting news we want to tell you."

"You do?" he responds, *"and what news is that?"*

"I'm expecting a baby, Giancarlo. I'm pregnant." Placing his knife and fork down on his plate with a loud clink, he wipes his mouth with his napkin and stares at her with a growing smile. Standing and kissing her once again, he then wraps his arm around Mario's shoulders.

"That's exciting...very exciting. Congratulations to both of you. And how are you feeling, Antonella?"

"I'm fine...just a little morning sickness sometimes. That's all."

"And what does the U.S. Army have to say about this Mario? Will they allow you to have a baby?" Giancarlo asks with a bit of a smirk.

"Not much they can do if they don't allow it, right?" answers Mario. As they laugh at Giancarlo's teasing, he lifts his wine glass and says,

"I wish you both the very best. To your new family." The festive mood carries well into the evening, and Mario and Antonella begin to prepare themselves for the arrival of their first child.

In the succeeding months, the romantic and intimate privacy of their young marriage is gradually lost to the demands of a yet-to-be-born baby. As her child grows inside her, Antonella's body changes drastically. Her swollen breasts and enlarged belly prevent her from wearing many of her favorite clothes. When Mario is working on the base, she spends much of her time at her mother's apartment sewing new clothes for herself and her baby. With her mother's guidance, she plans the many details of the birth event. Antonella wants the baby to be born in her own apartment, and they make preparations to have Assunta stay there in the final week of her pregnancy. Mario borrows a cot from the base for Assunta to use during that time. Hank's resourcefulness has also provided ample towels and linens to be used when the baby is born.

In addition to her physical changes, Antonella's personality changes daily, forcing Mario to constantly adjust to her varying wants. Her unpredictable mood swings surprise and sometimes anger him. She is often laughing one minute and crying the next, and her unpredictable behavior tests Mario's love for her daily. She has strange cravings and sleeping difficulties. Their marriage now demands endless patience from him, as the arrival of their child grows near. The base becomes Mario's temporary haven of relief from the constant pressure. Sitting with Frankie and George in the mess hall, he shares his frustrations with them.

"I can't wait till this baby's born. I'm walkin on eggshells tryin to keep Antonella happy."

"That's your job," replies George with a loud laugh. "I knew this guy back home…his wife would only eat mashed potatoes for the last month before their kid was born. Damn near drove em crazy."

"I know how he feels."

"Let's show em what we found. Maybe that'll cheer em up. Finish yer coffee and follow me," says Frankie. Dragging Mario from the mess hall, Frankie and George lead him to the repair center. Pulling a large, burlap bag from behind a workbench, Frankie opens it and dumps out an old, disassembled baby crib. Looking at the discarded relic, Mario asks,

"How's this supposed ta cheer me up?"

"Me and George are gonna fix it up and give it to Antonella. Whaddaya think?"

"Looks like it needs one helluva lot of fixin if ya ask me."

"Just give us a few days…ya won't recognize it the next time ya see it," states George.

"Good luck," replies Mario, shaking his head as he leaves. Working almost around the clock, Frankie and George clean, sand and paint the old crib until it shines like new. After they add newly-machined hardware, it works as well as it looks. Standing back and admiring their handy work, George says,

"Wait'll Mario gets a load of this. He's gonna sing a different tune." After seeing the restored crib several days later, Mario is astonished by what his friends have done.

"Damn, you guys weren't kiddin around, were ya? This thing looks brand new. Antonella's gonna love it."

"We'll put it inna a truck and bringin it over tonight...ta surprise her, okay?"

"Sure. Of course. You two are amazing."

Later that evening, after carefully securing the crib into the rear of a personnel carrier, Frankie and George drive the hulking vehicle to Mario's apartment.

"I'll go tell em we're here. Make sure no one swipes this thing in the meantime," says George.

"Ya better not say nothing to Antonella bout this crib until I get there. Ya got it?"

"Yeah, yeah. Don't worry. I'm just gonna tell Mario we're bringing it up, that's all." Staring through the truck's windshield, Frankie watches George vanish up the apartment stairway. He returns a few minutes later with Mario.

"Come on, Frankie. Let's get it up there now. Antonella's takin a nap, and we can sneak it in before she wakes up."

Holding the crib at each end, Frankie and George scale the narrow staircase under Mario's watchful eye.

"Nice an easy does it. Don't bang it into the wall and scratch it all up now," warns George.

"Jus git yer ass up the stairs, fer Christ's sake. This thing's gettin heavy," complains Frankie. The scene reminds Mario of an old Laurel and Hardy movie he once saw, and he begins chuckling.

"Will you guys quit foolin around? She'll be havin the kid before ya get up here at this rate." After they reach the apartment, Mario directs them to place the crib in a corner of the room.

"I heard her movin around, so I think she's wakin up. This is going ta be great," he says.

Awakened by the scuffling sounds coming from the main room, Antonella lies comfortably in her bed, trying to resist the curiosity pulling her from the sweet sleep she enjoys. While still clutching her pillow, she hears muted conversation drifting through the closed bedroom door.

"Mario, is there someone here?" she calls out. Peering into the room, Mario says,

"You're awake. I thought I heard you moving around earlier. Frankie and George stopped by, and they brought something for the baby. Come and see."

"I will. I just need a few minutes to dress." Slowly rolling upright, she sits on the edge of the bed and runs a brush through her hair. After checking her appearance in a small, handheld mirror, she slips into her housedress and joins Mario and his friends.

"Ciao, Frankie e George," she says, and she gives each of them a hug. Moving away from the crib and revealing it to Antonella, Frankie exclaims,

"We brought ya something…for the bambino."

"Do you…like?" asks George in halting English. Covering her mouth with her hands, she gasps and her eyes fly wide open. Slowly approaching the crib, she glides her hands over its newly painted railings and frames. A wide smile replaces the look of surprise on her face.

"E belissimo! Grazie tante."

"I guess she must like it, huh Mario?" asks George. Before Mario responds, Antonella rushes to each man and gives him another embrace and a kiss on the cheek.

"Yeah, George. She likes it," replies Mario with a laugh. After placing the crib in the bedroom at Antonella's request, Mario says, "Let me buy you guys a drink before ya go. I found some good homemade liquor the other day." The three friends sit at the dining table sharing several rounds of drinks, and Antonella relaxes on the small settee. Pleased that Mario's friends have become hers as well, she enjoys their company and their generosity. Careful not to overstay their visit, however, George and Frankie shake Mario's hand, exchange a final hug with Antonella and say goodnight. As they start down the stairs, Antonella waves and shouts to them in her improving English,

"Thanka you so much. Gooda night, Frankie. Gooda night, George." Returning to the bedroom again, she stares at the crib and tries to imagine what her life will become once the baby arrives.

Now well into the final months of her pregnancy, Antonella finds that even the simplest tasks are time-consuming and often painful. The weight of the growing child prevents her from walking up and down the apartment stairs easily and confines her to the apartment for days at a time. Even when she does little more than sleep or rest, she has a constant backache and various muscle pains. With her normal sleep patterns disrupted, she remains awake late into the night on many occasions. On one of those sleepless evenings, Mario massages her back and shoulders, trying to relax her. In the quiet solitude of their old bed, she lies on her side staring at the tiny lamp across the room, as his fingers and hands bring temporary relief to her constant discomfort.

"Mario, who do you think the baby will look like?"

"I'm sure, if it's a girl, she'll look exactly like you."

"And if it's a boy?"

"A boy? Maybe he'll look a little like me...or even his grandfather. Pa will go crazy over a grandson. He's been giving John and Joe holy hell for not having any kids yet."

"I hope it's a boy too, Mario. I want you to have a son...to please your father."

"He's already excited about meeting you. If we bring him a grandson...God, I can't even imagine how thrilled he'll be."

"I pray for a baby boy every day Mario. Maybe God will answer my prayers again."

"We'll know soon enough." Mario gently rubs her shoulders.

With the baby nearing full term, Assunta becomes a permanent resident in her daughter's apartment. Her loving care is only part of all she does. From preparing meals to doing laundry, she tends to Antonella's every need in excited anticipation of delivering her first grandchild. Examining her daughter daily, Assunta is certain the baby will be born at any time.

"This baby will not wait much longer, my darling. This will all be over soon."

"Mama, it hurts so much. Does everything look...I mean...is everything normal?"

"Everything is fine, Antonella. You've gained enough weight, and I think the baby is going to be big and healthy." On the dresser next to the bed, Assunta has neatly organized the towels, sheets and assorted medical supplies Mario's friends from the base have provided. Not being accustomed to the luxury of so many supplies with which to deliver a baby, she's grateful for the peace of mind they bring. With preparations complete, there is little more to do except wait for Antonella's baby to arrive. They will not have to wait very long.

Recoiling from the searing pain in her belly, Antonella paws at a sleeping Mario and screams,

"Oh...dear God. Mario, tell Mama to come in here...right away. It hurts...Mario...it hurts so much." Scrambling from the bed, he pulls on his pants and races into the main room. Assunta is already awake and dressing herself.

"I...I think it's time, Assunta. She wants you to come...now."

"Yes, yes, I heard. Mario, fill the pans with water and begin to heat them. We'll need some hot water soon." Seeing her mother enter the bedroom, Antonella cries out,

"Mama, is it time? I...I can't breathe. Is the baby...coming?"

"Yes, my dear. Try and relax. Take deep breaths while I have a look at you." Another contraction stops Antonella's breathing once again. Releasing a gush of air when the pain passes, she screams,

"Mario. Where are you, Mario?"

"You're doing fine, Antonella. Your water broke and the baby is dropping. You must keep breathing and pushing. This is almost over, darling," says Assunta. Entering the room moments later, Mario takes Antonella's hand and kisses her forehead.

"I'm here, I'm here, now. Do what your Mama says and you'll be fine," he says, *"What can I do, Mama?"*

"Bring me some towels for right now...and some water when it's ready."

Antonella claws at her swollen belly and another wave of contractions causes her to moan and grimace. Kissing her once again before he steps out of the way, Mario whispers,

"I'll be right here. I love you."

The concept of time loses its meaning for Antonella during the painful hours that follow, and early morning becomes midday. Although soaked in perspiration and exhausted to the point of collapse, her excellent health and youthful energy help bring the ordeal to an end.

"Push Antonella, push. I can see the baby's head, my darling," encourages Assunta. *"It's almost here."* Gripping Mario's hand as tightly as she can, Antonella takes one more deep breath and pushes with one last scream.

"That's good, that's good. We're nearly done," says Assunta while gently pulling the baby into the world. Antonella lifts her head and watches Assunta whisk the infant away to a small bathing pan. After clearing its throat, she gently slaps the baby's backside, resulting in a loud, piercing scream that fills the room. She washes the baby and wraps it in a towel, then returns it to her anxious daughter. Tears stream down her cheeks as she hands the child to Antonella.

"It's a...a boy, Antonella. A beautiful, little boy." Holding the baby in her arms for the first time, she stares into his tiny, dark eyes and gently touches his face. The fatigue and pain of the past seven hours instantly vanish when her son instinctively wraps his miniature hand over her finger. She looks up at Mario with tears in her eyes.

"Look, Mario. You...you have a son. Isn't he beautiful? God answered our prayers."

Looking at his son's face in the first few moments of the baby's life, Mario's heart pounds heavily and his legs suddenly feel unsteady. In awe of the miracle he's just witnessed, his joy is distilled with feelings of wonder and disbelief. With tears pooling in the corners of his eyes, Mario reaches out and touches the infant's cheek. The baby flinches gently, and Mario smiles nervously at Antonella.

"He's amazing. He's even got some hair. I can't get over this...a boy. I...think he has your eyes."

"Do you want to hold him? Mama, can you help?"

"Is it all right? I mean...so soon?"

"He's big and healthy, Mario. You won't hurt him. Antonella is going to fall asleep, so the baby must go in his crib now. Here, let me hand him to you. Just be sure to cradle his head," says a smiling Assunta. Watching her handle the baby with such ease, Mario is reminded of how many times she has done this. After she places the child in his arms, she tenderly brushes the baby's forehead with the back of her hand and says,

"You see how easy it is?"

"He's heavy, isn't he?"

"Yes. We must weigh him," replies Assunta with a soft laugh. Mario gently places the baby onto a small scale she uses.

"Eight pounds and fourteen ounces. He's a very big baby," says Assunta. Antonella watches Mario pick up the child and carry

him around the bedroom. He appears hypnotized by the arrival of his infant son.

"Come and put him in the crib, Mario. Everyone needs some rest," says Assunta. After kissing the baby's forehead, Mario places him in Hank and Frankie's crib and returns to Antonella's side. Holding her hands, he sees she's exhausted and fighting to stay awake.

"Get some sleep. Your Mama and I will watch over him." Bending over Antonella and kissing her, he whispers, *"Thank you...I love you very much."*

With Antonella and the baby sleeping comfortably, Assunta also naps on her cot. In spite of the lengthy ordeal, Mario remains far too excited to sleep. In the quiet of the late afternoon, he sits at the small dining table and sips coffee he's made for himself. His thoughts are complex and varied. What will Giuseppi's reaction be? His brothers? He wishes he could tell them right away, but of course he can't. He looks forward to sharing the news with Lucia and Giancarlo, as well as his friends on the base. He cannot find enough ways to thank Assunta for all she has done. In the furthest corner of his thoughts, however, he's deeply troubled over certain sadness she will suffer when her daughter and grandson must leave Napoli. A knock on the door interrupts the unpleasant image in his mind. Letting herself in, Lucia sees her mother sleeping and rushes to Mario.

"Tell me, Mario. Did she have the baby yet?" she whispers. Mario's smile is answer enough, and she covers her mouth to muffle her joyful gasp.

"Oh, my God, she did. What did she have?"

"A boy," Mario proudly tells her, *"and they're both doing fine. She's sleeping right now."*

"I must see him. I'll be very quiet." Approaching the crib, she stares at the infant in silent fascination. *"Oh Mario, he looks just like you. You must be so proud,"* she whispers.

"Isn't he something? He weighs nine pounds." After leaving the bedroom, Lucia embraces Mario.

"I'm so happy for you and Antonella. This is wonderful. Wait until Giancarlo gets here. He'll be so surprised."

"Lucia, when did you arrive?" asks Assunta, as she wakes from her nap. *"Did you see the baby yet?"*

"Yes, just now. He's so precious. I can't wait to hold him. How are you feeling, Mama? Can I get you anything?"

"Maybe a little coffee. Is that coffee I smell, Mario?"

"Yes. I made some earlier for myself." While Lucia pours her mother some coffee, Assunta asks,

"Do you know where Giancarlo is, Lucia?"

"He's coming. I told him I thought the baby could be born soon. When he finds I'm not home, he'll be right here. Come sit with Mario and drink your coffee. I'll make you both something to eat." After placing her mother's coffee on the dining table, Lucia prepares

a platter of food for them. Her exuberance transforms the simple meal into a spontaneous celebration, and everyone's spirits soar over Mario and Antonella's son.

A heavy knock on the door signals Giancarlo's arrival. He enters the apartment without waiting for someone to answer. Finding everyone sitting and laughing together, he is bursting with excitement over the possible birth.

"She had the baby, didn't she?" he says in a loud voice.

"Shhhh..." warns Assunta, *"they're still sleeping in the other room."*

"There's nothing wrong, is there? What did she have?"

"Antonella's doing fine. She had a beautiful, baby boy, Giancarlo," says Assunta gleefully.

"A boy! That's wonderful. Congratulations, Mario. You must be overjoyed," he says, as he shakes hands with the new father.

"Thank you. I'm still a little shocked...it's hard to believe. Do you want to see him?" asks Mario.

"Of course," replies Giancarlo with a beaming smile. An opportunity to view the infant once more is too tempting for Lucia and Assunta, and they follow the men into the bedroom. Although they try to be quiet, the infant squirms and fusses while they encircle his crib. Assunta quickly lifts the child into her arms.

"He must be getting hungry. We'll have to bring him to his mother now." Placing his hand on Mario's shoulder, Giancarlo quietly tells him,

"Our father would be very, very proud of his new grandson, Mario." The simple statement fills Mario with a deep sense of belonging to this family for whom Giancarlo cares so much.

"Is he awake?" asks a groggy Antonella. Hearing her sister's voice, Lucia dashes to her. Wrapping her arms around her, she says,

"Yes, he is. How do you feel?"

"I'm fine. A little tired, that's all." Assunta brings the infant to Antonella, and the others take great pleasure in watching her hold him.

"Your son is making this a very exciting day for us," says Giancarlo, as he kisses Antonella's cheek.

"Everyone must leave the room, now so Antonella can nurse her baby in quiet." Mario is the last to leave her side. Before turning away, he holds the baby's hand between his fingers and smiles proudly at his infant son. Unaware of suddenly speaking in English, he murmurs,

"He's really something, ain't he?"

Mario rejoins Lucia and Giancarlo in the adjacent room.

"Lucia and I are going to leave. You all must be very tired," says Giancarlo.

"I know I am. I didn't sleep too much last night. None of us did," replies Mario.

"Have you decided on a name, Mario?" asks Lucia. The question momentarily halts their departure as they wait for Mario's response.

"Antonella and I agreed, if it was a boy, we'd name him Vincenzo. Vincenzo Carlucci is a nice name, don't you think?"

"Vincenzo! It's a wonderful name, Mario," replies Lucia laughing. *"Tell Antonella good night for us. We'll be back tomorrow."* After they leave, Mario follows Assunta into the bedroom. Antonella has finished nursing and is resting comfortably with the baby cradled on her lap.

"Did he eat for you, dear?" asks Assunta.

"Yes. I think so. How do I know if he gets enough?"

"He'll let you know. Mario told us his name is Vincenzo."

"Do you like it?" she asks.

"Yes, I love it. Come Vincenzo, time to go in your crib," she says in a hushed voice. Taking the baby from Antonella, she hands him to Mario, saying, *"Do you want to hold your son before he falls asleep again?"* Mario answers the question by simply holding out his arms and taking the infant from her. He watches his son's eyes close, and he gently places him into the crib. Assunta kisses the baby's forehead and whispers,

"Good night, little Vincenzo. I love you."

Sergeant Thompson wanders through the barracks searching for Mario. Wondering why he hasn't seen him in several days, he questions Hank, Frankie and George during breakfast.

"You guys seen Mario around here in the last couple of days?"

"No, Sarge. We was wonderin if you knew anything," answers Hank. "Do ya think Antonella had the baby?"

556

"He asked me for permission to take some time off right after the baby was born, and I said it would be okay. I'll bet the baby came." Jumping from his bunk, Frankie paces wildly up and down the center of the barracks, yelling,

"What other reason is there for Mario ta be gone like this? She musta had the kid. Let's head over there right now." For a rare moment, no one questions Frankie's logic. They all pile into a truck and drive to Mario's apartment to see for themselves.

They rush up the small stairway leading to the apartment. Crowding next to the door, they listen for any signs of activity inside. Hearing nothing at first, the Sergeant prepares to knock when the unmistakable sound of a crying baby confirms Frankie's suspicions.

"Holy shit, Frankie was right. Antonella had the baby!" Hank whispers. Giggling under their breath, they shake each other's hand in misdirected congratulations.

"Go on, Sarge. Knock," encourages George. After rapping lightly three times, the Sergeant puts his ear a little closer to the door, listening for any response. He's set aback when Mario swings the door open.

"I thought I heard someone knocking. You guys surprised me," says Mario.

"We thought we heard a baby cryin," says Frankie. "Did she have the kid?"

"She sure did. A couple of days ago…it's a boy, you guys. Wait'll ya see how big he is."

557

"Is it okay to come in? Can we see him?" asks the Sergeant.

"Yeah, it's okay. Come on in. Antonella's feeding him right now. All the little guy does is eat, sleep and fill his diapers. I'll ask her to bring him out in a few minutes." Following a round of backslaps, handshakes and congratulations, the Sergeant tells Mario,

"Write down the baby's name and birthdate for me, and I'll see that his paper work gets processed when I get back to the base. Did you give him a name yet?"

"We named him Vincenzo. Whatta ya guys think?"

"I like it...sounds important or special or something," says Frankie with a chuckle.

Antonella hears the commotion Mario and his friends are making, and she recognizes their voices. While holding Vincenzo securely against her shoulder, she joins them in the next room. She gives them their first look at the baby by cupping the infant's head in her hand to give them a clear view of his face. The four men immediately surround her.

"Will ya look at that? He's a good looking little guy, ain't he?" says Hank, gently touching the baby's exposed foot.

"Thanka you. He'sa beautiful, yes?" replies Antonella, in her heavily accented English.

"Bella, bambino," adds the Sergeant, using his limited Italian. After a short visit with Mario's friends, Antonella tells Mario,

"I should put him down to rest, Mario. He's had enough excitement today."

Smiling proudly, the four men take one last look at Mario's son before Antonella disappears into the bedroom with him.

"I should be back to the base in a few more days, Sarge. Is that okay?" asks Mario.

"Okay. Do what you have to do, and we'll see you back at the base when you're done."

Life begins to design new routines for Mario and Antonella in the weeks following Vincenzo's birth. Assunta returns to her own apartment, and Antonella discovers the joy and sacrifices of being a mother. Mario is reporting to Pomig on a regular schedule again. Mario sits at the table of his little apartment one quiet afternoon and writes a letter to his father, telling him of his first grandson.

Dear Pa,
    I hope everyone's doing ok. I'm sorry for not writing very much, but there's been a lot of important things going on. Antonella and I are living in a small apartment near the base. The Army lets me live off base now that the war's over in Italy. We're doing good. Her family and I get along great. I really like them more and more all the time. I got some wonderful news to tell you, Pa. Antonella got pregnant right after we got married, and she just had the baby a few weeks ago. Sorry for not telling you sooner but I been so busy getting the apartment ready, I didn't have time until now. It's a boy. He weighs nine pounds and has a head full of hair. I guess that makes you a grandpa now.
    His name is Vincenzo, and he's terrific, Pa. He's big and healthy, and I can't wait until you meet him. You're going to be crazy about him like everyone here is. I think he even looks a little like you. My

Sergeant told me he's already an American citizen, and he'll even get his own American passport.

Rumors are flying about shipping out soon. Don't know anything official yet. I'm looking forward to coming home with my new family. Tell John and Joe the good news.

Mario

He seals the letter in its envelope and will deliver it to the post office on base the next day. Holding it in his hands, he studies Giuseppi's address and tries to imagine his father's reaction when he reads of his new grandson. He wishes he could be there in person to tell him of the most important event ever to occur in their family.

CHAPTER 20

Arriving at Pomig one morning, many weeks after Vincenzo's birth, Mario stops at the post office to see if he's received any mail from home. Although he realizes he is unlikely to find a letter from his father so soon after telling him of his grandson, he checks anyway. Finding nothing, he reports to the nearly empty repair center. The vacant building is evidence that the war is coming to an end. Returning to the barracks, Mario stops to talk with Sergeant Thompson.

"Hi ya, Sarge."

"Morning, Mario. How's that kid of yours doing?"

"He's growin like crazy. I'll bet he's doubled his weight already. He can almost roll over now."

"That's great. I want to come over and see him again sometime soon. Oh, I just received his papers the other day. Here,

561

have a look," says Sarge, handing Mario an envelope. It contains Vincenzo's birth certificate and U.S. passport.

"I guess he's legal now, eh Sarge?" replies Mario, as he studies the documents.

"That's his ticket back to the States, so take good care of those papers. Trying to replace them could be a nightmare."

"Ya don't have to worry about that. Thanks for takin care of this for me. Whatta ya hear from the brass…you know, about goin home?"

"I don't know much more than you do right now, but until the war's officially over, we won't be going anywhere."

"I heard the Russians got Hitler trapped in Berlin? Is that true?"

"I'm not sure about that. You know how rumors fly around this camp. But I've read some reports saying the Germans have been getting their ass kicked real good lately, so this thing won't last much longer. I'm expecting to hear something from Capitan Brunell about shipping out in the next few weeks."

"What about Antonella and the baby?" asks Mario, with some apprehension.

"I don't know how that works yet, but I'll be sure to find out for you." Sergeant Thompson's lack of an answer troubles Mario, but he keeps his thoughts to himself. The prospect of going home with his new family suddenly sounds more complicated than he had expected it to be.

Assunta visits her new grandson almost daily. The only time she doesn't is when her midwife services are needed elsewhere. When out delivering babies, she constantly looks for used infant clothing, small blankets and even simple toys, such as rattles and stuffed dolls, to bring Vincenzo. The joy her grandchild brings to her surpasses anything she's ever imagined. By helping Antonella with everything from changing his diapers to preparing fresh juices for him, Assunta establishes an intimate bond between herself and the baby. Of all the delightful moments she enjoys with Vincenzo, bathing him is clearly her favorite. As his size and alertness increase, the baths become a loving battle, resulting in water being splashed in all directions. Holding him in her arm after one of his feedings, Assunta says,

"Come with me, Enzo. We'll wash you and put some clean clothes on you before you take your nap. Your Mama can rest for a while." After removing his sleep shirt and diaper, she gently lowers him into the old, porcelain washtub. With her free hand cupped, she scoops up warm water and sprinkles it all over him. She pours a handful over his head, and Vincenzo suddenly rocks his head back and smiles at her for the first time. His toothless grin fills her with even greater pleasure. She kisses him and excitedly calls out to her daughter.

"Antonella! Come quick. You must see what Enzo has done."

"What is it, Mama?"

"He just smiled for me. Watch." Pouring another handful of water over the baby's head, Assunta is able to make him repeat the smile for his mother.

"He has such a beautiful smile. I just want to smother him with kisses," says a joyous Assunta. Holding the baby's hand in hers, Antonella says,

"Vincenzo, I think your grandma will never be the same now that you've shown her your smile."

Antonella's prediction rings true. Assunta arrives at the apartment several days later with yet another gift. Rushing into the apartment, she tells her daughter,

"Antonella, bring Enzo and come down to the street. I have a surprise...hurry." Carrying Vincenzo in her arms, Antonella follows her mother.

"Be careful on the stairs. Wait until you see what I have," says Assunta.

At the foot of the stairs is an old baby carriage. Its spoke wheels are slightly rust-covered and the rubber tread is worn smooth. The black, leather body is covered with hairline cracks, the result of many years of service under the hot sun. In spite of its appearance, however, it remains very functional, and Assunta is excited.

"Where did you get this, Mama?"

"It belonged to one of the neighbors. They have no use for it anymore and asked if I wanted it. I said yes, of course. Let's take Enzo for a walk, shall we?"

Placing Vincenzo in the carriage, Antonella and Assunta proudly guide it through the neighborhood. Stopping often to greet Antonella's neighbors, Assunta eagerly picks up the baby to show him off. Her voice sparkles with excitement when she explains his father is an American soldier from Sicily. Assunta's love for her grandson is like nothing she's ever experienced before. She cherishes every moment she can spend with him, for she knows her time with Vincenzo is fleeting. She tries not to think of that dreadful day.

Vincenzo is growing rapidly and, at four months, he is able to recognize his father. Whenever Mario approaches the crib, the baby kicks his legs and waves his arms until his father picks him up. His son's behavior brings an immediate smile to Mario's face, and he finds it impossible not to pick him up. He spends many happy hours carrying Vincenzo in his arms on short walks to the nearby market. Having to report for duty at the base becomes difficult for him as the baby becomes a more important part of his life.

Hank, George and Frankie frequently stop to see Vincenzo. Arriving at Mario's apartment one afternoon, Frankie notices the baby carriage.

"Hey, Mario, kin we take the baby for a little ride in that buggy?"

"I dunno, Frankie. Antonella might not like the idea too much."

"Aw, we'll be real careful and won't go too far away," adds Hank.

"Okay, I'll ask, but I ain't promising she'll go along with it." Mario finds Antonella in the bedroom where she is putting clean clothes on Vincenzo. He nervously asks,

"The guys, uh...they want to know if they can take the baby for a ride...in the carriage."

"Oh, I don't know, Mario. He's so little. What if something happens?"

"They won't go very far, and I know they'll be real careful. I think it'll be all right."

"I'll agree, but they must promise to go no further than the bus stop on the corner." She carries Vincenzo from the bedroom as Mario follows her.

"She'll go along with it, but ya can't wander off," he says. After hearing the good news, the men surround Antonella and Vincenzo in anticipation.

"Grazie, Grazie, Antonella," says George. Hank picks up the baby carriage and starts down the stairs, followed by Frank, George and Mario. Antonella is the last to descend. After she reluctantly places Vincenzo in the carriage, the three men are gone in seconds. Mario laughes at the sight of his three American buddies pushing a baby carriage through the streets of Napoli.

"Do you think Vincenzo will be safe?" asks a concerned Antonella.

"You don't have to worry. Those guys won't let anything happen to him."

Sergeant Thompson and the other NCO's at Pomig are ordered to report to the base commander's office for an important morning briefing. Crammed into a squadron meeting room usually reserved for pilots, the men mill about in small groups waiting for the C.O. to arrive. There is much speculation that the war will soon be declared over, and the men expect the subject of the briefing to be demobilization. Dozens of conversations immediately cease when Captain Brunell enters the room.

"Good morning, gentlemen. Will everyone take a seat, please? I have some good news for a change. You've all heard the rumors. Well, now it's official. As of tomorrow, the war in Europe is over. Berlin has been captured and the German army has surrendered," announces the Captain. A round of applause shatters the silence, as the men welcome the exciting news. "Okay, settle down for a few more minutes; it gets better. Pomig will be one of the first bases in Italy to demobilize. The first troop transports will begin arriving in Naples within a few weeks." Another loud cheer explodes from the men.

"Have any departure schedules been worked out yet, Sir?" asks one of the men.

"You'll be given all that information before you leave. And let me remind each of you of something very important to pass along to your men. No one misses his ship…period. To do so means to risk a delay in being discharged. It could even result in charges of desertion. We don't want to be chasing G.I.'s around the Italian countryside, so make sure they get the message. Any questions?"

"Yes, Sir. I have a question," responds Sergeant Thompson. "I have one man with a wife and baby. What's the procedure to get his family to the States?"

"We will do the same thing they are doing in England, Sergeant. Any man with family members can arrange passage for them through the C.O.'s office. They'll be booked on a commercial ship after all our guys leave."

"You mean he goes and they stay, Sir?"

"That's how it works, Sergeant."

"How long a period will that be, Sir?"

"It's difficult to say, but I estimate it'll be between four and six months."

At the conclusion of the briefing, each man is given a schedule with specific departure dates for his company. While Sergeant Thompson looks forward to sharing the exciting news with his men, he knows Mario's going to be very upset by the news regarding his family.

Returning to his barrack's office, Sarge spends the next several hours reviewing the demobilization plan for A Company. His men will split up and ship out on two different dates. After completing the roster, he calls the squad together to explain the details. News of demobilization has spread through Pomig like wildfire, and the squad is anxious to get the official version from

Sergeant Thompson. Smiling and slapping each other on the back as they shake hands, the men wait in great anticipation. The Sergeant shouts out,

"Okay guys, quiet down. I have something important to say. We're going home." The squad erupts in another round of ear-piercing whistles and screams, as long-awaited orders finally arrive. Smiling broadly, the Sergeant raises his hands to settle the men down again. "Troop transports will begin arriving in several weeks. I'm posting a roster with your name and date of departure on the wall next to my office. Make sure you check it and know when you're supposed to leave. Missing your ship is big trouble, so don't do anything stupid." Crowding around the roster, the men study the alphabetical listing and instantly memorize the important information. They joke at the possibility of missing their ride home, then begin comparing dates to determine with whom they'll be shipping out.

Sitting on the edges of an empty bunk, Mario, Hank, George and Frankie cluster together and compare their dates.

"I'm goin on June 19. Anyone else got that day?" asks George.

"Yeah, me," replies Hank. He then directs his question to Mario and Frankie. "What about you guys?"

"I got June 29. Whadda ya got, Mario?" answers Frankie.

"The same. June 29. Looks like they're goin to split the four of us up," replies Mario solemnly.

"What about Antonella and Vincenzo? Do you know anything about getting them home with you?" asks Hank.

"No. I'm not sure what the hell is goin on. I gotta go see Sarge right now and get this straightened out." Working his way through the noisy barracks, Mario knocks on the Sergeant's open door.

"Can I talk to ya for a minute, Sarge?" he asks.

"Yeah. Come on in, Mario. I've been expecting you," says the Sergeant, closing the office door behind him.

"You know why I'm here, Sarge. What about my family? Has the C.O. said anything yet?"

"Take it easy, Mario. I know you're nervous, but just listen to me for a few minutes, okay?"

"The Army's not gonna let me bring em home with me are they?" says Mario. Sarge stares at the floor for a second and then looks straight at Mario.

"Your wife's an Italian citizen, and your baby is technically a U.S. civilian, but they can't make passage on a military transport ship. Even if they could, you don't want your family on one of those things. You know what shit holes they are."

"Then what the hell's gonna happen?"

"Will you let me finish? You're not the first G.I. to get married over here, Mario. The Army will arrange to have your family brought to the States after all the troops have shipped out. That's what they're doing in England, and it'll be the same thing here."

"How long is that gonna take?"

"The C.O. said it could be anywhere from four to six months," replies the Sergeant reluctantly.

"Six months? Jesus Christ, Sarge, I can't leave Antonella and the baby for six months. Why can't I just take my discharge here? That way I can bring em home with me."

"You can't do that. If you miss your transport ship, you'll be arrested and forced to go. If you go AWOL, you'll end up with a dishonorable discharge. You've worked too hard to let that happen," warns the Sergeant. Running his hand through his hair and pacing around the office, Mario becomes more frustrated and angry. He finally explodes.

"This is fuckin bullshit, Sarge. How do I tell Antonella I gotta leave and she can't come with me? I got a five-month-old son to take care of. How do I leave without him?" Standing in the middle of the office with his hands on his hips, Mario stares hopelessly at the ceiling. He turns his back to his friend and wipes tears from his eyes as his anger turns to fear. Trying to calm Mario down, Sarge approaches him, rests his hand on his shoulder and says,

"Come on, Mario, why don't you sit down and listen to me for a minute? I can help a little." Mario slumps into a chair as the Sergeant leans against the edge of his desk and says, "I'll be one of the last guys scheduled to leave Pomig. I'll make sure that Antonella and the baby are on the first civilian ship headed for the States.

That's a promise. Between your brother-in-law and me, they'll be well cared for until they can join you."

"Not much of a choice, is there?" answers Mario.

"No, there isn't."

"Look, Sarge. I know this ain't your fault. I'm…uh…sorry for blowin up at ya like that."

"That's okay. I know this is tough. What are you going to do?"

"I guess I better get home…and tell Antonella. Thanks for your help, Sarge." Feeling like he's just been kicked in the gut, Mario leaves the office wondering how to break the awful news to Antonella.

After hearing most of Mario's conversation through the thin walls of Sarge's office, Frankie, Hank and George are waiting for him in the barracks. The unpleasant news steals some of the excitement of being told they are shipping out.

"We couldn't help overhearing what Sarge told ya, Mario. That's a real bad deal. Is there anything we kin do?" asks Hank.

"Yeah, anythin at all?" adds Frankie.

"No. I don't think so, but thanks for asking. I'm the only one who can tell Antonella. I just gotta figure out how." After leaving the base, Mario wanders around Napoli for several hours before returning to his apartment. He parks the Jeep along the beach, stares out over the ocean and tries to think of some way to explain this to her. He realizes that, no matter how or what he tells her, she'll be devastated by the idea of their family being separated. He starts the Jeep's engine and returns home. Entering the apartment, he finds Vincenzo awake in his crib. The baby turns his head when he notices Mario in the room. The baby's first teeth are coming in, and his chin glistens with saliva. He flashes his father a big grin. Immediately drawn to him, Mario lifts his son from the crib.

"So, did any of those teeth pop up yet?" he asks, wiping the baby's face with his handkerchief. Vincenzo suddenly reaches out with his wet hands and paints Mario's face with saliva.

"Now look what you've done," he says with a smile. His son's reaction allows Mario to forget about the awful news for this brief moment. Antonella soon joins them.

"Mario. You are home early. How nice," she says and gives him a kiss. *"I was just going to feed Vincenzo some fresh fruit Mama prepared for him."* Antonella takes the baby and holds him on her lap. She tugs on Vincenzo's shirt to cover his bare stomach and enjoys the baby's reaction to her fussing.

"He's growing so fast. This shirt fit him last month. Don't you think he's getting big, Mario?" she asks.

"Yes...he changes every day." Noticing Mario's unusual seriousness as she feeds Vincenzo, Antonella asks,

"You seem worried, Mario. What's wrong?"

"We heard the war in Europe...is over. The Germans surrendered. Sarge told us this morning."

"Why do you seem upset? That's wonderful news."

"That means they'll be closing Pomig. I'll...be shipping out...in just a few weeks." His announcement unnerves Antonella. She stops feeding Vincenzo, places him back in his crib and sits next to Mario. Holding his hand, she asks,

"What about Vincenzo and me? Are...we going with you?"

"No. They...they won't allow it. I have to go back on a troop ship."

Mario's words send a chilling fear through Antonella. Her smile vanishes as she anxiously bites her lip. Tightening her grip on his hands, she tries to summon up her courage to cope with the frightening news.

"Mario, I'm scared. I thought we were going to America together. What...what am I to do now?"

"All this means is that we can't travel together. Sarge told me the Army will arrange passage for you and Vincenzo on a commercial liner later this year...after the troops are gone." Trembling and near tears, Antonella cannot believe such a terrible thing has happened.

"How...how long will it take...before we can join you?

"Four months, maybe six. It's hard to know right now," Mario answers sadly.

"Six...months? Dear God, how can we be apart for six months? You...you can't go like this, Mario. You can't leave us this way. Please, Mario, please don't go. I'm so afraid," she screams. Mario takes her into his arms and gently kisses her cheek as she sobs.

"I...I don't want to raise our baby...alone, Mario. Can't you see how he loves you?" Her unrelenting fear gives way to total panic, and she tears herself away from him. Taking Vincenzo in her arms, she runs into the bedroom. She sits on the edge of the bed and rocks the baby back and forth as she attempts to grasp the horrible news. A distraught Mario follows her.

"Please...don't cry," he says. *"You know I love you and Vincenzo too much to ever leave you. I promise you, we'll be together as soon as we can...even if I must come back and get you myself."* His heartfelt promise restores little of Antonella's shattered confidence in their future. The news leaves her numb with shock, and only Vincenzo's innocent demands force her to put her fears temporarily aside and attend to his needs. She embraces Mario tightly but says nothing. On this darkest day of their lives together, the often-ignored sacrifices she knew she would one day have to make have reared up and confronted her in a most brutal manner. Her love, courage, and devotion will be severely tested in the weeks and months ahead. Her life is about to change forever.

The long, dreadful night deprives Antonella of sleep. In the morning, her fear is amplified by a swelling anger. Grim-faced, she goes about her normal routine of caring for her baby, while Mario makes every effort to comfort her.

"Being mad at me won't do us any good, Antonella. This is not my fault."

"I know, Mario. But what do you expect? I...I can't help how I feel."

"I'm sure your mother will want you to move back with her. And Giancarlo...he'll take good care of you and the baby while I'm gone, you know that. Sergeant Thompson...he promised me he'd take care of all the paperwork. I know you're upset, but the time will go by fast; you'll see."

"And what about Vincenzo? He's going to miss you and...and I won't be able to tell him why you're not here," she replies tearfully. Holding her in his arms again, Mario says,

"I'm going to miss him, too, but there's nothing I can do about it. I...even pleaded with Sarge to let me stay, but he said I'll get arrested if I do." Antonella reluctantly begins to accept the unavoidable events that lie before her. Her anger subsides, but her fear remains, gnawing away at her confidence like the rats in the old wine cellar.

The unpleasant task of telling Antonella's family of the disturbing news still awaits Mario. He and Antonella travel to Assunta's apartment the following day. Mario parks the Jeep, carries Vincenzo and follows Antonella up the stairs.

"Mama, where are you?" she calls out.

"I'm here in the bedroom, Antonella. I'll be right there." Assunta appears in the bedroom doorway while still brushing back her hair. She is delighted to see her grandson.

"Let me hold him, Mario. Come to Grandma, Enzo. How are you, my angel?" Taking the baby in her arms, she kisses him several times before greeting Mario.

"Mario, I'm sorry. I don't mean to ignore you," she laughs.

"I understand, Mama. I know the baby is more important than I am now," he teases.

"Oh Mario, you know that's not true, but he's such a joy. Sometimes, I can't help myself. What brings you here today? I wasn't expecting you."

Antonella looks at Mario and tries to decide how to answer her mother's question.

"Where is Lucia, Mama?" she asks nervously.

"She is helping Senora Tucci hang curtains. She'll be back soon. Is something wrong, Antonella?"

"It's Mario. The Allies are closing the base and...he'll be shipping out."

"Shipping out? Dear God...when? Do you know?" Lucia bursts into the apartment before Antonella can answer her mother's question.

"I knew you were here when I saw the Jeep on the street. Hello, Vincenzo. Let me hold him, Mama," says Lucia. Assunta hands the infant to her and says,

"Lucia, Antonella says the Allies are closing Mario's base. They will be leaving for America soon, isn't that right, Antonella?"

"Mama, you don't understand. Only Mario is leaving. Vincenzo and I can't go...not until later," replies Antonella, while fighting back more tears.

"You have to leave without them, Mario? But why? This is terrible," says Lucia.

"I don't have a choice. This is the way the Army is going to do it. If I don't follow orders, I'll be arrested."

"And when will you leave, Antonella?" asks Assunta.

"Mario says I may have to wait...maybe for six months."

"Dear Mother of God...how awful," says Lucia.

The news shocks Lucia and Assunta. Assunta puts her arms around Antonella and holds her. She can think of nothing to say that will ease her daughter's pain. Turning to Mario, she embraces him and then holds his hands.

"Antonella and Enzo will come and live with me after you leave, Mario. I will see that your family is safe. We all knew this day would come, but I don't think we understood how difficult it will be to say goodbye."

"I know you'll take good care of them. I...I don't know how to thank you, Mama."

"Your beautiful son is my blood, and you are my family, Mario. You don't have to thank me for doing this."

Mario receives permission from Sergeant Thompson to stay with Antonella and Vincenzo until he must report to the transport ship. His son has become an incredible source of contentment, and

Mario devotes countless hours to him in hopes of finding a way into the child's budding memory. Of all the troubling events facing him and his family, the fear of leaving Vincenzo and being forgotten plagues him the most. He takes his son on frequent trips through the neighborhood, feeds him the mashed fruit Assunta prepares and even rocks him to sleep. The closeness he feels to Antonella and his son intensifies his fear of leaving them. The grim image of leaving Napoli without them often tempts his better judgment. He even considers going AWOL and taking his chances with the military police, but Sergeant Thompson's friendship and advice prevail. In spite of Mario's deep concern over leaving his family, he begins to feel an uncomfortable excitement about returning to America and reuniting with his father and brothers. The thrill of going home and the sadness of leaving his family tear at his emotions simultaneously, flooding him with unexpected guilt. It is a guilt he will never understand nor overcome.

Mario hears a knock at the door. He opens it and finds Giancarlo standing there.

"Hello, Mario."

"It's good to see you, Giancarlo. You know...about my leaving, don't you?"

"Yes. I've been in Rome for the last week, and I just got home. When Mama told me the news, I rushed right over. How are you and Antonella?"

Mono V. D'Angelo

"It's been hard...for both of us. We didn't expect this. I'm sorry; please come in." Antonella appears from the bedroom with Vincenzo. Seeing her brother, she welcomes him with a kiss and he takes the baby into his arms.

"He's getting so big," says Giancarlo, smiling at his nephew.

"Did Mama tell you? Mario must return to America in a few weeks."

"I know, Antonella. I'm...so sorry. I know you had hoped to go with him. Are you all right?"

"No. I'm afraid and...some days, all I do is cry and worry. I'm so glad you're home."

"Please sit down, Giancarlo," says Mario. They all sit around the wooden dinner table, and Giancarlo asks,

"Mario, do you know when Antonella can go to America?"

"No, that's part of the problem. All I know right now is it can be up to six months. No one knows for sure. Sergeant Thompson promised me he'll arrange passage for her and the baby on a ship as soon as he can."

"Your Sergeant's a good friend, isn't he?"

"He's the best friend I've ever had. I'll never be able to thank him for everything he's done for me."

"I know you are both upset. This disturbs me very much, too, but I'll make sure that Sergeant Thompson has all the help he needs. Antonella and Vincenzo will be safe and well cared for until she can join you, Mario. I promise you that."

"I know that, Giancarlo. When they told me I had to leave Napoli alone, I knew I could depend on you to look after them for me. You're a good man...Giancarlo. I'm...I'm going to miss you a lot," says Mario, in a quivering voice.

"We're all going to miss you, as well, Mario. You've become such an important part of our family in such a short time. I know our father would have liked you very much." Giancarlo hands the infant to Antonella, kisses her cheek and prepares to leave. He shakes hands with Mario, and the two men exchange an embrace.

"Thank you for your help. Knowing she has you to look after her and the baby is a great relief for me."

"If you need anything...anything at all, just ask me."

Pomig swarms with activity, as men and machines begin moving to the main harbor of Naples. Many companies have already boarded waiting transports and are returning home. In this time of high jubilation, Mario takes the time to say goodbye to the first members of his squad scheduled to leave Italy. The men exchange names and addresses and make excited promises to try and look one another up. Of the four men with whom he's become so close, Hank and George will be the first to go. The energized mood in the barracks is exciting, and Mario finds his two friends anxiously packing their duffel bags amid the constant laughter and cheering of soldiers going home.

"Looks like you guys are all set to go."

"You bet your ass, we are. 1100 hours tomorrow, we're gone. Shit, it sounds good to say that," says George with a laugh.

"Do ya know who else is going with you two?" asks Mario.

"I think it's Collier, Martensen and Racoski. There's a bunch more guys from a coupla other squads, too."

"Mario, can we come over later…you know, to say goodbye to Antonella and see the baby one more time?" asks Hank.

"I think she'd like that. I'll try ta find some good booze. We gotta have a proper goin away party, right?"

"Damn right. After what we been through together, we better."

Stopping at the PX on his way back to his apartment, Mario asks the supply sergeant,

"McCarthy, you ain't got any good whiskey stashed away someplace, do ya?"

"You know stuff like that's only for officers, Carlucci."

"Come on, McCarthy. Hank and George are shippin out tomorrow, and I want to get something special to celebrate. You ain't forgot all the money ya won ridin my shirttails when we were playin craps, have ya?" The supply sergeant smiles, shakes his head and disappears into the storage bay. Returning a few minutes laters, he hands Mario a paper sack containing a bottle.

"If you get caught with that, I don't know nothin about it," says the sergeant. Opening the bag and peeking inside, Mario finds a fifth of Vat 69 whiskey.

582

"Damn, McCarthy. Thanks. I didn't expect anything this good."

"Just get the hell outta here with it, will ya? And tell Hank and George I wish em good luck."

"You got it, Sarge." Mario tucks the bag under the seat of the Jeep and returns to his apartment.

A familiar creaking of the stairs, immediately followed by a loud, pounding knock on the door signal that Hank and George have arrived at the apartment. Mario opens the door and says,

"Come on in. I was getting worried ya might not make it."

"Aw, it's a little crazy on base right now. Guys runnin around all over the place, you know, sayin goodbye and visitin their girlfriends before they go, shit like that," replies Hank with a grin. Moments later, Antonella joins them. She is carrying Vincenzo.

"*Ciao*, Hank anna George. I'ma so appy to see you, tonight," she says in her struggling English. They greet her with a friendly hug, and she kisses them on their cheeks.

"Can I hold him?" asks Hank, smiling at the baby. Antonella gladly hands Vincenzo to him. The baby looks at her, and she can tell he's confused and slightly frightened. She smiles and gently strokes his head.

"You don't need to be afraid, Vincenzo. I'm right here." Soon, the baby is smiling comfortably as Hank and George take turns holding him.

"He sure is a handful, ain't he, Mario?" says George.

"I know. He loves to eat and it shows. I swear I can see em grow sometimes," replies Mario with a laugh. "Why don't you guys grab a seat at the table? I got a little surprise for ya." Mario opens the paper sack containing the whiskey and holds the dark, green bottle high in the air.

"I called in a favor from McCarthy today."

"Is that Vat 69?" asks a surprised Hank.

"Sure as hell is. I can't let you guys leave without a headache, can I?" Hank and George laugh as Mario fills three small glasses with the amber liquid. Lifting his glass up in front of them, he says,

"To the best damn friends I ever had. Good luck when ya get home." They all touch their glasses together and down their drinks in one rapid gulp. Mario promptly refills their glasses, and they discuss what waits for them when they return to the States.

"Whatta ya gonna do when ya get back, George?" asks Mario.

"I...uh, don't know just yet. Probably see if my old job is still there. Gonna be nice to see my folks again. I can't wait to get some of my mom's cookin again. I been dreamin of her fried chicken and homemade biscuits ever since they said we're goin home."

"How bout you, Hank? You goin back to Chicago?"

"Yeah. I got nowhere else to go. I ain't got no family there, so I guess I'll look up my old boss and see if he kin find me some work and a place to stay."

"Well, if ya ever get bored, Detroit ain't that far away."

"Thanks, I just might look ya up sometime."

After several more rounds of drinks and a lot of laughter, the evening quickly slips away. George checks his watch and says,

"Do ya think we outta get back to the base, Hank?"

"I suppose we should. We don't wanna miss our ride." Antonella has since put Vincenzo to sleep, and she stands quietly at Mario's side. The three men don't hide their feelings as they say goodbye to each other for the last time. With right hands clasped in a firm, emotional handshake, Mario and George embrace and slap one another on the back.

"You, uh…take care of yourself, will ya?"

"I…will, Mario. You got a great wife and a terrific kid. I hope everything goes okay for ya…you know, with getting them back to the States and all."

"Thanks, George. It's goin to take a little time, but we'll be all right." George looks at Antonella, smiles and puts his arms around her one last time.

"Ciao, Antonella. I'm goin to miss you. Kiss Vincenzo for me, okay?" She kisses his cheek and says,

"*Arrivederci, George.*"

Grabbing Mario's hand with both of his own, Hank holds on tightly while searching for words to express himself.

"Goddamn it, Mario, I ain't too good at sayin important things, but these past four years…well, they been somethin really special. I know I ain't never gonna have a friend like you again." Taking a deep breath, Mario rests his hand on Hank's shoulder.

585

"I feel the same way. You and the guys...well, you're like brothers to me. The way all of you helped with the wedding...man, you were my family."

"No one's ever asked me ta do that before. I won't forget that old church as long as I live. And look at you now. Goin home with a beautiful wife and baby. Your family's in for a helluva surprise when you git back."

"Yeah, we had a lot of surprises over the last four years, ain't we?"

"We better get going, Hank," says George.

"Okay, gimme a second here." He wraps his arms around Antonella once more. "Ciao, Antonella."

She kisses him again and wipes the tears from her eyes. The two men head for the door. George waves his hand one last time and starts down the stairway. Hank is about to do the same when Mario calls out,

"Hank, wait a minute. I almost forgot. I got something for ya." Reaching into his shirt pocket, Mario pulls out the little bag containing Donnie's lucky dice.

"These are for you. You got more use out of them then I did lately. I figured you could use a little luck on that transport for the next two weeks." Staring at the bag for a moment, Hank looks up and asks,

"Mario, these are your lucky dice. You sure about this?"

"I'm sure. Go ahead; take em."

"Hank! What the hell ya doin up there?" shouts George, from the street below.

"I better go before I start cryin. Thanks, Mario…I don't know what else I kin say."

The two men hug once more and Hank dashes down the stairs, waving wildly as he goes. Mario remains on the landing until he hears their truck vanish into the night. Closing the door, he leans against it with his back. He instinctively runs his hand across his face and stares down at the floor in silence for a moment. With tears in his eyes and sadness in his face, he looks up at Antonella and takes her into his arms. Holding her tightly, he realizes that, after almost four years with his friends, he may never see them again.

Mario's remaining time in Napoli passes with alarming speed. With most of Sergeant Thompson's squad already on their way back to the U.S., Mario and Frankie are among the last group to leave. Mario has only a few days left before he must ship out, and he concentrates on making sure his family is well prepared for his absence. Most of Antonella's belongings, along with many of the baby's things, have been moved to Assunta's apartment. Mario's mind skips from one important matter to another with growing anxiety.

"Do you have the baby's birth certificate and passport in a safe place? You can't get into the country without them," he reminds Antonella.

"Yes, Mario. You don't have to worry. I have all his papers and my passport together."

"I paid for the tickets...for you and Vincenzo. Sergeant Thompson said he'll bring them to you when they arrive. He'll tell Giancarlo the name of the ship and the departure date. I...I can't think of anything else. Is there anything you need?"

"No. I don't think so, Mario." She sits with her arms folded across her chest, and the despair in her voice screams out at him. He holds her hands.

"You and the baby...you're going to be all right. Everything is taken care of, and you got your family and the Sergeant...to watch over both of you."

"I know...I know. I just can't stop being scared. What if I get to America and...and I can't find you? What if..."

"That's not going to happen, Antonella. Sarge is going to send me a telegram telling me when you leave Napoli. I'll be there, no matter what." Having done all that he can to insure Antonella's safety, he's still deeply troubled by her ever-increasing fear of their separation. The dark days ahead will be their most difficult yet.

Mario spends his final day in Napoli with Antonella and her family. Having packed his duffle bag and attended to the few personal matters on the base, he tries to enjoy every minute he has left. While Assunta and Lucia prepare a wonderful dinner, he carries Vincenzo in his arms and plays with him constantly. Sitting next to Antonella with the infant on his lap, Mario delights in tickling his son and making him giggle. Their somber mood is briefly forgotten each time the child squirms at his touch.

"That's enough, Mario. Quit teasing him like that," says Antonella, wiping the drool from Vincenzo's chin.

"He likes it. Look at him laugh when I touch him on his stomach."

"Come, Mario. Sit and eat. Dinner is ready. Giancarlo, can you carry this bowl to the table for me?" asks Assunta. With food and wine on the table, they pass bowls and plates around in quiet reflection. Similar gatherings have usually been cheerful and spontaneous, but there is no joy for them today. The guarded conversation creates a greater tension. No one can find words that will sooth the undertone of fear and uncertainty in the room. Mario attempts to return to some sense of normalcy, saying,

"Thank you for cooking like this tonight, Mama. Everything is delicious."

"I don't want you to leave Napoli hungry."

"I won't get a meal like this again for a long time. I'll miss that." The evening is awkward and uncomfortable. Still holding Vincenzo, Mario says,

"We should go home, Antonella. I think Vincenzo is getting tired. He's starting to rub his eyes."

Carrying his son, Mario surveys the little apartment one last time. He stands at the window where he first saw Antonella. His thoughts flash back to the day he stood on the street in wet pants, trying to talk his way into her life. Because of a wrong turn on a nearby street, he'll return to America with a family of his own. How and why such things happen are a mystery to him, but he considers himself extremely fortunate.

"Mario, are you ready to go?" asks Antonella.

"Uh...yes. We can leave anytime."

"Mario. I'll be happy to watch Vincenzo...if you and Antonella want to be alone tonight," offers Lucia.

"No, but thank you for asking, Lucia. I want to take him home with us tonight."

After he embraces Lucia and Assunta and says goodnight, Mario hands Vincenzo to Antonella and discusses the next day's events with Giancarlo.

"I've arranged for two taxis to pick us up tomorrow, Mario. Will that be all right?" asks Giancarlo.

"Yes. Sergeant Thompson is coming by my apartment in the morning...to pick up the Jeep. I have to be ready to board the ship by 1500 hours, so that should give us plenty of time." After Mario shakes Giancarlo's hand, Mario and Antonella return to their own apartment to spend their last night together in Napoli.

Cradling a sleeping Vincenzo in her arms as Mario drives them back to their apartment, Antonella stares into the infant's face. She shields him from the evening breeze by pulling the corner of his small blanket around his head and shoulders. When they arrive home, she carefully steps from the Jeep to avoid waking the baby. Once inside the apartment, she places him in his crib and covers him with a blanket. She feels Mario's arms around her. He kisses her neck and looks over her shoulder.

"He's sound asleep. It's been a long day for him," whispers Mario. Antonella turns, embraces him and buries her face against his chest. She doesn't want to wake Vincenzo, so she weeps in muffled sighs. Fear edges its way into her last night with Mario.

"He...he'll wonder where you are...why you don't...play with him. What...what will I do when...he looks for you and you're not there?" she asks. Mario doesn't respond to her question, but she can feel his heart racing. They cling to each other in the darkened room, and she can already sense an emptiness beginning to creep into her world. Her cheeks glisten from the tears that stream down her face, and her fear turns to desperation.

"Mario, please don't go. I'm so afraid...please."

"You know I have to go. Don't do this...don't make it any harder than it is. We're going to be all right; you'll see. There are a lot of people who will look after you. I'll write to you every day; I promise." Wiping her eyes, she kisses him.

"Let's go to bed." She leads him into the bedroom, lies on the bed and pulls him down next to her. *"Just hold me...for a little while,"* she asks. Curled up in his arms, she feels the reassuring warmth of his touch momentarily calm her fear and trembling. As she relaxes, her kisses become more passionate.

"I love you, Antonella."

Mono V. D'Angelo

"I want to make love to you, Mario." The precious little time they have left together is as passionate as the night they were married.

Vincenzo's crying pulls Antonella from her bed the following morning.

"He's always so hungry in the mornings. I'll change his diaper and feed him. Do you want some coffee, Mario?" she asks, putting on her robe.

"That's all right. I'll make it myself. I think he wants his breakfast right away."

After starting the coffee, Mario bathes himself from the small sink in the bathroom and puts on his fatigues. His duffel bag is packed, and there is little left for him to do. He pours some coffee in his cup and carefully sips the steaming brew while watching Antonella care for Vincenzo. What was once simple and mundane is now vitally important to him on his final day in Italy. He wonders how long it will be before they can be part of his life again. Antonella puts clean clothes on the infant and carries him to Mario.

"You go with your Papa while I get dressed."

"Come on, big boy. Did you get enough to eat this morning?" Vincenzo squirms wildly, as he reaches out to Mario and falls into his arms.

"Easy...easy. Slow down," he says with a laugh. Antonella kisses the baby's cheek and returns to the bedroom to dress. Holding his son in one arm, he tries to drink his coffee with the other, but the cup soon becomes a target of Vincenzo's interest. As he plays an

592

impromptu game of grab and release with his son, Mario hears a knock at the door.

"Who is it?"

"It's Sarge, Mario." Rushing to open the door, he says,

"Come on in, Sarge. I'm glad you're here this morning."

"You didn't think I'd let you get out of here without saying goodbye, did you? How is the little guy doing?" says Sarge, grabbing Vincenzo's hand.

"He just ate and he's rarin to go. Antonella's gettin dressed. Ya want a little coffee?"

"No thanks, I'm not going to stay long. How's Antonella takin all this?"

"It's been pretty hard on her...and me too, for that matter. Today's gonna be...bad. I...I just can't let myself think about it too much."

"That's what I figured. Look, you got a lot on your mind, so I'll get going. I won't see you again today and...well, good luck to you, Mario."

"Thanks Sarge. You know when you're goin home yet?"

"In a few months, I guess. Soon as the company gear is all packed up."

"Wait a second while I go get Antonella. I know she'll want ta see you."

"No, that's okay, Mario. She's probably not feeling very well today…just tell her I'll be back with her papers as soon as I get them. I'll make sure your family gets to the States."

"I know ya will, Sarge. I can't thank you enough for everything you've done for me. It's been a pleasure to serve with you. If ya ever find yourself in Detroit, ya better look us up, deal?"

"It's a deal. Have a safe trip, huh?" says Sarge with a slight smile.

"I will; you take care of yourself, too." After they share a final hug and handshake, Sarge begins to leave the apartment, and Mario says, "Oh, one last thing. Here's the key to the Jeep. I guess I won't be needin it any more." Sarge smiles, takes the key and starts down the stairs. When he reaches the bottom, he stops and looks back up at Mario and the baby and waves one last time.

The quiet morning is soon filled with frantic anxiety, as the time to leave for the harbor draws near. Giancarlo, Assunta and Lucia arrive at the apartment shortly after Sergeant Thompson has left. The mood is tense. Each of them greets Mario and Antonella with a long embrace.

"I…can't believe you are leaving today," says an emotional Assunta.

"We had better go, Mario. The taxis are waiting."

"I know, Giancarlo. Will you carry my bag for me? I'll want to hold the baby on the way to the harbor." Carrying Vincenzo in his arms, Mario walks through the apartment one last time before he

594

leaves. He stares at the bed in which his son was born and slides his hand across the refurbished crib. It reminds him of Hank and George, and he wonders where they are and how they're doing.

"It's time, Mario. Everyone's waiting," says Antonella. He holds her hand as they make their way down the stairs and into a waiting taxi. They sit in silence during the short ride to the harbor. Mario holds Vincenzo in his lap, and he can feel Antonella trembling. She grips his arm tightly. He's grateful the baby is too little to understand what is taking place. The child's innocent smile seems to be the only thing that keeps Antonella from openly crying. Mario repeatedly kisses his son on the cheek, and he savors these last moments in Napoli.

"You like riding in the car, don't you?" Making sure the baby can look out the old taxi's window, Mario enjoys the look of wonder on the infant's face. His pleasure is short-lived, however. The taxi lurches to a stop behind the one carrying Antonella's family. Through the window of the taxi, Mario sees the transport ship he is to board. Hundreds of G.I.'s are already swarming over its decks.

"Is that your ship...Mario?" asks Antonella.

"Yes, it is. It's the only ship leaving today."

"Dear God, Mario. I don't know if I can take this," she whispers. Tears drip onto her dress and she can no longer hold back the fear raging inside of her. Mario's heart begins to pound violently at the painful reality of leaving her and his son. He puts his arm around Antonella and kisses her tenderly.

"We'll be together soon. I love you, you must remember that."

Climbing from the taxis, the family gathers together in the shadow of the rust-stained vessel. The muffled, pulsing of the ship's giant engines warns them that their time is short. The dock is crowded with ecstatic soldiers waiting to return home, but Mario cannot share in the celebration. Holding Vincenzo until the last possible moment, he kisses him once again before handing him to Antonella.

"You be a good boy for your mother." The child reaches out and touches Mario's mouth with tiny, wet fingers. Mario takes his son's hand into his and kisses it.

"No, Vincenzo. I can't take you this time. You...have to stay with your Mama, now." Tears trickle down Mario's face. His heart feels like it's just been ripped from his chest, as he must ignore his son's gesture to hold him. Two loud blasts from the ship's horn indicate all soldiers must board immediately.

"I...I have to go." Feeling a heavy hand on his shoulder, Mario turns to face Giancarlo.

"I'm going to miss you, Mario. But remember, you are going home. Your father and brothers will be excited to see you again."

"I know. I want to see them again, too. But leaving Antonella and Vincenzo...like this...it's the hardest thing I've ever had to do."

"I hope we can see each other again someday," says Giancarlo.

"I do too. I have to say goodbye to your mother and sister before I run out of time." Mario wraps his arms around Giancarlo's shoulders in a final goodbye gesture.

"Antonella will have a good life in America, Giancarlo."

"I know you'll take good care of her, Mario. I know." Mario gently pats him on the back and then looks at Assunta. Openly crying and distraught, she wipes her eyes as her grief becomes too unbearable to restrain. Taking her in his arms, Mario can feel her trembling. He kisses her on the cheek and caresses her face with his hand.

"I...never knew my own mother very well, but...I hope she was like you. You always treat me like your son. Thank you for that. I'm going to miss you very much, Mama."

"I...I love you like my own son. Seeing you leave like this, it's...it's so sad. I...can't stop crying." Holding him tightly, Assunta kisses him one last time. Reaching into a small bag she is carrying, she takes out a neatly wrapped bundle and hands it to Mario.

"Here...this is for you, Mario. It's bruschetta...I know you like it. I got up early and made it for you." Her kindness brings more tears to Mario's eyes, and he stuffs the gift into his bag. Struggling to keep from crying in front of her, he says,

"I...I love you, Mama. Thank you." Standing next to Antonella, Lucia is also crying. When Mario turns toward her, she rushes to him, throws her arms around his neck and weeps upon his chest.

"I...I can't believe...you are actually leaving, Mario. I'm going to miss you so much. May God watch over you on your journey home."

"Thank you, Lucia...for everything." The ship's horn bellows out its warning once again, and Mario shares one last moment with Antonella. He takes Vincenzo into his arms, holds him tightly against his chest and kisses him again. Handing the baby to Lucia, he embraces his sobbing wife once again before he must leave.

"I love you. I love Vincenzo. We'll be together again. Please believe me."

"I believe you...please, write as soon as you can; promise me you will."

"I promise...I'm sorry...so sorry for putting you through this."

From inside the fenced entrance to the pier, Mario hears a familiar voice shouting out to him.

"Mario! Hey, Mario. Come on, will ya? We gotta go," shouts Frankie. Picking up his duffel bag in one hand, Mario holds Antonella's arm as her family escorts him to the gateway. Kissing her and his son one last time, he feels the pain of leaving them becoming too unbearable. He finally has to turn his back and pass through the gate. He joins Frankie.

"Let's go before I change my mind." After walking a short distance, he's compelled to look back again. He sees Vincenzo raising his arm, as if waving goodbye to him. With tears streaming down his face, Mario instinctively waves back at him and his Italian family. Wiping his eyes with his hand, he can't remember ever feeling so guilty and alone.

"Let's get aboard, Mario. This ain't gonna get any easier," says Frankie. Grabbing Mario's bag from his hand, he hurries him through the crowded pier and up the gangplank of the old transport.

They are among the last men to board the vessel. The ship's crew hoists the gangplank, and the shore men cast off the ship's dock lines. Every vantage point from which to see his family is blocked with G.I.'s, and Mario begins to aggressively push his way through the crowd.

"Hey, give the guy some room, will ya? He's got family down there," shouts Frankie. Oblivious to the growling threats from the other men, Mario reaches the rail as the great ship slowly maneuvers away from the pier. From there, he is able to see Antonella and Vincenzo looking up at the massive collection of soldiers. He waves wildly, but they can't see him amid the throng of cheering and applauding soldiers. The transport is guided out of the harbor, and the loud thuds and increasing vibrations from the ship's giant engines heighten the bleakness of the moment. Seeing the still shattered remains of Napoli for the last time, Mario is repulsed by the thought of leaving his family alone in this war-torn part of the world. He misses them already.

Vincenzo begins to fuss as Antonella watches the transport steam away from the harbor. Weeping softly, so as not to frighten him, she is in a state of shock. The great ship is soon swallowed into the dark blue vastness of the Mediterranean. She is certain Vincenzo realizes his father is gone.

"Don't cry, Enzo. We'll see your Papa soon. Don't cry, my darling."

"Why don't we go home, Antonella?" asks Giancarlo, putting his arm around her. *"His ship has nearly disappeared."*

"Can we stay...for just a few more minutes?   Please, Giancarlo? I can't leave...not yet."

"We will stay for as long you want, Antonella."

The glare of the afternoon sun obscures the western horizon, and Mario's ship eventually vanishes. With her family surrounding her, Antonella leaves the pier and returns to her mother's apartment. The rolling motion of the taxi puts Vincenzo to sleep, and he rests his head on her shoulder. While tenderly rubbing his tiny back, she stares at the passing neighborhood, but she sees nothing. Her thoughts leap ahead to the day when she and her baby will make this same journey alone.   After today's painful experience, she questions her own courage to endure another, even more tragic, farewell. She recalls the words Father Bertulucci spoke at her wedding. He understood, all to well, the price she would have to pay for her decision to marry Mario. Today, she has learned what a terrible price that is.

CHAPTER 21

Sitting at his kitchen table, Guiseppi gulps down the last few mouthfuls of his luke-warm coffee. It's ten-thirty in the morning, and the telltale squeak from the lid of the old mailbox signals the postman's arrival. Like every other time he's heard the annoying sound, he reminds himself to put a few drops of oil on the rusty hinge, but he never does. Hurrying to the front door, he catches the mailman descending the porch steps.

"Morninga, Sammy," he calls out.

"Mornin, Mr. Carlucci. Nice day for early April, huh? You got a letter there, from Italy. Hope it's good news. See ya tomorrow."

"Thanka you, Sammy. I think it's froma my son, Mario." Opening the tiny mailbox, he retrieves the small stack of envelopes and carefully studies each piece of mail. Recognizing Mario's handwriting on one of them, he anxiously returns to the kitchen, pulls a sharp knife from the drawer and carefully slits open the envelope. After refilling his cup with the last of the morning coffee, he sits at the table, puts on his glasses and gently unfolds his son's letter. Always eager for any news from Mario, he reads the letter with keen interest. Since the local newspapers are reporting that the war in Europe is nearly over, he hopes the letter will tell him when Mario and his Italian wife will return. Not wanting to overlook anything, he reads each line several times until his attention becomes riveted on one startling comment in the middle of the letter. He places his coffee cup onto its saucer, holds the letter in both hands and carefully reads the passage again. 'I guess that makes you a grandpa'…Guiseppi can scarcely believe his eyes. Realizing that he has a grandson, he feels his heart pound with excitement. With the letter in his hand, he pours over it again and again, while roaming the house. Nervously running his hand across his head, he looks at the date on the letter and sees that the child is already several months old. He's elated that his first grandson was born in Italy. No longer able to contain his exhilaration, Guiseppi rushes to call his other sons and tell them the news.

Picking up the handset, he jams his first finger into the rotating dial and completes the first four digits of John's phone number before making a mistake.

"Goddamn a phone," he mutters. Redialing more slowly, he listens to the mysterious clicks and hums with impatience, until the call finally goes through. John's phone rings several times before he picks it up.

"John, it'sa me."

"Morning, Pa. Everything okay?"

"I hava something to tell you…froma Mario. I got a letter froma him thesea morning. You know hisa Italian wife? She had a baby…a boy. I can'ta believe it."

"A baby? Jesus Christ. When? Does he say when the baby was born?"

"I thinka just a few months ago. Hisa name is Vincenzo."

"So, how does it feel to be a grandfather?" asks John with a laugh. Guiseppi's own loud laughter quickly answers John's question. "Does he say anything else? Like when he'll be comin home with his wife and baby?"

"Alla he says isa he will be shipping out soon. Will you calla Joe anna tell him about Mario's baby?"

"Sure, Pa. I'll call em right…" With his mind already spinning over preparations that he'll have to make, Guiseppi sets the handset down before John can finish his thought.

Living alone since John and Joe moved out, Guiseppi expects Mario and his new family will have to live with him when they arrive from Italy. The anticipation of sharing his home with Mario's wife and son fills his days with endless pleasure, as he prepares the upper level of his home for them. Discarding unused clothing and old furniture, thoroughly cleaning all the rooms and even replacing worn shades and broken light bulbs become an obsession in the weeks that follow. Shopping at the nearby Sears and Roebuck store becomes a weekly pastime, and exploring the toy department is mandatory. The store clerks come to know him by name as he proudly tells them with every purchase all about his new grandson. An empty bedroom becomes a nursery, and he soon fills it with a new crib and dresser, a hand-painted rocking horse and an assortment of stuffed animals. He hopes for the next months to pass quickly.

Even after several days at sea, Mario suffers from the anguish and guilt of leaving his family in Naples. He cannot escape the image of Vincenzo's outstretched hand or the look of fear in Antonella's eyes on the day he left them in Naples. Spending time either lying in his bunk or staring at the vast expanse of the Atlantic, he finds it impossible to participate in the continuous celebration aboard the ship. Frankie is his only relief from the guilt and depression.

"Ya didn't have no choice, Mario. Ya know ya did the only thing you could do. Hell, if ya got yourself arrested for going AWOL, that woulda just made things worse," says Frankie.

"I shoulda stayed and took my chances, Frankie. No one should leave his family in a place like that."

"Quit bein so stupid, will ya? Getting yer ass thrown in the brig ain't gonna help nobody." Frankie's brutally honest remark temporarily eases Mario's guilt.

"I suppose you're right, but I'm still worried. The whole damn city's still got landmines and booby-traps hidden all over the place. Hell, anything can happen there," says Mario.

"Yeah, it can, but it won't. Not ta them. They'll be showin up in Detroit before ya know it. Wait and see." Frankie's determined loyalty and relentless support bring a slight smile to Mario's face.

"How'd ya get so smart all of a sudden?"

"All of a sudden? What in blue Jesus does that mean?" Frankie's joking eventually has Mario shaking his head and laughing a little. Mario's grateful that he and Frankie are able to make this final leg of their journey together.

Sitting in the mess hall having lunch, Mario spots Frankie charging through the maze of tables and benches and screaming out his name.

"Mario! Let's go topside. You can see land. Hurry, goddamn it, hurry. We're almost home." Mario stuffs the last bite of his sandwich in his mouth as Frankie drags him by the arm to the crowded bow of the ship. Hundreds of excited men watch and cheer as the Eastern seaboard of the U.S. gradually stretches across the entire horizon.

"Son of a bitch. Ain't that one helluva view?" says Frankie, slapping Mario on the back.

"Sure is. It's been a long time comin; that's for damn sure."

"Ever been to Norfolk, Mario?"

"No. I never been there."

"Me, either, but I'm looking forward to it now."

With the ocean passage nearly over, a heightened air of excitement sweeps over the men. Celebrations explode on every deck, as the thousands of jubilant soldiers roam about ship exchanging handshakes and sharing drinks with one another. Every available inch of rail on the starboard side of the ship is lined with cheering G.I.'s, wanting to watch the old transport maneuver its way into harbor at Norfolk, Virginia.

Within a few hours, the ship is secure in its berth, the crew lowers the gangplank and the war-weary troops go ashore. Throngs of cheering civilians welcome them. The feeling of being on U.S. soil again simply overwhelms many of the soldiers. Some men laugh, some cry, while others find themselves in a mild state of shock from the reality of just having survived the war. From Norfolk, they will all board trains to wherever they call home. Mario and Frankie leave the ship together.

"Damn, it feels good ta be back. Look at all these people wavin flags at us and cheerin. Kinda reminds me a when we was goin ta Naples. Remember all them Italians waving flags at us there, Mario?"

"Hell yes, but this is better. The war's over this time."

"We gotta find the debarkation center...to git our train tickets. I guess that must be it there," says Frankie, pointing to a building surrounded by soldiers.

"There's a long line, so that must be it." Using their duffle bags as seats, Mario and Frankie wait their turn in the slow-moving human chain. Once they get inside the building, clerks check I.D.'s and issue railroad vouchers for the last leg of the trip home.

"When's your train leavin?" asks Mario.

"2300 hours. How bout you?"

"2130. That gives us a few hours to kill. Let's see if we can find a drink around here." A brief tour of the train station reveals only a small liquor store open for business. Now full of returning soldiers, the store has a supply of booze that the men are depleting rapidly. Working his way to the counter, Mario asks the haggard proprietor,

"Hey, pal. Got any Canadian whiskey?" Without pausing to look up from the cash register, he says,

"Only whiskey I got is what ya see on the shelf behind me. Take it or leave it."

"Gimme that bottle a Four Roses, then."

Mario pays for the bottle and tucks it safely under his arm as he pushes his way out of the shop to rejoin Frankie.

"Man, that place is a madhouse," he says.

"Did ya find anything?"

"All they had was this bottle a cheap Kentucky bourbon. Guess it's better than nothin." With only a few hours before they are to return to their very different worlds, Mario and Frankie wander through the busy station looking for an empty bench on which to share a final drink. Few are available, and they resort to propping their bags against a wall near Mario's boarding platform. Twisting off the top of the bottle, Mario takes a long drink and hands it to Frankie.

"Shit, that stuff's bad," he says with a grimace. Frankie puts the bottle to his mouth and gulps down a mouthful. Red-faced and coughing, he says,

"Ain't this a bitch? After travelin round the whole goddamn world together, we gotta say goodbye like a coupla fuckin hobos hidin out in some train yard."

"We drank in a lot worse places than this. Hell, at least we can buy some booze here. Not like that North African shit hole we were stuck in."

"I couldn't wait ta get the hell outta there. I don't wanna see any more goddamn sand again as long as I live. And I'll betcha those British bastards are still wonderin where that fuckin Nazi flag came from," says Frankie, curling over in laughter.

"If you're gonna keep yappin, hand me the bottle," jokes Mario. Frankie takes another long swig and hands the bottle to Mario.

"I owe you a lot Mario, and I wanna be sure and thank ya, proper-like."

"Whatta ya mean? You don't owe me nothing."

"Oh yeah, I do. When I left Tylerville for the war, I didn't know much about anythin outside a Arkansas. Now, I kin fix damn near anything, I kin shoot craps and win, and I kin even talk a little Italian. Thanks ta you, I ain't jus some dumb hillbilly anymore."

"You don't have ta thank me for anything, Frankie. You and me…and Hank and George, we were pretty damn lucky together. Not too many guys got the breaks we got. Hell, I joined the army cause I thought some guys were gonna kick my ass, and I come home with a wife and a baby. I never figured on that."

"I hope I kin find me a gal like Antonella someday. You be sure ta give her a big hug fer me when she gets here."

"I will. I promise," says a smiling Mario. A slowing, northbound train enters the station and comes to a stop. Checking the time on the station clock overhead, Mario knows the train is his and that he has only a few more minutes before he must board.

"Looks like this is my train, Frankie. I guess I better get goin." Mario stands, grabs his bag and slings it over his shoulder. Frankie is a bit wobbly from the effects of the bourbon, but he stands and grabs Mario's hand.

"Ya got my address, right?" he says.

"It's right here in my shirt pocket."

"You take care a yourself, ya hear? Yer one helluva good guy, Mario. I'm gonna miss ya a lot. Good luck…with yer family and all."

"I'm gonna miss you too, Frankie. Thanks for helping me out on the boat. Ya made things a little easier for me." Still holding on to the whiskey bottle, Frankie gives Mario a clumsy hug and says,

"Ya better git on this damn thing before they leave without ya."

"Good luck back in Tylerville," says Mario, stepping onto the train car.

Throwing his duffle bag onto the overhead luggage rack, he takes a window seat overlooking the platform. Mario feels a subtle lurch of the train as it begins to inch its way out of the station. He raises his hand and waves to Frankie one last time before he sees his good friend vanish in the darkness.

Unlike the trip to Fort Dix four years earlier, the rail car is only half-full and quiet. Still, Mario gets very little sleep during the thirteen-hour ride. His excitement over returning home and his ongoing concern for Antonella and Vincenzo keep him awake. He misses his wife and son terribly and worries about how they are doing. Feeling the train starting to slow down, he asks the conductor,

"Are we in Detroit already?"

"No sir. This is Toledo. We'll be stopping here for a few minutes to let some passengers off, and then we'll be on our way again. Should be in Detroit in about an hour."

"Thanks." Mario's mind flashes back to the Green Door, to Mia and that fateful event that changed his life so dramatically. He wonders where he would be today if he hadn't gone to Toledo that night. Would he have gone to war? Would Antonella and Vincenzo be in his life today? He cannot dwell on the mystery for very long, for the train soon arrives in Detroit. Grabbing his bag, he steps from the rail car and makes his way toward the main entrance of the station. A clock mounted on a lamppost inside the station shows that it's eleven o'clock. He figures his brothers are probably working, so he decides to take a taxi home. Stepping out onto the street, he raises his hand and hails a passing cab. When a battered sedan pulls up in front of him, Mario throws his bag into the rear seat and climbs in. Staring into the rearview mirror with great interest, the elderly driver smiles.

"Ya just getting home, soldier?"

"Just got in from Norfolk, Virginia."

"Where ya been? Did ya see any action?"

"I just shipped in from Italy after bouncin around North Africa. It was pretty rough there for a while."

"Well, welcome home. Where do ya wanna go?"

"Ya know where Maxwell and Gratiot is?"

"Near the big Sears and Roebuck store, right?"

"Yup…you got it. Right behind the Sears store. I'll show ya where the house is when we get there." Lighting up a Pall Mall, Mario watches the once familiar landmarks pass by. Briggs Stadium, its flags waving in a strong breeze, appears on the left. There is a crowd milling about outside the ticket window, and he assumes there must be a ballgame today. Cadillac Square is full of shoppers and businessmen enjoying their lunches on a warm afternoon. It seems strange to find no ocean or war rubble a part of the landscape. The driver slows the cab to a crawl.

"Here's Maxwell Street."

"It's up on the right. See that Ford sedan? That's the house," says Mario.

The driver stops, turns to Mario and shakes his hand.

"Good luck, soldier."

"Thanks. How much I owe ya?"

"Gimme two dollars. That's good." Mario pays him the money and steps from the cab.

The mid-day sun feels warm and muggy, and Mario pulls his collar open a little bit wider. Standing there after his four-year absence, he suddenly feels like a stranger. Guiseppi's neatly manicured lawn and bushes look the same, the cracks in the walk are still there, but the sense of being home is, somehow, incomplete. It's a strange feeling that he doesn't understand, and he tries to put it aside for the moment. Dragging his duffle bag beside him, he climbs the porch steps and stands at the front door. Putting his hand across his forehead to decrease the sun's glare, he peeks into the window to see if his father is around. There is no sign of Guiseppi, so Mario twists the doorknob and finds it unlocked. After opening the door, he places his duffel bag in the corner of the foyer and drinks in the sight of the familiar surroundings again. Lamps and chairs are in their same places; the large dining room table remains exactly as he remembers it, and he even smells the faint, but distinctive, aroma of simmering garlic and tomatoes. The reminders flood him with the distant memories of wonderful days spent in this house. He finally begins to feel at home again.

Moving quietly through the dining room, Mario hears the soft ruffle of a newspaper. The sound is coming from the kitchen. Standing in the doorway between the two rooms, he feels his heart racing when he sees Giuseppi sitting at the kitchen table. He takes a deep breath, rubs his hands together and quietly says,

"Hi, Pa. I'm...I'm home."

Startled, Giuseppi slams his hands down on the table and bolts upright in his chair after hearing Mario's voice. With his eyes bulging, he looks at the doorway, leaps from his seat and screams,

"Mario! Oh my God, Mario...you arra home." Giuseppi rushes to him, wraps his arms tightly around his shoulders and holds him in an emotional embrace. With tears in his eyes, Giuseppi repeatedly pats Mario on the back and kisses his cheek.

"It's okay, Pa. It's okay."

"I...I can'ta believe you are really here. Look atta me. You make a me cry," says Giuseppi, wiping his eyes with his sleeve.

"I got into Norfolk yesterday and caught the train. I just got in a little while ago."

"Arra you alone? Where'sa your wife anna baby? I hava the upa stairs all ready for you."

"They're...they're still in Naples, Pa. I had ta come home without them," he says with falling voice and troubled expression.

"But when willa they come? Do you know?"

"I don't know for sure yet. I think it'll be about four or five months. My Sergeant's gonna send me a telegram to tell me exactly when they'll get ta leave."

"I'ma so sorry, Mario."

"Leavin em there…in that bombed out city…that was the worst thing I ever had ta do, Pa. I been worried sick ever since."

Mario's passionate concern for his family moves Giuseppi. He can see how difficult it is for his son to talk about leaving them, and he tries to change the subject.

"You musta be hungry. Sit downa here anna I'll make a you some lunch. I hava some peppers an eggs already cooked. I justa heata them up," he says. He seats Mario at the table, pours him some coffee and carefully prepares a heaping plate of food for him.

"Here, Mario, eat. Ifa you want more, I'll cooka soma sausage I justa made thisa week."

"This is plenty, Pa, really." Watching Mario eat in his home again is a great relief to Giuseppi. He's content to wait until his son is ready to talk again before asking him some of the many questions he has regarding the war and his new family. He notices Mario has lost some weight and has tiny furrows across his forehead, giving him a more mature appearance. He is no longer the wild, young man who left home four years earlier.

"You have enougha to eat, Mario? I'll make a more eggs ifa you want."

"No...Pa. I'm full. But, you'll never know how good that tasted. Thanks. That was delicious."

"I'm gonna go call John anna Joe. They will be so surprised when I tella them that a you are home."

"Wait a minute, Pa. I wanna show ya somethin first." Returning to the foyer, Mario opens his duffle bag, pulls out a thick envelope and returns to the kitchen table. Inside the envelope are the wedding pictures George took in Naples. Placing the stack of photographs on the table, Mario says,

"I got some pictures I want ya to see...of Antonella and the wedding."

Giuseppi's joy over his son's return soars even higher when Mario presents him with the pictures. Smiling, Giuseppi looks up at Mario and then down at the collection of photographs.

"Theesa...arra your wedding pictures, Mario?"

"Uh huh. My buddy George took em for me. They turned out real good." After putting on his reading glasses, Guiseppi picks up the stack of photographs. With Mario looking over his shoulder, Giuseppi carefully studies each one before placing them into a neat pile.

"Antonella...she isa very beautiful, Mario. Your wedding...thata old church...it'sa so beautiful, too. I'ma very happy for you and proud, Mario. I see why you love a her."

"I got one more picture to show ya, Pa." Reaching into his shirt pocket, Mario finds a picture of Vincenzo that George took just prior to leaving Italy. Wearing only a grin and a tiny undershirt in the picture, Vincenzo clearly looks like Giuseppi's grandson. Handing the picture to his father, Mario says,

"Pa, this is Vincenzo." Cradling the photograph in his hand, Giuseppi stares at it in awe. Placing the picture on the table after a few moments, he removes his glasses and wipes away the tears in his eyes. After putting on his glasses again, he holds the picture in his hand and continues to gaze at the tiny image of his grandson in silent amazement. His ability to speak is choked by his emotions, and it takes him a few moments to regain his composure.

"Is…thisa the only picture you hava of him, Mario?"

"That's the only one, Pa. I'm sorry. I wish I had more."

"He'sa so beautiful, Mario. I…I can'ta believe I hava such a beautiful grandson."

"By the time he gets here, he'll be pretty big. Some of his teeth could even be in. Wait until you meet em, Pa. You're gonna go crazy over him."

"I…I thinka I already hava," replies Giuseppi with a smile.

Elated over the pictures, Guiseppi stands and hugs Mario again.

"I musta call John anna Joe to tella them the good new. We go to the Littla Café tonight…to celebrate. Isa that okay, Mario?"

"Yeah, Pa. That'd be great. I'd like to see Enzo again." Giuseppi hurries into the dining room and makes the calls to Mario's brothers. Listening to his father yell into phone, Mario's earlier feeling of not belonging completely vanishes in the warmth of Giuseppi's welcome. His father has changed as much as he has in the last four years. Mario sits in one of the overstuffed chairs in the living room and waits for Giuseppi to join him.

"Joe's gonna close a the store and coma right over with Edna. He'sa so excited," says Giuseppi with a smile.

"Were you able to talk to John?"

"No, but they gonna giva him a message. His shift isa over soon, so he will come a right home." Mario watches Giuseppi sit on the sofa and study the wedding pictures again. Even more fascinated by them now, Giuseppi wants to know much more about the people shown in each photograph. Suddenly the front door swings open and crashes into the wall behind it. John charges into the house, finds Mario and gives him a vigorous bear hug.

"Holee shit! Ya wanna give someone a heart attack showin up like this? Why didn't ya call or somethin? Goddamn, it's good ta see you," he says, with a thunderous laugh. Returning his hug, Mario affectionately pats his brother on the back.

"I just figured you guys would be working, that's all. Besides, I don't get too many chances ta scare the shit outta ya like this." John's wife is the next to greet Mario. Giving him a hug and a kiss, she says,

"Welcome home, Mario. Pa says you got married and had a baby. My God, that's wonderful. Congratulations. We're all so happy for you. Where are they? Can we meet them?"

"They're not here yet. The first civilian ships can't leave Naples for a coupla more months. But Pa's got some pictures I brought home. He'll be glad to show them to ya." Only a few minutes later, Mario is suddenly attacked from behind. Grabbing Mario's shoulders and leaping off the ground onto his back, Joe screams,

"It is you. I thought Pa was bullshitin' me. It's so great ta see you. Ya lost some weight, but you look good. How's it feel ta be home?'

"Git off my back and I'll tell ya," says Mario with a laugh. After exchanging hugs and handshakes with him, Joe says,

"What's this I hear you got married to an Italian girl and had a baby already?"

"It's true, Joe. Look at the pictures Mario brought home," says Pauline.

"Welcome back, Mario. We're all so excited and proud," says Edna, Joe's wife.

"Thanks, Edna. It still feels a little strange ta be home, but that's changin in a hurry."

"Edna, come and look at these pictures. Mario, your wife and baby...they're gorgeous. You must be very anxious to see them again," says Pauline.

"I'll feel a lot better when Antonella and Vincenzo get here. Naples is still a dangerous place." Mario's return becomes a major celebration for the family. Giuseppi puts wine and liquor on the dining room table, and the rest of the afternoon is spent listening to Mario describing his incredible experiences of the past four years. Enduring North Africa, discovering Sicily and meeting Antonella in the amusing way that he did are stories that rivet his family's attention to his every word. He's certain they would listen to him all night, but his long journey on the train begins to catch up with him.

"Pa. Is my room still available? I need to get a little rest before we go out for dinner tonight."

"Yes, Mario. It'sa the same way whenna you left. Go. I'll wake a you up when we arra ready to go."

"Yeah. You look like you could use a little sleep, Mario. We'll see ya later at Enzo's," says John. After his brothers leave, Mario grabs his bag and climbs the stairs to the second floor of Giuseppi's house. His old room appears exactly as he left it four years ago. After kicking off his shoes and removing his uniform, he pulls the blanket back and sits on the edge of his bed. His fatigue is not enough to put his mind at ease, however. What are Antonella and Vincenzo doing right now? Have his friends returned home safely? With his head full of such questions, he lies down, closes his eyes and hopes some sleep will put aside his concerns for a little while.

"Mario. Mario, wake up. It'sa time to go pretty soon," says Giuseppi, gently poking him on the shoulder.

"Oh…Okay, Pa. Wow, I must a really been tired. What…time is it?"

619

"6:30. I tolda Enzo we arra gonna be there at eight. He'sa very exited to see you."

"I just wanna take a shower and shave. I'll be ready in a half hour." After showering, Mario goes to his closet and finds all of his civilian clothes still hanging there, exactly as he left them. For the first time in four years, he will not be going out in military fatigues. Giuesppi enters Mario's room soon after his son is dressed.

"I want to show you somathing, Mario. It'sa for the baby," says Giuseppi. Leading Mario to the other bedroom, he stands just inside the door and smiles proudly.

"Thisa room isa for Vincenzo. Do you thinka he will like it?" Moving through the room, Mario examines the crib and the large collection of toys his father has already purchased for his unseen grandson.

"Pa...you didn't have ta do all this. But yeah...he's gonna like it. This is great. I don't know what else...to say. Thanks."

"I want him a to like hisa new home. Do you think Antonella willa like me, Mario?"

"She's gonna love ya, Pa. Vincenzo's never had toys like this before. Wait'll she sees all this." Giuseppi's face lights up with a big smile after hearing Mario's answer.

"That'sa good. Let's go...you musta be hungry by now," he says. Dumbfounded by his father's unexpected generosity, Mario puts his arm around Giuseppi's shoulder and says,

"It's good ta be home, Pa. I...really appreciate all this."

"Stopa, please. Before you make a me cry again," says Giuseppi with a soft laugh.

Arriving at the Little Café, Mario opens the door, let's his father enter and then follows him in. Above the din of the evening customers, Enzo's voice can suddenly be heard from behind the bar.

"Mario, Mario. *Benvenuto.* Whatta wonderfula surprise. How are you?" he yells. After dashing through the dining room, he shakes Mario's hand and gives him a friendly hug.

"I'm fine, Enzo. It's good to see you again. I see the restaurant hasn't changed very much."

"He looks good, eh, Giuseppi. You musta be very happy he'sa home," says Enzo, shaking Giuseppi's hand.

"Enzo. Mario isa married. And he has a baby. A son."

"Married? You arra married? Mario, that'sa so exciting. Come, I hava nice a table inna the alcove for you. You must tella me everything," says Enzo with a laugh. After guiding Mario and Giuseppi to the table, Enzo brings a pitcher of wine and the familiar porcelain cups to the table. He fills the cups and sits between Mario and his father. Giuseppi reaches into his coat pocket, pulls out the envelope containing Mario's wedding pictures and proudly says,

"Look at a these pictures, Enzo. It'sa Mario's wife an hisa baby." With help from Mario, Giuseppi describes each picture in painstaking detail. "And, thisa is Vincenzo. My grandson."

"It'sa miracle, Mario. You go away a to war, anna come home with thisa beautiful family. Congratulations. You hava been blessed."

"Thank you, Enzo. I guess it is a miracle in some ways."

"Vincenzo...such a nice name. Do you know Enzo isa short for Vincenzo, Mario?" asks Enzo with swelling pride.

"His grandmother...she calls him Enzo sometimes," says Mario with fond recollection. Soon, John, Joe and their wives join them, and the evening becomes a chorus of exuberant toasts and endless stories, combined with plenty of Enzo's veal and chianti. It's a wonderful reunion party, and Mario enjoys getting reacquainted with his family. He lights a cigarette while they look at his wedding pictures again, but the distant look on his face catches John's attention.

"Hey, you okay? You look like you're someplace else right now," says John quietly.

"Oh, I'm all right. I was just thinking about Antonella and the baby...you know, how they're doin."

"Anything I can do?"

"No, there's not much anybody can do. I just gotta wait it out. But I'm so goddamn worried, John. I never counted on this...you know, leavin em there like this."

"But, she's got people there, right? Her own family?"

"Sure, and they're good people. Her brother is an officer in the air force. He won't let anything happen to em. I just can't stop thinking about em, that's all."

"Look, Joe can use some help at the store. That's a little easier than goin back to the plant right away. You need to do something ta take your mind off it. The time will pass a lot faster that way."

"Maybe you're right. That way, I can be ready to go pick them up when they get here." Mario welcomes John's advice again. With much to consider in the coming months, he will certainly need his brother's help.

After dinner, Mario drives home while Giuseppi leans his head against the door glass and falls asleep. Parking the car in front of the house, Mario tugs on his father's coat.

"Wake up, Pa. We're home." Groggy from the long day and big meal, Giuseppi makes his way into the house. Looking at his pocket watch, he says,

"Midanight. It'sa late for me. I'ma going to sleep, Mario. Goodnight."

"Night, Pa. Oh, wait a second, Pa. Do ya have a pen and some paper?"

"Inna the drawer, there," he says, pointing to a small lamp table.

"Thanks Pa. See ya in the morning."

Still feeling tormented over his separation from Antonella, Mario sits at the dining room table and writes the first of many letters to her.

My darling Antonella,

    I miss you and Vincenzo very much. I feel terrible being away from you. I hope you and the baby are well. My trip home was awful after leaving you behind. I arrived in a place called Norfolk and took a train to Detroit. I can't wait until you come here. I hope Sarge will bring you your shipping papers, soon and then we can make our plans to be together again.

    It was good to see my family again. John and Joe are doing good. They are very excited about meeting you and Vincenzo. I showed them pictures of our wedding and one of Vincenzo. Pa has a room in his house all ready for Vincenzo. He bought a crib and lots of toys already. I think he is going to spoil him a lot.

    Say hello to your family and tell them that I miss them. I hope you can read my Italian writing. I'll write again every chance I get. Please kiss Vincenzo for me. I love both of you very much.

                                    Mario

After sealing the letter in an envelope, Mario rubs his eyes, turns off all the lights and goes to his room. He knows the thrill of being home again will remain empty until he is reunited with his wife and son.

Mario takes John's advice and begins to work with Joe at the seafood store. He enjoys the casual days and relaxed pace there.

"Joe, ya shoulda seen the fish market in Bagnoli," says Mario. "They'd catch everything from swordfish to squid in the morning, and be cutting it up and sellin it in the afternoon. If we had that much fish ta sell, we'd be livin on easy street."

"Where's Bagnoli? Is that near Naples?" asks Joe.

"Yeah. It's just north a Naples. It's where I met Antonella." The phone rings before Mario can say any more. After Joe picks up the receiver, he says,

"It's Pa. He's all worked up about something and wants ta talk to you." Taking the phone from Joe, Mario says,

"What's a matter Pa? Is something wrong?"

"It'sa telegram, Mario. From a Sergeant Thompson. You wanta me to bring ita to you?"

"No, Pa. Just open it and read it to me right now. It's gotta be news about Antonella and Vincenzo," shouts Mario. He impatiently listens to the clunking sounds coming through the earpiece, as Guiseppi drops the phone down on the table and opens the telegram.

"Arra you still there, Mario?"

"Yes, Pa. What's it say?"

"You arra right, Mario. It'sa about your Antonella."

"Okay, Pa. Please read it to me. Read everything it says."

"To Mario Carlucci, STOP. Mario, your family departs Naples NOV 9 aboard Algonquin. STOP. Arriving American Export Lines Dock, New York City NOV 21. STOP. Confirm with shipping line. STOP. Good luck, my friend, Sarge."

"November? That's only a coupla months away," says Mario.

"Whatta do we do now, Mario?"

"I'll be right home. I need to contact the shipping line and get the details. Man, I been waitin for this news since the day I left Naples." Mario hangs up the phone and smiles.

"My Sergeant sent me a telegram sayin Antonella and Vincenzo are arrivin in New York on the twenty-first of November. Ain't that great?" he says.

"That's terrific, Mario. So what da ya gotta do? Go to New York and meet her?"

"I have to. I don't want them ta be alone there for a minute. Ya wanna go with me?" asks Mario.

"Sure. Let's all go. I'm sure the old man will wanna be there."

"I gotta go home and figure this out. I'll talk to ya later."

*   *   *

Tearful and despondent, Antonella often cries herself to sleep during the first few months after Mario's departure. Feeling like her world has come to a complete stop now that he's gone, she is helpless to do anything about it. She worries Vincenzo is becoming too attached to her brother and will forget about Mario. She prays his letters will arrive and reassure her that he has not forgotten her. Even with the support of her family, Antonella cannot put aside her constant fear of never seeing Mario again.

Holding Vincenzo on her lap while Antonella bathes, Lucia says,

"Antonella. When you're finished, why don't we walk to the post office again? Maybe there will be a letter from Mario."

"Do you think we'll get one today?"

"I don't know, but it's been many weeks now since he left. A letter could get here any day now. I'll put some clean clothes on Vincenzo, and we can go." With Vincenzo in his carriage, Antonella and Lucia trek the many blocks to the post office.

"Do you have any letters for a Cappodanno or a Carlucci?" she asks the postal clerk. The clerk fingers through a stack of sorted envelopes and asks,

"Antonella Carlucci?"

"Yes...yes. Is it from America?"

"I think so. It's from Detroit," answers the clerk, handing her the letter.

"Lucia. You...were right. I want to read it now. I can't wait until we get home." Standing on the street in front of the post office, Antonella carefully opens the envelope and unfolds Mario's letter. Her eyes feast on the long awaited news, and she begins to smile again for the first time in long while.

"Is he all right? What does he say, Antonella?" asks Lucia.

"Yes. He says he got home and misses everyone very much."

"You see. You had nothing to worry about all this time."

"Oh, listen to this Lucia. Mario showed our wedding pictures to his family, and he says they're all very excited about meeting Vincenzo and me. And his father...he bought Vincenzo a crib and lots of toys already." Mario's first letter clears away much of the doubt and fear that Antonella has felt since he shipped out. Her ordeal, however, is not over.

The first letter from Mario takes nearly two months to arrive in Naples, but others soon follow on a regular basis. Antonella looks forward to each one and always writes back to him immediately. She tells him about Vincenzo sitting up for the first time or pulling himself up in his crib. She tells Mario about all the little things he is missing as his son grows. The letters ease the loneliness of their separation, but for Antonella, they also consume much of her remaining time in Napoli. Giancarlo's visit, one afternoon, brings Antonella her first glimpse of the ominous events she's been expecting.

"Antonella, I've spoken with Sergeant Thompson, and he will be stopping by today. He...has your paperwork completed...to leave for America."

"He knows...the day? What did he say to you?"

"He's asked me to explain everything to you...so there will be no misunderstandings."

"I...I see. What day is it, Giancarlo? Tell me, please."

"November 9. You and Vincenzo are booked to sail to New York on the Algonquin."

"That's less than two months...it's so soon," says Antonella.

"The Sergeant has sent Mario a telegram with this information, so he can be there to meet you."

"New York? It's such a big city, Giancarlo. Are you certain it's New York?"

"There's no need to be afraid, Antonella. Mario is going to be there, waiting for you." Knowing her actual departure date sends a slight chill tingling over her skin.

"What...do you know...about the ship?" she asks.

"All we know is that it was used as a hospital ship. There will be hundreds of other women on the ship with you." A knock at the door interrupts Antonella's questioning. It is Sergeant Thompson. Antonella invites him in, gives him a gentle hug, and says in her improving English,

"I ama appy to see you."

"Grazie, Antonella," he replies. After shaking hands with Giancarlo, Sergeant sits at the table and asks him,

"Have you told her, yet?"

"Yesa, Sergeant. I was justa explaining it to her. Do you hava the tickets?"

"Right here," says the Sergeant, handing them to Giancarlo. He looks over the tickets and gives them to Antonella.

"These are your tickets. Keep them with your passports and other papers. Do you have any questions you want me to ask the Sergeant?"

"What about Vincenzo? Where will he sleep on the boat?"

"Sergeant, she wants a to know where the baby will sleep on the ship?"

"I understand there'll be cribs for the children...in their mothers' cabins."

"The Sergeant says Vincenzo will have his own crib, Antonella. He'll be fine."

Staring at the tickets in her hands, Antonella realizes she may never see the sergeant after today. She nervously clears her throat and asks,

"An whenna do you go home, Sergeant?" Holding up the four fingers on his right hand, he answers,

"Quattro giorno." Antonella is suddenly distracted by the sound of Vincenzo stirring in the bedroom, and she jumps up to go check on him. Holding him in her arms, she returns a few moments later.

"May I...hold him," says Sarge, extending his arms toward the baby.

"Si, Si. Andiamo, Vincenzo. Be good a boy," she says, handing the baby to him. Sarge holds Vincenzo with one arm while the baby toys with his lapel buttons. Looking at Giancarlo, he says,

"Mario's going to be surprised when he sees how big this little guy is getting. I...uh, should get going. Thank you for your help, Giancarlo."

"It'sa not you who should thanka us, but it is we who should thanka you, Sergeant. I do this because it'sa my family, but you...you do thisa because you are a good friend. *Grazie, grazie tante.*" Antonella feels tears welling up in her eyes once more. She gives Sarge another emotional embrace, gently places her hand on his left cheek and kisses him on the other. Taking Vincenzo from him, she says,

"Ciao, Sergeant, buon viaggio. I will not a forgeta you."

"Good luck to you...*bouno fortuno,* Antonella," says Sergeant, kissing her lightly on the cheek. Shaking Giancarlo's hand one last time, Sarge says,

"You take care of yourself, too. You hear?" Giancarlo smiles and nods his head, as the Sergeant leaves the apartment. Antonella will never see him again.

After sharing the news of her departure with Assunta and Lucia, Antonella discovers how truly difficult leaving her family is going to be. Holding Vincenzo, her mother studies the paperwork that will take them away forever.

"November the ninth? That...is...your last day with us?" asks Assunta.

"Yes, Mama. I must be aboard the ship...in the...the morning."

631

"My God, Antonella. There...there is so little time left...to prepare." Assunta cuddles Vincenzo against her chest and gently rocks him back and forth. Antonella can see her mother's chin quiver in fear. The frightening thought of Antonella's departure has always been at a safe distance from their day-to-day existence. It is like a dark, family secret they must eventually confront. They can no longer ignore it.

"Please, Mama. Try not...to cry. Please...for the baby," pleads Antonella.

"I know, sweetheart. I know. I don't want to scare him. But, I...I can't bear to..." Her voice trembles so badly, she cannot speak easily of her grief. She wipes her tears with a small handkerchief and lovingly kisses Vincenzo's forehead. Scarcely able to suppress her own emotions, Antonella embraces a weeping Lucia.

"We...can write to each other...and maybe someday...you and Mama can come to visit me in America. Wouldn't that be wonderful?" says Antonella. She realizes such a visit is merely wishful thinking, but tries to remain hopeful. Lucia, too, understands such a wish is futile, and she hugs her courageous sister more tightly.

"I'll write to you, Antonella. I...I promise. I will miss you...so much," says Lucia.

During her final weeks in Napoli, Antonella and her family live under a cloud of sadness. Joined by Lucia and Assunta, she walks Vincenzo along the Via Pozzuoli and tries to enjoy the beach with them again before she leaves. The joy she knew there as a young girl, however, is no longer possible. She visits Theresa Minelli and the many other neighbors who have come to know her so well and says goodbye to them. On her final Sunday in Napoli, she attends Father Bertulucci's mass to thank him for all he's done. Holding Vincenzo in her arms, she greets the priest on the front steps of the cathedral at the conclusion of the service.

"Antonella, it's so good to see you. Look at this child. He's such a joy, isn't he?" asks Father.

"Yes, Father. He's a good baby."

"How are you, my child? I know your husband has returned home alone."

"Our life...it's very different now. You knew, didn't you, Father? You knew how awful it would be to watch him go. I must go and join him soon. I've never been so afraid, Father." Putting his arm around Atonella's shoulder, Father Bertulucci guides her back into the church.

"I knew because I've had to say goodbye to loved ones of my own. But I also know you will survive this sadness you feel. This baby, and hopefully others, will fill your life with happiness. I know you are strong enough to do this, but it will not be easy. Allow me to bless you and your baby, my child." After dipping his fingertips in holy water, he makes a small cross on her forehead and then Vincenzo's.

"In the name of the Father, the Son and the Holy Ghost. May God watch over you, Antonella and Vincenzo," he says.

"Thank you, Father. Thank you for everything."

"You are welcome, my child. I'll pray for you."

Not even Father Bertulucci's inspiring words and final blessing can eliminate Antonella's dread of leaving her family. During her last few days in Napoli, she concentrates on the final preparations for her voyage and tries to put the impending anguish out of her mind. With only one suitcase in which to pack all her belongings, she knows she cannot bring all of her beautiful dresses with her. With Lucia's help, she begins to sort through the collection and select the ones she will take to America with her. The old, leather suitcase is soon full, its sides bulging like an overgrown melon.

"This is all I can pack, Lucia. The suitcase is too full already."

"But, there are so many left, Antonella. What will you do with them?"

"I...I want you...to have them."

"But Antonella, these...these are your most beautiful designs. I can't take..."

"Take them, Lucia. Please. It will make me happy to know you have them." Sitting on the edge of the bed they have shared for so long, Lucia holds one of the dresses and begins to cry.

"How...can I...how will I wear these and not think of you?" she says tearfully.

Antonella is also overcome with emotions. She holds Lucia in her arms and says,

"I...I will never forget about you, and I don't ever want you...to forget me, Lucia. I'll always love you."

"I won't Antonella. I never will. I love you, too."

Giancarlo takes time away from his military duties in order to spend it with his sister. They cherish her last few days in Napoli, and Giancarlo looks after all the details of her voyage to allow her more time with Assunta and Lucia. He makes sure all her paperwork is complete and safely stored. It's only days before she is scheduled to leave her family, and the anguish of watching yet another loved one leave Napoli begins to take its toll on all of them.

With his military efficiency, Giancarlo makes certain that Antonella is thoroughly prepared for her voyage. On this, her last night in Napoli, she sits and listens to him go over the details.

"I visited the Stazione Marittima earlier today, Antonella. Your ship, the Algonquin, is there." The Algonquin's presence in the harbor represents the last part of the complicated plan she and Mario have discussed so many times.

"You...saw it, Giancarlo?" she asks, solemnly.

"Yes. We will have to leave here early. I imagine the dock will be crowded. I have arranged for a cab in the morning...at nine o'clock. Do you have all your papers?"

"I have them all in my purse. Do you want to see them again?"

"Let's be sure everything is in order." Antonella opens the purse and carefully organizes all the documents on the table.

Passports, Vincenzo's birth certificate, her marriage license and the tickets for her passage are all there. Giancarlo inspects them and hands them back to her.

"There is little more to do except make sure you are packed. I found another small suitcase for you. You can pack the baby's things in it."

"Thank you for doing all this, Giancarlo. I...could never do it alone." With tears in her eyes, she puts her arms around her brother and holds him in a long, emotional embrace.

"It's going to be all right, Antonella. You'll see. You and Vincenzo are going to a wonderful place."

Carrying Vincenzo in her arms, Antonella joins her mother in the kitchen. Assunta has tried to keep herself busy in these final hours before Antonella's departure by preparing a nice dinner for her family. When Assunta stops what she's doing to kiss her grandson, Antonella sees the pain in her mother's face. Dark circles surround her watery, red eyes, and she nervously bites her lower lip trying to remain calm.

"Dinner is...is almost ready, Antonella. Here, come with Grandma, Enzo," she says, taking the baby into her arms.

"Mama, why don't you take him into the other room. Lucia and I will bring the food to the table." Only Vincenzo's tiny hands, exploring her face, can bring a slight smile to Assunta. Antonella is sickened by the grief her mother will have to endure over losing this child forever.

Sharing a quiet dinner with her family on her last night in Napoli, Antonella, once again, questions the wisdom of her decision. There are no smiles, and even passing plates of food around the table becomes awkward. They avoid direct eye contact. The awful mood reminds Antonella of her father's funeral. The only joy is watching Assunta feed Vincenzo carefully mashed portions of her meal. The evening passes quickly, and Giancarlo prepares to return to his own apartment.

"I'll be here early in the morning. Do you need anything else from me before I go, Antonella?"

"I...can't think of anything, Giancarlo." Antonella begins to weep, as she holds him, kisses his cheek and whispers,

"Giancarlo...I...can't do this alone. I'll need you tomorrow...more than ever before."

"I know. I'll be with you for as long as I can, I promise."

That night, Antonella gets very little sleep. At breaking dawn, she is standing at the window and watching the early stirrings of the neighborhood. Men carrying fishing equipment and peddlers making their way to markets are scenes she has witnessed her entire life, but this morning they become some of her final memories of Napoli. The baby's crying pulls Assunta from her bed. Antonella and her mother feed, bathe and dress Vincenzo. Antonella then dresses herself, inspects the contents of her suitcases once more, and then carries them into the living room to await Giancarlo's arrival.

"Are...you sure you have everything?" asks Lucia.

637

"I think I do. There is no room in the suitcases for anything else."

"You didn't pack your...wedding dress, Antonella. What about your wedding dress?"

"Will you please take care of it for me? I...I'll write to you and tell you where to mail it. Can you do that for me?" Tears soon glisten in Lucia's eyes.

"Yes, of course...I will," she weeps.

They hear Giancarlo's heavy footsteps on the stairs. He enters the apartment and kisses his mother and sisters.

"The taxi is waiting, Antonella. We must go."

"I...I think I'm ready, Giancarlo. My papers are...here...in my purse, and the bags are all packed." Giancarlo picks up the suitcases and carries them to the street.

Holding Vincenzo in her arms, Assunta makes her way down the stairs. As she stands in the doorway, Antonella looks at the little apartment for the last time. Even the anticipation of reuniting with Mario does not keep the tears from her eyes. She closes the door on this part of her life forever. Giancarlo places the suitcases in the trunk of the taxi and patiently waits for her to get into the car. She stares at the familiar neighborhood through the window of the cab. The scene becomes another important memory for her.

Holding Lucia's hand tightly in hers, Antonella tries to console her weeping sister. Lucia's muted sobs continue all the way to the Stazione Marittima. It is only Vincenzo's smiling reaction to riding in a car that prevents Antonella from sobbing too. The taxi driver winds his way along the crowded pier, stops in front of the Stazione and says,

"I'm sorry, Signor, but this is as far as I can go."

"This is fine. We can walk from here," replies Giancarlo. Antonella steps from the cab and gazes up at the massive ship. The name, Algonquin, is clearly visible on the bow, and she can suddenly feel her heart pounding much faster. It is like the many ships she remembers coming and going from the harbor, but knowing this one will carry her away forever causes her legs to tremble. Gray, with three decks and two large smokestacks, the ship is an ominous backdrop to the profound sadness that fills the Statzione. Holding on to Giancarlo's arm, Antonella follows him through the hundreds of crying families who are saying their painful goodbyes to their own.

"There are so many others," says Antonella in astonishment.

"I'm afraid the ship will be crowded, but maybe that's good. Let's go aboard and find your cabin. Mama, I think it's best if you and Lucia wait here with the baby," says Giancarlo. Finding the entrance to the passenger's boarding area, Antonella presents her tickets to a gruff-looking man standing guard at the end of the gangplank. The sailor cross-checks the ticket against a passenger manifest and says,

"It says here you're supposed to be traveling with a baby. Is that a mistake?"

"She speaks very little English. Her baby isa there, witha his grandmother," says Giancarlo, pointing to Assunta.

"And who are you?"

"I'ma her brother. I wanta to find her cabin for her. Isa that possible?"

"Yeah, okay, but don't take all day. We have to shove off in two hours. Her cabin number is 231. It's on the port side, second deck."

"I don't understand, Giancarlo. What is he saying? Is there a problem?" asks Antonella.

"Everything is fine. He says we can go aboard and find your room."

"What...about Vincenzo?"

"He'll be safe with Mama for a few minutes. We will drop off your bags and come right back." Carrying her suitcases, Giancarlo leads Antonella up the gangplank and onto the ship.

The cold, impersonal decks of the transport remind Antonella of the British ship on which she was nearly raped. This unlikely connection adds to her numbing fear. Staring down at the pier from the second deck, she sees the many women who will be making this journey. She can hear the strains from a distant band somewhere on the dock. Their music seems so strangely out of place today. Giancarlo stops abruptly and checks the number on the cabin door.

"Here it is, Antonella. This is your cabin." Pushing open the door, he takes Antonella by the arm and leads her into the darkened

room. When he turns on the single overhead light, Antonella sees the wretched conditions in which she will spend the next fourteen days. There are eight bunks, stacked four high, along both sides of the narrow cabin. Each bunk provides only two and a half feet of space, their well-worn guardrails and tattered curtains offering very little privacy. There are two small cribs adjacent to the lower bunks. Behind another door is a single toilet and washbasin. The stale, musty air is already making her nauseous. Trembling and crying, Antonella says,

"My God, Giancarlo, look...at...at how awful. How can...I bring Vincenzo in here? He'll be terrified." Giancarlo takes her into his arms and holds her until she is able to calm herself.

"What have...I done, Giancarlo? What have I done to our family?"

"I know you're afraid, but I've seen your courage many times before. You have to try and be brave, again. Here, stop crying and let's go find your son." Giancarlo wipes her cheeks with his handkerchief.

After placing her bags on her bunk, Giancarlo puts his arm around Antonella and escorts her back to the pier for their final goodbyes.

Growing restless without his mother, Vincenzo lifts his arms in excitement when he sees her returning. She takes him into her arms and kisses him.

"What's wrong, Vincenzo. Are you hungry all ready?"

"I...have something for him, Antonella. You...you can take these with you," says Assunta. She takes a soft cookie from a small bag she carries and hands it to the baby. Tenderly, she runs her hand through his hair and watches Vincenzo enjoy the sugary treat. Tears stream down her face, and she places her hand over her mouth, trying to muffle her crying.

"My beautiful little Enzo. My...my heart is breaking, Antonella. Forgive me, but I...I can't stop...crying. Oh dear God, I...I can't believe I'll never see him...again."

Giancarlo takes his mother into his arms, and she begins to sob uncontrollably. Several loud blasts from the ship's horn warn that final boarding is underway. Lucia puts her arms around Antonella and Vincenzo and holds them as tightly as she can. Her grief is so devastating that she struggles to speak.

"I...love you. I'll...always love...love you, my dear sister," she whispers.

"I love you, too, Lucia. Please forgive...me...for leaving you." The sadness ultimately steals their voices, and they can only kiss each other one last time. The ship's horn sounds again, and Giancarlo knows it is time to see Antonella onto the ship.

"Antonella, it's time. You must board the ship," he says softly. She kisses Assunta and Lucia, turns away and follows her brother to the gangplank. With her face awash in tears, she reaches out and touches Giancarlo on the cheek.

"I don't know what to say...how to...to thank you. I...I love you, Giancarlo." He is not immune to the feelings of grief and sorrow this day brings, and his own tears begin to trickle down his face. He pulls her close to him and kisses her and the baby.

"Mario's a good man. I know you'll have a good life with him. I'll take...good care of Mama and Lucia. Oh, God, Antonella, I'm...going to miss you so much."

"Goodbye, my...dear brother."

Carrying Vincenzo in one arm and the bag full of cookies in the other, Antonella walks up the steep gangplank without looking back. Reaching the second deck, she finds a place along the rail and begins to look for her family as the dock men release the ship's lines. Moments later, the transport slowly eases away from its berth, and Antonella's terror becomes nearly unbearable. Finding her family clustered together among the hundreds of well-wishers on the dock, she waves at them repeatedly. She is unsure whether they see her until Assunta and Lucia wave their white scarves in the air.

Thinking she might faint from the fear and sadness she is experiencing, she steps away from the rail to protect her son. Overcome by crushing despair and loneliness, she weeps uncontrollably as the huge ship churns its way out onto the Mediterranean. From her place behind the railing, she is able to watch her sister and mother wave their white scarves until they become nothing but flickering, white specks on the dock. Looking out over her beloved Napoli for the last time, she sees the beautiful

Mono V. D'Angelo

San Martino Castle perched atop its familiar hill, the imposing outline of Mt. Vesuvius and the bay she adores so much. Alone with her baby, she watches for hours until all these landmarks and the only life she has ever known, vanish below the horizon.

CHAPTER 22

Leaping up the porch steps in two long strides, Mario rushes into Giuseppi's house and yells,

"Pa? Where are ya, Pa? Where's the telegram?"

"It'sa there, inna the dining room," answers Giuseppi, emerging from the kitchen. Mario finds Sergeant Thompson's telegram neatly folded atop its envelope in the middle of the large, mahogany table. After reading it carefully several more times, he folds the telegram and stuffs it into his pants pocket.

"Do you know whatta you gonna do, Mario?"

"I think I'm gonna go down ta Fort Wayne. Maybe someone there can tell me how to get in touch with this American Export. Can I borrow your car for a while, Pa?" Giuseppi barely has time to nod his head before Mario flies out the door.

Entering the Fort Wayne recruitment office, Mario approaches a young private sitting behind a desk.

"Can I help you, sir?"

"I hope so. I was discharged a few months ago, and I just got a telegram sayin my wife and son are gonna be arrivin from Italy in November. They're comin into New York, but I don't know where or when. Do ya think someone here can help me...you know, ta figure out when they're comin?"

"I should be able to find something out for you. Can I see the telegram and your I.D.?" After reading the telegram, the clerk checks Mario's I.D. and says,

"Why don't you wait here for a couple minutes while I go make a few telephone calls? I gotta talk to my sergeant, but I'm pretty sure we can get in touch with the shipping line for you."

Bolstered by the encouraging news, Mario impatiently waits while the private steps into the office at the rear of the building. Lighting a cigarette, Mario nervously paces about the room. A collection of old recruitment posters hanging on the walls holds his interest momentarily. The next fifteen minutes drag by slowly, but the young private eventually returns.

"Any luck?" asks Mario.

"Yes sir. My sergeant gave me a telephone number for American Export. I guess there are a lot of guys who have wives and kids coming into the States. Anyway, I talked to the shipping line, and a clerk confirmed your wife's passage on the Algonquin for

November 9. He said, if there's no bad weather, it should arrive at pier twelve in New York's main harbor terminal on November 24."

"That's right after Thanksgiving, ain't it? Great. Did they give ya any idea what time the ship might come in?"

"No sir. I guess that's too hard to predict. They said the best thing to do is to get there early in the morning. The guy I talked to said that, if you take a train to New York and hop on the subway, it'll take you right to the harbor. I wrote all that down for you on the bottom of the telegram. Hope it helps."

"Thanks a lot, private. It helps a hell of a lot."

"Good luck, sir."

That evening, John and Joe show up at Giusesppi's house, anxious for more details regarding the arrival of Mario's wife and baby.

"So I hear ya got a telegram. Did ya find out anything yet?" asks John.

"Yeah. I went ta Fort Wayne, and a private called American Export in New York for me. Antonella's gonna be on the Algonquin, and it should get inta New York on November 24. That's the Saturday after Thanksgiving."

"Did ya find out where?" asks Joe.

"Yeah. I got it right here...on the telegram," says Mario, carefully removing it from his pants pocket. "Main terminal, New York Harbor. Her ship will dock at pier twelve."

647

"Mario and I was sayin we should all go ta New York and meet her. Whaddya think?" asks Joe.

"I'm game. How 'bout you, Pa? Ya wanna go ta New York and meet Mario's family?" asks John with a smile.

"Well, of a course I'm a gonna go. Why do you ask a such a thing?" replies Giuseppi sternly. His three sons begin laughing, and Mario says,

"He's just givin ya a hard time, Pa. We all know you're gonna go."

"How we gonna get there?" asks Joe.

"The shipping line said it's easier ta take the train inta New York and then jump on the subway to get to the harbor. We can leave on Friday night...after the holiday. That way, we'll get there in the morning. If that's okay with you guys, I'll go buy the tickets tomorrow," says Mario. They all agree, and the plan is in place. The most difficult thing for Mario to do now is wait the six weeks until the Algonquin arrives in New York.

With only weeks to go before meeting his first grandson, Giuseppi's excitement sends him off to the Sears and Roebuck store in search of a gift to bring him. Knowing late November can be cold and wet, he wanders through the many racks of infant clothing looking for something that will keep Vincenzo warm. With hundreds of different sizes and styles to choose from, he's unsure of what to buy. Placing one hand on his hip and scratching his head with the other, he's confused and frustrated by the vast selection.

"May I help you with something?" asks a young woman with a pleasant voice.

"Uh...yes. Thanka you. You see, I want a to buy some a warm clothes...butta...I'm a not sure what's a right. It'sa for my new grandson."

"Well, if you tell me how old he is, we can find the right size and then choose something."

"I'm a not a sure. I never hava seen him yet. He'sa coming from Italy in a few weeks. I, uh...think he'sa eight or nine months old. I have a picture. Willa that help?" he asks.

"Yes. It might." After viewing Vincenzo's photograph, the young woman replies with a smirk,

"He's a handsome little boy, isn't he? Why don't we look at something for one-year-olds? That way he can grow into it if it's a little big for him." Leading Giuseppi through the maze of aisles, the clerk removes a tiny, double-breasted coat from one of the hanging racks.

"This is the same material they make Navy pea coats from. It has a matching cap and leggings. It's very warm, and I'm sure he'll look adorable in it." Giuseppi studies the coat and strokes the fabric, trying to convince himself it will be warm enough. Satisfied, he says,

"I thinka you are right. This issa perfect. Can a you please put it into a nice a gift box for me?"

"Yes sir. Is there anything else you might want to get for him? Gloves or maybe a scarf?"

"It mighta be very cold in New York...yes...I will a need them, too, please."

When the clerk finishes boxing up the little outfit, she hands Giuseppi the package and says,

"Here you are. I'm sure these will keep your grandson very warm, no matter how cold it gets. Good luck to you."

"Thanka you so much a for your help. I can't a wait to give it to him." After paying the clerk, Giuseppi returns home trying to imagine how his grandson will look wearing it.

Mario and his brothers celebrate the Thanksgiving holiday together in their father's house. Nibbling on roasted chestnuts and homemade sausage while the turkey slowly cooks, Mario enjoys the wonderful traditions of one of his father's holiday dinners again. This holiday, of course, brings its own special excitement.

"How thrilling, Mario! Can you believe your wife and baby will be here in just two days?" asks Pauline.

"I know. I hope her ship gets in when it's supposed to. I'm not gonna get any sleep for a few days; I just know it," replies Mario.

"You got the tickets, right?" asks Joe.

"Yup. Even remembered to buy two more for the trip back. We're on the 6:15 train tomorrow night. That gets us to New York by about seven in the morning." While enjoying his first holiday dinner since returning home, Mario's thoughts are never far from his reunion with Antonella and Vincenzo.

Mario tosses and turns throughout the night. Sitting up, he clicks on the small light and looks at the Big Ben alarm clock. It's 5:30 in the morning. He climbs from his bed, grabs his cigarettes and lighter and sits on the old chair next to the window. Lighting a Pall Mall, he waits for the dawn to put this long day in motion. It's not long afterwards that he hears his father roaming around the first floor of the house. He joins Giuseppi in the kitchen.

"What's a matter, Pa, you can't sleep either?"

"How a can I sleep today? I'ma too nervous a to sleep." Giuseppi busies himself preparing breakfast.

"What's in the box? The one on your dresser?" asks Mario. His father doesn't look up from the frying eggs, but a smile crosses his face.

"I buy a little a gift…for Vincenzo. I can't a meet your wife without a gift for the baby."

"What'd ya buy? Or is it a surprise?"

"It's a warm coat and cap, in a case it'sa cold in New York."

"That's a good idea, Pa. I'll bet it'll be cold on the pier." Mario and his father spend the rest of the morning and early afternoon cleaning floors and bathrooms, dusting lamps and tables, and for the first time, making sure there's baby food in the house.

It's soon 4:30 in the afternoon, and Joe and John arrive at Giuseppi's house.

"Where the hell are you guys? It's time to get going," shouts Joe. Racing down the stairs from the second floor, Mario excitedly greets his brothers.

"We're all set. We'll go as soon as Pa's done gettin dressed."

"I'll bet you'll be glad when this is over," says John.

"You can say that again. Hell, I ain't had a decent night's sleep in a weeks." When Giuseppi joins them in the living room, the conversation stops abruptly. Dressed in his finest pinstriped suit and floral tie, the old man's dapper appearance catches his sons by surprise.

"Whoa! Get a look at this guy, will ya?" teases John.

"Hey Pa, ya better watch out. Some gal gonna wanna take you home with her after seein ya all dressed up like that," jokes Joe.

"Just a shut uppa, you two. This issa big a day for Mario. I want to looka nice for hisa new wife. Let'sa go." After putting on his hat, he grabs the crumpled Sears and Roebuck bag containing Vincenzo's gift and walks out the door.

"Go on, before you guys piss 'em off," says Mario with a smile.

The frequent November gales whip the Atlantic up into towering, froth-covered mountains of murky, green water. The bitter conditions cause the huge vessel to pitch and roll for days at a time, making it impossible for Antonella to venture out of the cabin with Vincenzo. Of the seven other women sharing the cabin with her, six are expecting and one is traveling with an infant daughter. None of the women have ever been aboard a large ship in rough seas, and seasickness quickly confines most of them to their bunks. In a few short days, the odor in the tiny bathroom becomes so nauseating, the women must cover their faces with hand towels to use it. The Spanish-speaking crew is rude and indifferent, the food is certainly not Italian, and there are reports of numerous miscarriages aboard the ship. Cradling Vincenzo in her arms during the first dreadful days of the crossing, Antonella frequently cries herself to sleep amid the strangers she travels with.

Antonella and Sophia, another woman in her cabin with a small child, are drawn to each other by their similar circumstances. The need to care for their children under these wretched conditions literally forces them to become friends. They take turns watching the infants while one of them makes the difficult trip to the ship's galley for food.

"Antonella, the weather...it's getting warmer today and...and the fresh air it's...wonderful. Let's go out on the deck after we feed the babies. It will do us good to get out of this awful cabin," says Sophia, after returning with food.

"Yes, that's a wonderful idea, Sophia. What good news. Thank God. I must get Vincenzo out of this cabin. He's always such a good baby, but he cries all the time now. I know he's not used to being locked up like...like this. Your baby's fever...is it going down, Sophia?"

"She still feels warm to me, but I'll wrap her in a blanket before we go out on deck. Maybe the fresh air will make her feel better."

"I...have some cookies. My mother gave them to me. Maybe Angela will like one."

"Thank you. You're...very kind to...to share them, Antonella. I'm sure she'll feel better if we can go on deck. I will give it to her there." The improving weather allows many of the women aboard to leave their cabins and venture to other decks. Antonella and Sophia explore the ship whenever possible, often discussing what awaits them in America.

"Is your husband going to meet you in New York, Sophia?"

"No. He lives far away from New York. I must take a train to Colorado. Do you know where that is?"

"No. I...don't. How...will you get there? Do you speak English?"

"Oh no. But Paul, that's my husband, he said the soldiers will see that I get on a train that will take me there."

"Aren't you afraid to travel alone like that?"

"Yes, a little. But...I have no family in Italy any more. They...they were killed by the Germans. This is all I can do...for me and my baby."

Sophia's desperate condition upsets Antonella even more than her own circumstances. She pulls the blanket around herself and Vincenzo a little tighter, the sea air suddenly feeling a little colder after hearing of Sophia's misfortune. Antonella is deeply grateful her family has survived the war. And through Mario's many letters, she's confidant he will be in New York when she arrives. Facing her new world alone, as Sophia must do, terrifies her, and she cannot imagine having such courage. She wonders how many other 'Sophias' there are among the many hundreds of women who have made this painful voyage.

A rare morning sun warms the air, and Antonella looks forward to leaving the cabin.

"Sophia, it looks like we have good weather for a change. Let's take Vincenzo and Angela to the galley for breakfast."

"I...I better not, Antonella. Angela's fever is worse today and...and she's...I think she's very sick."

"Are there any doctors on the ship? Did you check?"

"There...there is no doctor, Antonella. I asked the crew and...and all they can do is radio for a doctor...when we arrive."

"I'll bring something back for her. Maybe...if she eats, she'll feel better," says Antonella. After wrapping Vincenzo in a warm blanket, Antonella holds him tightly against her breast and makes her way along the deck. She worries about Sophia's baby and, even worse, worries that Vincenzo may become sick. Feeding Vincenzo in the galley is a welcome change from feeding him in the rancid-smelling cabin. It is there that she hears several women shouting into the galley.

"Land! We can see land. Come quickly," they scream. She can feel her heart start to beat a little faster in her mounting excitement. After feeding Vincenzo the last few spoonfuls of his breakfast, she bundles him up.

"Let's go see our new home, Vincenzo. Soon we'll be with your Papa again. You've missed him, haven't you?"

Placing several slices of bread and a small bottle of milk in her bag for Sophia, Antonella rushes to the forward part of the ship. There, she sees a long, burgundy shadow, sandwiched between the sea and the sky. The blurry image rekindles the dream she's shared with Mario. It's the place where she can have her own garden and take her son to a movie house. With her much anticipated reunion with Mario only hours away, a great deal of the pain she's endured is temporarily forgotten. She returns to her cabin to tell Sophia the good news.

"Sophia, did you hear? We'll be in port in a few hours. Then the doctor can look at Angela. I've brought you a few slices of bread...and some milk. Do you think Angela can eat?"

"She's awake, but I don't know if she will eat. I...I'll try and feed her. Thank...you, Antonella, for bringing her something."

Antonella dresses Vincenzo in the last of his clean clothes and packs his suitcase. She changes into the same dress she wore on her honeymoon and then makes sure all her important papers are safely stored in her purse. Holding her son, she stands along the rail and watches the spectacular skyline of New York glide by the slowing ship. She is astonished by the gray-green majesty of the Statue of Liberty passing by. Soon, tugboats encircle the massive ship, and begin to guide it through the maze of barges and piers.

Like most of the women aboard the ship, Antonella finds the size of this great city intimidating. With the voyage nearly over, her thoughts begin to dwell on Mario. Will he look the same? What will his family be like? Their five months apart suddenly make him seem like a stranger to her. It's a terrible feeling, but it won't go away. She tries not to think about it. She still loves him, of that she is certain, and she believes he loves her. But she can't keep from becoming increasingly nervous. She kisses her baby, waits and watches.

Arriving at New York's Grand Central Station, Mario and his family are directed to the subway by a friendly conductor. After the short ride to the harbor, they locate the American Export Lines' terminal office.

"I'm gonna go inside and check on her ship. I'll be right back," says Mario.

"We're gonna go find some coffee. We'll meet ya right here in a few minutes," says John. Entering the terminal office, Mario sees only one man working behind a long counter.

"Need something?"

"I'm expecting someone…I'm tryin to find out if her ship is comin in today. Can ya help me out?"

"What's the name of the ship?"

"The Algonquin."

"Left Naples on the ninth?"

"Yes, that's the one."

"She'll be in today, but she's still a few hours out. Pier twelve. That's where she'll tie up."

"Where's Pier twelve from here?"

"This one…right in front here? That's seven. Twelve's down there on the right." Stepping from the terminal office, Mario rejoins his brothers and father.

"Here, gotcha one. Black," says Joe, handing Mario a steaming cup of coffee.

"Coulda they tell a you anything?" asks Giuseppi.

"We're right on time. She's gonna show up in coupla hours, the guy said. Pier twelve is down to the right. He said we kin wait there. Damn! I…I can't believe there're finally gonna be here."

"That's terrific. Wow…a few hours, eh? Are ya nervous?" asks Joe.

"Wouldn't you be? Jesus, I wonder if the baby's changed a lot? Five months is a lot a time for a kid to grow."

"Let's go find the pier," says John.

Even at this early hour, the pier is crowded with people awaiting the arrival of the Algonquin. Sitting together on a bench, John, Joe and Giuseppi drink their third cups of coffee. Too impatient to sit, Mario walks around holding the hot coffee between his hands. He sips from the steaming cup and repeatedly stares out onto the busy harbor.

"Why don't a you sit down anna try to relax, Mario? You gonna make a us all a crazy, the way you jumpin around."

"I can't sit down, Pa. It's been a coupla hours already. Where the hell could it be?" Then, three short blasts from a distant ship capture the attention of everyone on the pier. Mario scans the harbor again and sees a large vessel being guided toward the pier.

"I'll bet that's it. Whatta ya guys think?"

"Looks like they're linin it up with this dock, that's for sure. It's gotta be her. It won't be long now," says John, slapping Mario on the back. Moving steadily for the pier, the ship is soon close enough for them to read its name on the bow. Straining to make out the letters, Mario is able to read the white block letters: SS ALGONQUIN. With his heart soaring, he spins around, rushes to his brothers and father.

"That's it. That's the Algonquin!" Mario's sense of anticipation is contagious. His brothers jump up, surround him and shake his hand in laughter.

"Are ya gonna be alright?" asks John, with a smile.

"I think so…as long as she's on the ship. Man, I'm more nervous now than when we got married."

The crowded pier is chaotic. With military personnel setting up barricades and medical workers waiting to board the ship, there is a great confusion everywhere. Once the gangplank is secured, those in need of medical help are the first to leave the ship. Standing at the rail holding Vincenzo, Antonella stares at the mass of humanity on the dock, hoping to find Mario. A nurse suddenly approaches her.

"Are you the one with a sick baby?" she asks. Understanding a little of the nurse's English, Antonella points to the cabin.

"No, no. Notta my baby. Sophia. See a Sophia." The nurse enters the cabin and emerges a few minutes later holding Angela in her arms. Following her out, a tearful Sophia stops to hug Antonella.

"Angela...is...very sick...but I...I don't understand the nurse...what she is saying. What...what should I do, Antonella?"

"It's all right, Sophia. Don't cry. The nurse is going to help Angela. You go with her...I'm sure someone speaks Italian."

Watching Sophia being lead away in such terror brings Antonella to tears. Feeling helpless to do anything for her friend, she again turns her attention to searching the crowded dock and finding Mario. The decks are teeming with people, either yelling at someone on the pier or greeting a loved one who's come aboard. She sees a man dressed in civilian clothes, standing at the end of the gangplank. He resembles Mario, but she can't be sure. Not until he gazes up at the ship and they make eye contact. Suddenly, he begins jumping wildly and waving his hands in the air.

"Antonella! Here, Antonella. It's me," she hears him shout in Italian. It is Mario. With tears streaming down her face, she waves to him.

"I see you, Mario. Oh dear God, it's you."

"Stay where you are," he shouts. *"I'll come up and get you. Don't move."*

She watches Mario show his I.D. to the military staff, rush up the gangplank, and then disappear into the lower level of the ship. Within minutes, he's pushing his way through the congested second deck and calling out to her.

"Antonella, here I am." Seconds later, he's standing directly in front of her. Dressed in civilian clothes, he looks very different to her. But when she looks into his face, their separation quickly becomes part of the past. Crying with joy, she kisses him.

"Do...you want to say...hello...to your son, Mario?" Holding Vincenzo on his arm, Mario eyes are soon glazed with tears, as he touches his son's hand and kisses his forehead.

"Look at how big you've gotten. And all these teeth...do you remember me, Vincenzo?"

Frightened at first, the baby looks at Mario for a few minutes with ever-increasing curiosity. But when he smiles, Mario begins laughing.

"You do remember your Papa, don't you?" says Antonella. Wrapping her arms around Mario, she kisses him tenderly and holds him in a trembling embrace.

"I'm so happy you're here at last. I missed you both so much," he says.

"I was so afraid...all these months, Mario. Afraid that...you wouldn't be here or...or that you wouldn't love me anymore."

"I love you, Antonella, like I've always loved you. And you're home now. My whole family is here...to meet you and Vincenzo today. There they are, on the dock. That's my father wearing the dark suit and holding the shopping bag." Antonella is not sure whom it is that Mario is pointing to on the swarming pier, but she says,

"I want to meet them, too. I'm sure your father wants to meet his grandson."

"He can't wait. He even brought him a gift."

Carrying Vincenzo, Antonella follows Mario along the deck, down several stairways and then to the gangplank. Her first few steps in America immerse her in the crowded and noisy mob on the pier. Toting Antonella's suitcases, Mario weaves his way through the crowd to his waiting family.

"Stay close behind me. We'll be through all this real soon."

"Mario, wait. That woman there...holding the baby...she was in my cabin. Her baby's sick and the woman speaks no English. I'm very worried about her. Can we stop...and see if she's safe?"

"Sure. She looks very scared," says Mario, working his way in her direction.

"Sophia...Sophia. It's me, Antonella. What did the nurse say?"

"Antonella! Thank you. Thank you for stopping. No one can...can tell me anything, Antonella. They only speak English. I don't know...what to...to do."

662

"Mario, can you talk to the nurse? Maybe they will tell you something to help Sophia," says Antonella.

"I'll see what I can do." Finding the nurse, Mario speaks to her for several minutes while Antonella and Sophia watch. When he returns, he translates the nurse's information for Sophia.

"Your baby has pneumonia, Sophia, and she needs to go to the hospital. The nurse is waiting for an ambulance to take you there. They're going to take care of your baby. Do you understand?"

"A hospital? Oh dear God...I have no money...for a hospital...I..."

"You don't need money. It's an Army hospital. They'll have someone there who can speak Italian. They will treat your baby and see that you get on the right train when she's able to travel. Everything will be all right."

"Thank you, Signor...you're a saint. Goodbye Antonella," says Sophia, as the nurse leads her away.

"Goodbye, Sophia. I'll pray for Angela," says Antonella. *"Thank you for helping her, Mario. She was so afraid."*

"I'm glad we stopped. She's safe now. You don't have to worry about her any more. Why don't we go? I'm sure my family is getting very anxious."

Approaching the waiting area, Antonella can see Mario's family for the first time. She anxiously tugs on her dress and undoes the portion of the blanket wrapped around Vincenzo's head and shoulders. After setting down the suitcases, Mario takes her by the arm and introduces her to his brothers and father. Standing shoulder to shoulder, the three men smile in excited anticipation.

"Antonella, this is my brother, Joe, my brother, John and my father, Giuseppi."

"I'm so happy to meet you, Antonella. Mario's told us so much about you," says John, giving her a welcoming hug. *"And who's this little boy?"* he says, touching Vincenzo's chin.

"I'm...very glad to meet you, John. This is your nephew, Vincenzo. Can you smile for your new uncle, Vincenzo?"

"He's something, Mario," says John, of his new nephew. Joe follows John's lead and greets Antonella with a gracious hug.

"We're all excited to have you and Vincenzo here with us. I can't wait for you to meet Edna and Pauline when we get home," says Joe.

"I'm anxious to meet them, too. It's so kind of you to come from Detroit to meet us today. Vincenzo, he has very nice uncles. Don't you, Vincenzo?" she says, smiling at the baby.

"He's so big. How old is he now?" asks Joe.

"He'll be nine months in a few weeks."

Still tightly clutching the Sears and Roebuck bag, Giuseppi is overjoyed by the arrival of Mario's wife and baby. He cannot take his eyes off of them, particularly his grandson. Standing only a few feet away from Vincenzo, Giuseppi still can't believe this magical child from another world is his flesh and blood. His heart pounds and his legs begin to quiver when Mario introduces him to Antonella.

"Pa, this is Antonella and Vincenzo." Antonella smiles nervously, then leans forward and kisses Giuseppi's cheek.

"I'm excited to meet you...but I feel a little embarrassed. What...would you like me to call you?" asks Antonella. Giuseppi laughs out loud and puts his arms around her.

"The boys...they call me Pa. You...can call me that, if...you like. Mario has told me how beautiful you are, but you are even more lovely in person."

"Thank you...Pa. And this is Vincenzo. Would...you like to hold your...grandson?" Before he can answer, Antonella places Vincenzo in his arms.

"This is your grandpa, Vincenzo. You be a good boy for him."

The baby turns his head from side to side in anxious confusion. So many new faces have frightened him, and he reaches out to Antonella.

"Hold his hand, Pa. He'll get used to you in a few minutes," says Mario. Tears drip down Giuseppi's cheeks. This is the most incredible moment of joy he's ever experienced. Touching his grandson's tiny hands and soft cheeks, Giuseppi is thrilled beyond words by his grandchild's presence. With his voice choked with emotions, he puts his arm around Antonella and whispers,

"He's...such a...a beautiful gift. I don't...know how to...to thank you...for bringing him to us." Giuseppi's emotional gratitude reassures her that she and her son are with family again. Vincenzo's

uneasiness among so many strangers continues to frighten him, and he cries out for Antonella.

"What's wrong, my darling? You're all right. Maybe I better take him for a little while, Pa."

"That's good because I have something for him...a gift. Let me open it," says Giuseppi excitedly.

Taking the gift box from the Sears bag and placing it on the bench, Giuseppi proudly opens it and holds up the tiny coat.

"The clerk said it's a very warm coat. I thought he might need one today. There are gloves and a cap, too."

"Thank you, Pa. What a beautiful coat. He's never had anything like this...from a store, I mean. It's very generous of you to do this. Now I can take this old blanket off of him." After dressing Vincenzo in his new coat and hat, Antonella returns him to Giuseppi. *"They fit him perfectly, Pa. Look how handsome he looks. Do you like your new coat, Vincenzo?"*

Giuseppi's beaming smile lights up his face as he proudly carries his grandson around the pier. But for Antonella, his boundless joy is a bittersweet reminder of Assunta's love for this same child. The image of her mother's profound grief over losing her youngest daughter and only grandchild will forever haunt Antonella. Even amid the excitement of being reunited with Mario, the guilt of leaving her family is still very fresh in her mind. She knows it will always be with her. This new life she embarks on seems destined to be forever torn between these two different worlds that have become one.

For Antonella, the memory of those flickering, white scarves on the pier in Napoli will be a constant source of sorrow from which she'll never escape.

"Antonella? Are you all right? It's time to go. Do you have your papers?"

"Yes...yes. I have them here in my purse, Mario."

Mono V. D'Angelo

ABOUT THE AUTHOR

Born in Naples, Italy in 1945, Mono D'Angelo is the son of an American soldier and an Italian war bride. He was raised in and around the Detroit, Michigan region of the Midwest. After devoting thirty-some years to a career as an automotive design engineer and freelance artist, he is now focusing on his writing. He began writing seriously after joining several online writers groups. Bolstered by encouragement received from some members of the group, he began to promote his writing locally. He has since written articles for major-media newspapers, such as the Detroit News, as well as for the online travel magazine, Trips and Journeys.

As an Italian-American who's heritage is directly linked to the war bride experience, his creative non-fiction novel, *Powers of Fate*, is based upon the unique lives of his parents. Combining family folklore, personal memories and a great deal of historical research, he addresses the war bride phenomenon from the private and personal viewpoint of the participants.

He presently resides with his wife in Grosse Ile, Michigan, a quaint island community located on the northwest corner of Lake Erie. When he is not writing or painting, he enjoys racing his sailboat on the Great Lakes.